S0-BYN-232

Common Core State Standards

# Mathematics II

Integrated Pathway

**Student Resource**

*Units 5–6*

WALCH
INTEGRATED MATH

1    2    3    4    5    6    7    8    9    10

ISBN 978-0-8251-7168-0 V2

Copyright © 2013, 2014

J. Weston Walch, Publisher

Portland, ME 04103

www.walch.com

Printed in the United States of America

# Table of Contents

## Volume II

## Unit 5: Similarity, Right Triangle Trigonometry, and Proof

# Unit 6: Circles With and Without Coordinates

# Introduction to the Program

Welcome to the *CCSS Integrated Pathway: Mathematics II Student Resource Book.* This book will help you learn how to use algebra, geometry, data analysis, and probability to solve problems. Each lesson builds on what you have already learned. As you participate in classroom activities and use this book, you will master important concepts that will help to prepare you for mathematics assessments and other mathematics courses.

This book is your resource as you work your way through the Math II course. It includes explanations of the concepts you will learn in class; math vocabulary and definitions; formulas and rules; and exercises so you can practice the math you are learning. Most of your assignments will come from your teacher, but this book will allow you to review what was covered in class, including terms, formulas, and procedures.

- In **Unit 1: Extending the Number System**, you will learn about rational exponents and the properties of rational and irrational numbers. This is followed by operating with polynomials. Finally, you will define an imaginary number and learn to operate with complex numbers.

- In **Unit 2: Quadratic Functions and Modeling**, you will begin by exploring and interpreting the graphs of quadratic functions. Then you will learn how to build quadratic functions from a context and how to carry out operations with functions. This gives way to the exploration of other types of functions, including square root, cube root, absolute value, step, and piecewise functions. The unit progresses to analyzing exponential functions and comparing linear, quadratic, and exponential models given in different forms. The unit ends with transforming functions and finding the inverse of functions.

- In **Unit 3: Expressions and Equations**, you will reexamine the basic structures of expressions, but this time apply these structures to quadratic expressions. Then you will learn to solve quadratic equations using various methods, as well as how to apply structures of quadratic expressions in solving these equations. The structures of expressions theme continues into having you create quadratic equations of various forms; here, you will learn how to rearrange formulas to solve for a quadratic variable of interest. The unit builds on previous units by introducing the Fundamental Theorem of Algebra and showing you how complex numbers are solutions to quadratic equations. Then you will be introduced to rational functions. Again, you will learn to write exponentially structured expressions in equivalent forms. The unit ends with returning to a familiar topic—solving systems of equations—but now complex solutions can be determined.

- In **Unit 4: Applications of Probability**, you will start by defining events, applying the addition rule, and learning about independence. Then you will progress toward conditional probabilities and the multiplication rule. This builds into using combinatorics to count and calculate probabilities. Finally, you will learn to make and analyze decisions based on probability.

- In **Unit 5: Similarity, Right Triangle Trigonometry, and Proof**, you will begin by learning about midpoints and other points of interest in a line segment. Then you will work with dilations and similarity. This builds into learning about and proving the various similarity statements. Then you will learn about special angles in intersecting lines and about relationships among the angles formed by a set of parallel lines intersected by a transversal. You will then return to working with triangles and proving theorems about them, including the Interior Angle Sum Theorem, theorems about isosceles triangles, midsegments, and centers of triangles. The unit ends with an introduction to trigonometric ratios and problem solving with those ratios and the Pythagorean theorem.

- In **Unit 6: Circles With and Without Coordinates**, you will study the properties of circles, including central and inscribed angles, chords of a circle, and tangents of a circle. Then you build on this to explore polygons circumscribed and inscribed in a circle. You will then learn about the properties and construction of tangent lines. The measurement units of radians are introduced, and you will use radians to measure the area of a sector and the circumference and area of a circle. You build from a 1- and 2-dimensional arena to a 3-dimensional one by exploring more deeply the volume formulas for cylinders, pyramids, cones, and spheres. Then you will study the links between algebra and geometry by deriving the equations for circles and parabolas. Finally, you will use coordinates to prove geometric theorems about circles and parabolas.

Each lesson is made up of short sections that explain important concepts, including some completed examples. Each of these sections is followed by a few problems to help you practice what you have learned. The "Words to Know" section at the beginning of each lesson includes important terms introduced in that lesson.

As you move through your Math II course, you will become a more confident and skilled mathematician. We hope this book will serve as a useful resource as you learn.

# Unit 5
## Similarity, Right Triangle Trigonometry, and Proof

# Lesson 1: Line Segments

**Common Core State Standard**

**G–GPE.6**   Find the point on a directed line segment between two given points that partitions the segment in a given ratio.

**Essential Questions**

1. How can the midpoint of a line segment be found without measuring?

2. How are the midpoint formula and the distance formula related?

**WORDS TO KNOW**

| | |
|---|---|
| **distance formula** | formula that states the distance between $(x_1, y_1)$ and $(x_2, y_2)$ is equal to $\sqrt{(x_2 - x_1)^2 + (y_2 - y_1)^2}$ |
| **line segment** | a part of a line that is noted by two endpoints, $(x_1, y_1)$ and $(x_2, y_2)$ |
| **midpoint** | a point on a line segment that divides the segment into two equal parts |
| **midpoint formula** | formula that states the midpoint of a segment created by connecting $(x_1, y_1)$ and $(x_2, y_2)$ is given by the formula $\left( \dfrac{x_1 + x_2}{2}, \dfrac{y_1 + y_2}{2} \right)$ |

## Recommended Resources

- Math Open Reference. "Midpoint of a Line Segment (Coordinate Geometry)."

  http://www.walch.com/rr/00128

  Users can adjust a line segment by dragging the endpoints around a coordinate plane to see how the midpoint changes. The equations for each set of endpoints are displayed off to the side of the plane and change as the points are dragged.

- Purplemath. "The Midpoint Formula."

  http://www.walch.com/rr/00129

  This site explains why finding the midpoint can be useful and includes worked examples. A widget on the second page allows users to enter problems, view the steps to the solution, and then view a graph of the solution.

# Lesson 5.1.1: Midpoints and Other Points on Line Segments

## Introduction

The use of the coordinate plane can be helpful with many real-world applications. Scenarios can be translated into equations, equations can be graphed, points can be found, and distances between points can be calculated; but what if you need to find a point on a line that is halfway between two points? Can this be easily done?

## Key Concepts

- Lines continue infinitely in both directions. Their length cannot be measured.

- A **line segment** is a part of a line that is noted by two endpoints, $(x_1, y_1)$ and $(x_2, y_2)$.

- The length of a line segment can be found using the **distance formula**, $\sqrt{(x_2 - x_1)^2 + (y_2 - y_1)^2}$.

- The **midpoint** of a line segment is the point on the segment that divides it into two equal parts.

- Finding the midpoint of a line segment is like finding the average of the two endpoints.

- The **midpoint formula** is used to find the midpoint of a line segment. The formula is $\left( \dfrac{x_1 + x_2}{2}, \dfrac{y_1 + y_2}{2} \right)$.

- You can prove that the midpoint is halfway between the endpoints by calculating the distance from each endpoint to the midpoint.

---

**Finding the Midpoint of a Line Segment**

1. Determine the endpoints of the line segment, $(x_1, y_1)$ and $(x_2, y_2)$.

2. Substitute the values of $(x_1, y_1)$ and $(x_2, y_2)$ into the midpoint formula: $\left( \dfrac{x_1 + x_2}{2}, \dfrac{y_1 + y_2}{2} \right)$.

3. Simplify.

---

- It is often helpful to plot the segment on a coordinate plane.

- Other points, such as a point that is one-fourth the distance from one endpoint of a segment, can be calculated in a similar way.

| **Finding the Point on a Line Segment with Any Given Ratio** |
| --- |

1. Determine the endpoints of the line segment, $(x_1, y_1)$ and $(x_2, y_2)$.

2. Calculate the difference between the $x$-values: $|x_2 - x_1|$.

3. Multiply the difference by the given ratio, $\dfrac{m}{n}$.

4. Add the product to or subtract it from the $x$-value of the endpoint. This is the $x$-value of the point with the given ratio.

5. Calculate the difference between the $y$-values: $|y_2 - y_1|$.

6. Multiply the difference by the given ratio, $\dfrac{m}{n}$.

7. Add the product to or subtract it from the $y$-value of the endpoint. This is the $y$-value of the point with the given ratio.

# Guided Practice 5.1.1

**Example 1**

Calculate the midpoint of the line segment with endpoints (–2, 1) and (4, 10).

---

1. Determine the endpoints of the line segment.

   The endpoints of the segment are (–2, 1) and (4, 10).

---

2. Substitute the values of $(x_1, y_1)$ and $(x_2, y_2)$ into the midpoint formula.

   $$\left( \frac{x_1 + x_2}{2}, \frac{y_1 + y_2}{2} \right)$$  Midpoint formula

   $$\left( \frac{(-2) + (4)}{2}, \frac{(1) + (10)}{2} \right)$$  Substitute (–2, 1) and (4, 10).

---

3. Simplify.

$$\left( \frac{(-2)+(4)}{2}, \frac{(1)+(10)}{2} \right)$$

$$\left( \frac{2}{2}, \frac{11}{2} \right)$$

$(1, 5.5)$

The midpoint of the segment with endpoints $(-2, 1)$ and $(4, 10)$ is $(1, 5.5)$.

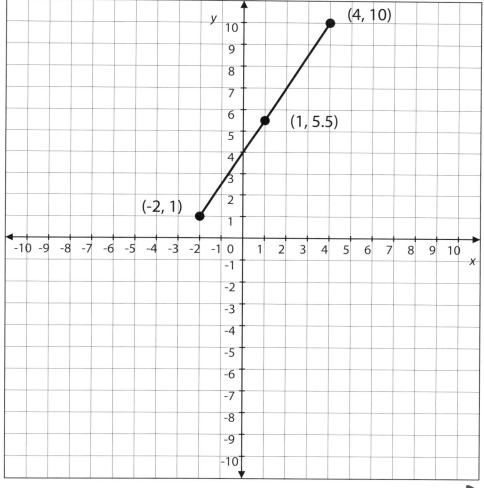

## Example 2

Show mathematically that (1, 5.5) is the midpoint of the line segment with endpoints (−2, 1) and (4, 10).

1.  Calculate the distance between the endpoint (−2, 1) and the midpoint (1, 5.5).

    Use the distance formula.

    $\sqrt{(x_2 - x_1)^2 + (y_2 - y_1)^2}$     Distance formula

    $\sqrt{[(1) - (-2)]^2 + [(5.5) - (1)]^2}$     Substitute (−2, 1) and (1, 5.5).

    $\sqrt{(3)^2 + (4.5)^2}$     Simplify as needed.

    $\sqrt{9 + 20.25}$

    $\sqrt{29.25}$

    The distance between (−2, 1) and (1, 5.5) is $\sqrt{29.25}$ units.

2. Calculate the distance between the endpoint (4, 10) and the midpoint (1, 5.5).

$$\sqrt{(x_2 - x_1)^2 + (y_2 - y_1)^2}$$    Distance formula

$$\sqrt{[(1) - (4)]^2 + [(5.5) - (10)]^2}$$    Substitute (4, 10) and (1, 5.5).

$$\sqrt{(-3)^2 + (-4.5)^2}$$    Simplify as needed.

$$\sqrt{9 + 20.25}$$

$$\sqrt{29.25}$$

The distance between (4, 10) and (1, 5.5) is $\sqrt{29.25}$ units.

The distance from each endpoint to the midpoint is the same, $\sqrt{29.25}$ units, proving that (1, 5.5) is the midpoint of the line segment.

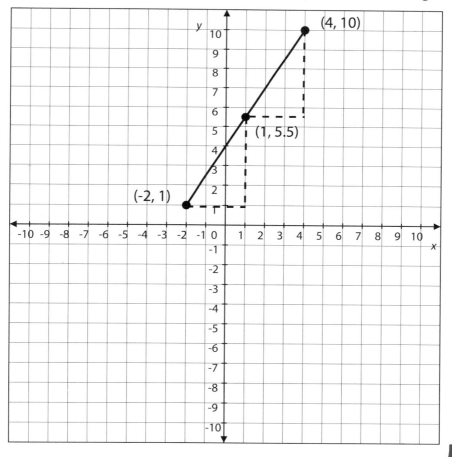

## Example 3

Determine the point that is $\dfrac{1}{4}$ the distance from the endpoint $(-3, 7)$ of the segment with endpoints $\overset{x_2\ y_2}{(-3, 7)}$ and $\overset{x_4\ y_1}{(5, -9)}$.

1. Draw the segment $(-3, 7)$ and $(5, -9)$ on a coordinate plane.

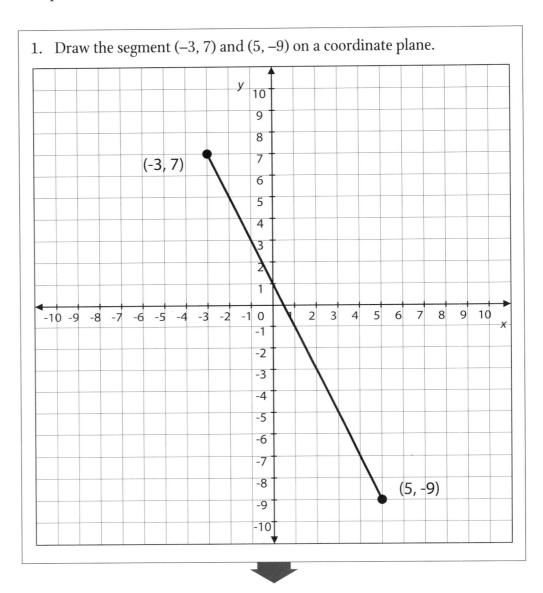

2. Calculate the difference between the *x*-values.

$|x_2 - x_1|$　　　　Distance between *x*-values

$|(-3) - (5)|$　　　Substitute the *x*-values.

$|-8|$　　　　　　Simplify.

$8$

The difference between the *x*-values is 8 units.

3. Multiply the difference by the given ratio, $\dfrac{1}{4}$.

$$8 \cdot \frac{1}{4} = \frac{8}{4} = 2$$

4. The *x*-value is to the right of the original endpoint; therefore, add the product to the *x*-value of the endpoint. This is the *x*-value of the point with the given ratio.

$$-3 + 2 = -1$$

5. Calculate the difference between the *y*-values: $|y_2 - y_1|$.

$|y_2 - y_1|$　　　　Distance between *y*-values

$|(7) - (-9)|$　　　Substitute the *y*-values.

$|16|$　　　　　　Simplify.

$16$

The difference between the *y*-values is 16 units.

6. Multiply the difference by the given ratio, $\dfrac{1}{4}$.

$$16 \cdot \frac{1}{4} = \frac{16}{4} = 4$$

7. The *y*-value is down from the original endpoint; therefore, subtract the product from the *y*-value of the endpoint. This is the *y*-value of the point with the given ratio.

$$7 - 4 = 3$$

The point that is $\dfrac{1}{4}$ the distance from the endpoint $(-3, 7)$ of the segment with endpoints $(-3, 7)$ and $(5, -9)$ is $(-1, 3)$.

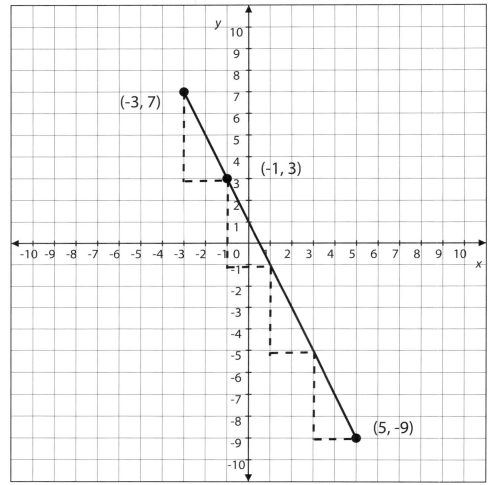

**Example 4**

Determine the point that is $\dfrac{2}{3}$ the distance from the endpoint (2, 9) of the segment with endpoints (2, 9) and (–4, –6).

1. Draw the segment (2, 9) and (–4, –6) on a coordinate plane.

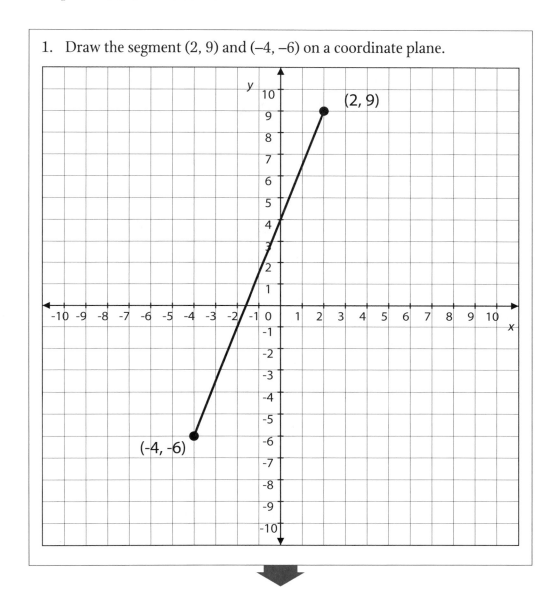

2. Calculate the difference between the x-values.

$$|x_2 - x_1|$$    Distance between x-values

$$|(2) - (-4)|$$    Substitute the x-values.

$$|6|$$    Simplify.

$$6$$

The difference between the x-values is 6 units.

3. Multiply the difference by the given ratio, $\dfrac{2}{3}$.

$$6 \bullet \dfrac{2}{3} = \dfrac{12}{3} = 4$$

4. Subtract the product from the x-value of the endpoint. This is the x-value of the point with the given ratio.

$$2 - 4 = -2$$

5. Calculate the difference between the y-values: $|y_2 - y_1|$.

$$|y_2 - y_1|$$    Distance between y-values

$$|(9) - (-6)|$$    Substitute the y-values.

$$|15|$$    Simplify.

$$15$$

The difference between the y-values is 15 units.

6. Multiply the difference by the given ratio, $\dfrac{2}{3}$.

$$15 \bullet \dfrac{2}{3} = \dfrac{30}{3} = 10$$

7. Subtract the product from the *y*-value of the endpoint. This is the *y*-value of the point with the given ratio.

$$9 - 10 = -1$$

The point that is $\dfrac{2}{3}$ the distance from the endpoint (2, 9) of the segment with endpoints (2, 9) and (–4, –6) is (–2, –1).

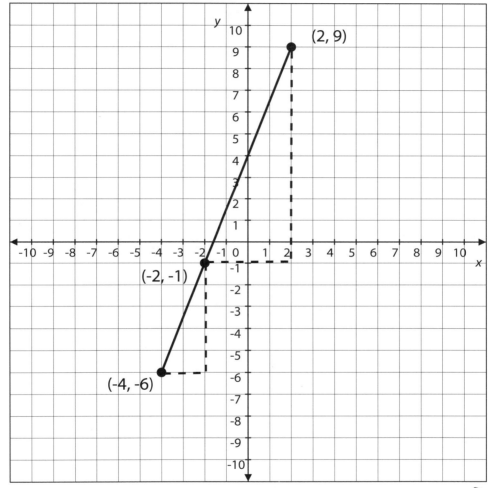

## Example 5

A line segment has one endpoint at $(12, 0)$ and a midpoint of $(10, -2)$. Locate the second endpoint.

---

1. Determine the endpoints of the line segment.

   One endpoint of the segment is $(12, 0)$.

   The other endpoint is unknown.

---

2. Substitute the values of $(x_1, y_1)$ into the midpoint formula and simplify.

$$\left( \frac{x_1 + x_2}{2}, \frac{y_1 + y_2}{2} \right)$$   Midpoint formula

$$\left( \frac{x + 12}{2}, \frac{y + 0}{2} \right)$$   Substitute $(12, 0)$.

---

3. Find the value of $x$.

   The midpoint $(10, -2)$ is equal to $\left( \dfrac{x + 12}{2}, \dfrac{y + 0}{2} \right)$.

$$\left( \frac{x + 12}{2}, \frac{y + 0}{2} \right) = (10, -2)$$

   Create an equation to find the value of $x$.

$$\frac{x + 12}{2} = 10$$   Equation

$$x + 12 = 20$$   Multiply both sides by 2.

$$x = 8$$   Subtract 12 from both sides.

---

4. Find the value of $y$.

   Create an equation to find the value of $y$.

$$\frac{y + 0}{2} = -2$$   Equation

$$y + 0 = -4$$   Multiply both sides by 2.

$$y = -4$$   Simplify.

   The endpoint of the segment with one endpoint at $(12, 0)$ and a midpoint at $(10, -2)$ is $(8, -4)$.

## Practice 5.1.1: Midpoints and Other Points on Line Segments

For problems 1–3, the endpoints of a segment are given. Calculate the indicated point for each segment.

1. Determine the midpoint of the segment with endpoints (22, −9) and (−8, 25).

2. Determine the point that is $\frac{1}{4}$ the distance from the endpoint (−6, −10) of the segment with endpoints (14, −2) and (−6, −10).

3. Determine the point that is $\frac{2}{3}$ the distance from the endpoint (12, 10) of the segment with endpoints (12, 10) and (−15, 1).

For problems 4 and 5, find the coordinates of the second endpoint given one endpoint and the midpoint of the segment.

4. endpoint (−24, −12) and midpoint (−2, 4)

5. endpoint (1, 5) and midpoint (2.5, 7.5)

*continued*

# UNIT 5 • SIMILARITY, RIGHT TRIANGLE TRIGONOMETRY, AND PROOF
## Lesson 1: Line Segments

Use the map and the information given to solve each problem that follows.

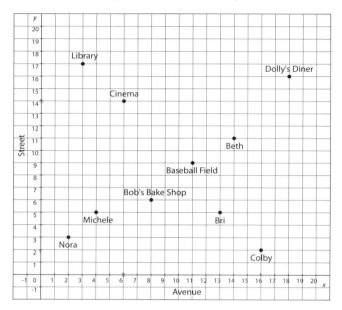

6. Carlos works at a cinema on 6th Avenue and 14th Street. Colby lives at the corner of 16th Avenue and 2nd Street. What is a possible location that is midway between them?

7. Nora lives at the corner of 2nd Avenue and 3rd Street. Beth lives at the corner of 14th Avenue and 11th Street. Their favorite music store is located midway between them. What is one possible location of the music store?

8. Bob's Bake Shop is located at the corner of 8th Avenue and 6th Street. Dolly's Diner is located at the corner of 18th Avenue and 16th Street. Located $\frac{4}{5}$ of the distance from Bob's Bake Shop is the bank. Where is the bank?

9. Michele and Bri both live on 5th Street. Michele lives at the corner of 4th Avenue, and Bri lives at the corner of 13th Avenue. $\frac{1}{3}$ the distance from Michele's apartment to Bri's apartment is a statue. Where is the statue?

10. The main entrance to the library is located at the corner of 3rd Avenue and 17th Street. On his way from the library to the market, Carlos stops at the baseball field located at 11th Avenue and 9th Street. The baseball field is the midpoint of this trip. What is the location of the market?

# Lesson 2: Investigating Properties of Dilations

## Common Core State Standards

**G–SRT.1**  Verify experimentally the properties of dilations given by a center and a scale factor:

    a.  A dilation takes a line not passing through the center of the dilation to a parallel line, and leaves a line passing through the center unchanged.

    b.  The dilation of a line segment is longer or shorter in the ratio given by the scale factor.

## Essential Questions

1. How are the preimage and image similar in dilations?

2. How are the preimage and image different in dilations?

3. When are dilations used in the real world?

## WORDS TO KNOW

| | |
|---|---|
| **center of dilation** | a point through which a dilation takes place; all the points of a dilated figure are stretched or compressed through this point |
| **collinear points** | points that lie on the same line |
| **compression** | a transformation in which a figure becomes smaller; compressions may be horizontal (affecting only horizontal lengths), vertical (affecting only vertical lengths), or both |
| **congruency transformation** | a transformation in which a geometric figure moves but keeps the same size and shape; a dilation where the scale factor is equal to 1 |
| **corresponding sides** | sides of two figures that lie in the same position relative to the figure. In transformations, the corresponding sides are the preimage and image sides, so $\overline{AB}$ and $\overline{A'B'}$ are corresponding sides and so on. |

| | |
|---|---|
| **dilation** | a transformation in which a figure is either enlarged or reduced by a scale factor in relation to a center point |
| **enlargement** | a dilation of a figure where the scale factor is greater than 1 |
| **non-rigid motion** | a transformation done to a figure that changes the figure's shape and/or size |
| **reduction** | a dilation where the scale factor is between 0 and 1 |
| **rigid motion** | a transformation done to a figure that maintains the figure's shape and size or its segment lengths and angle measures |
| **scale factor** | a multiple of the lengths of the sides from one figure to the transformed figure. If the scale factor is larger than 1, then the figure is enlarged. If the scale factor is between 0 and 1, then the figure is reduced. |
| **stretch** | a transformation in which a figure becomes larger; stretches may be horizontal (affecting only horizontal lengths), vertical (affecting only vertical lengths), or both |

# Recommended Resources

- IXL Learning. "Transformations: Dilations: Find the Coordinates."

  http://www.walch.com/rr/00017

  This interactive website gives a series of problems and scores them immediately. If the user submits a wrong answer, a description and process for arriving at the correct answer are provided. These problems start with a graphed figure. Users are asked to input the coordinates of the dilated figure given a center and scale factor.

- IXL Learning. "Transformations: Dilations: Graph the Image."

  http://www.walch.com/rr/00018

  This interactive website gives a series of problems and scores them immediately. If the user submits a wrong answer, a description and process for arriving at the correct answer are provided. These problems start with a graphed figure. Users are asked to draw a dilation of the figure on the screen using a point that can be dragged, given a center and scale factor.

- IXL Learning. "Transformations: Dilations: Scale Factor and Classification."

  http://www.walch.com/rr/00019

  This interactive website gives a series of problems and scores them immediately. If the user submits a wrong answer, a description and process for arriving at the correct answer are provided. These problems start with a graphed preimage and image. Users are required to choose whether the figure is an enlargement or a reduction. Other problems ask users to enter the scale factor.

- Math Is Fun. "Resizing."

  http://www.walch.com/rr/00020

  This website gives a brief explanation of the properties of dilations and how to perform them. The site also contains an interactive applet with which users can select a shape, a center point, and a scale factor. The computer then generates the dilated image. After users explore the applet, they may answer eight multiple-choice questions in order to check understanding.

# Lesson 5.2.1: Investigating Properties of Parallelism and the Center

## Introduction

Think about resizing a window on your computer screen. You can stretch it vertically, horizontally, or at the corner so that it stretches both horizontally and vertically at the same time. These are non-rigid motions. **Non-rigid motions** are transformations done to a figure that change the figure's shape and/or size. These are in contrast to **rigid motions**, which are transformations to a figure that maintain the figure's shape and size, or its segment lengths and angle measures.

Specifically, we are going to study non-rigid motions of dilations. **Dilations** are transformations in which a figure is either enlarged or reduced by a scale factor in relation to a center point.

## Key Concepts

- Dilations require a center of dilation and a scale factor.

- The **center of dilation** is the point about which all points are stretched or compressed.

- The **scale factor** of a figure is a multiple of the lengths of the sides from one figure to the transformed figure.

- Side lengths are changed according to the scale factor, $k$.

- The scale factor can be found by finding the distances of the sides of the preimage in relation to the image.

- Use a ratio of corresponding sides to find the scale factor:
$$\frac{\text{length of image side}}{\text{length of preimage side}} = \text{scale factor}$$

- The scale factor, $k$, takes a point $P$ and moves it along a line in relation to the center so that $k \bullet CP = CP'$.

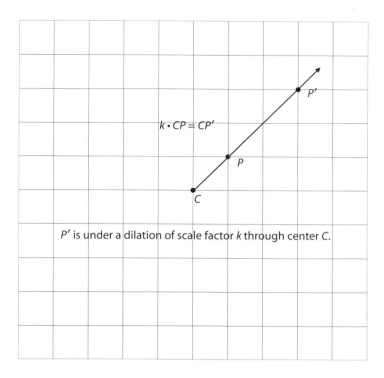

$k \cdot CP = CP'$

P' is under a dilation of scale factor $k$ through center C.

- If the scale factor is greater than 1, the figure is stretched or made larger and is called an **enlargement**. (A transformation in which a figure becomes larger is also called a **stretch**.)

- If the scale factor is between 0 and 1, the figure is compressed or made smaller and is called a **reduction**. (A transformation in which a figure becomes smaller is also called a **compression**.)

- If the scale factor is equal to 1, the preimage and image are congruent. This is called a **congruency transformation**.

- Angle measures are preserved in dilations.

- The orientation is also preserved.

- The sides of the preimage are parallel to the corresponding sides of the image.

- The **corresponding sides** are the sides of two figures that lie in the same position relative to the figures.

- In transformations, the corresponding sides are the preimage and image sides, so $\overline{AB}$ and $\overline{A'B'}$ are corresponding sides and so on.

- The notation of a dilation in the coordinate plane is given by $D_k(x, y) = (kx, ky)$. The scale factor is multiplied by each coordinate in the ordered pair.

- The center of dilation is usually the origin, (0, 0).

- If a segment of the figure being dilated passes through the center of dilation, then the image segment will lie on the same line as the preimage segment. All other segments of the image will be parallel to the corresponding preimage segments.

- The corresponding points in the preimage and image are **collinear points**, meaning they lie on the same line, with the center of dilation.

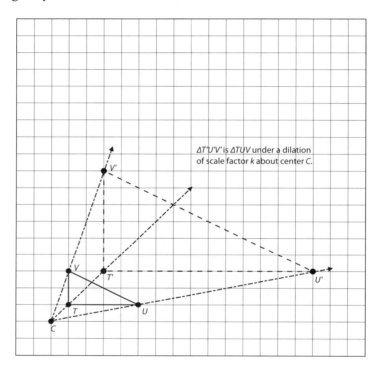

$\triangle T'U'V'$ is $\triangle TUV$ under a dilation of scale factor $k$ about center $C$.

| Properties of Dilations |
| --- |
| 1. Shape, orientation, and angles are preserved. |
| 2. All sides change by a single scale factor, $k$. |
| 3. The corresponding preimage and image sides are parallel. |
| 4. The corresponding points of the figure are collinear with the center of dilation. |

# Guided Practice 5.2.1

## Example 1

Is the following transformation a dilation? Justify your answer using the properties of dilations.

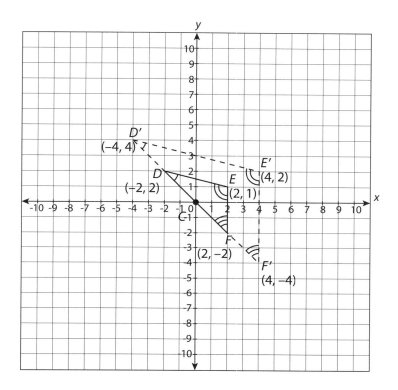

1. Verify that shape, orientation, and angles have been preserved from the preimage to the image.

   Both figures are triangles in the same orientation.

   $$\angle D \cong \angle D'$$

   $$\angle E \cong \angle E'$$

   $$\angle F \cong \angle F'$$

   The angle measures have been preserved.

2. Verify that the corresponding sides are parallel.

$$m_{\overline{DE}} = \frac{\Delta y}{\Delta x} = \frac{(2-1)}{(-2-2)} = \frac{1}{-4} = -\frac{1}{4} \quad \text{and} \quad m_{\overline{D'E'}} = \frac{\Delta y}{\Delta x} = \frac{(4-2)}{(-4-4)} = \frac{2}{-8} = -\frac{1}{4} \; ;$$

therefore, $\overline{DE} \parallel \overline{D'E'}$.

By inspection, $\overline{EF} \parallel \overline{E'F'}$ because both lines are vertical; therefore, they have the same slope and are parallel.

$$m_{\overline{DF}} = \frac{\Delta y}{\Delta x} = \frac{[2-(-2)]}{(-2-2)} = \frac{4}{-4} = -1 \quad \text{and} \quad m_{\overline{D'F'}} = \frac{\Delta y}{\Delta x} = \frac{[4-(-4)]}{(-4-4)} = \frac{8}{-8} = -1;$$

therefore, $\overline{DF} \parallel \overline{D'F'}$. In fact, these two segments, $\overline{DF}$ and $\overline{D'F'}$, lie on the same line.

All corresponding sides are parallel.

3. Verify that the distances of the corresponding sides have changed by a common scale factor, $k$.

We could calculate the distances of each side, but that would take a lot of time. Instead, examine the coordinates and determine if the coordinates of the vertices have changed by a common scale factor.

The notation of a dilation in the coordinate plane is given by $D_k(x, y) = (kx, ky)$.

Divide the coordinates of each vertex to determine if there is a common scale factor.

| $D(-2,2) \rightarrow D'(-4,4)$ | $E(2,1) \rightarrow E'(4,2)$ | $F(2,-2) \rightarrow F'(4,-4)$ |
|---|---|---|
| $\dfrac{x_{D'}}{x_D} = \dfrac{-4}{-2} = 2; \dfrac{y_{D'}}{y_D} = \dfrac{4}{2} = 2$ | $\dfrac{x_{E'}}{x_E} = \dfrac{4}{2} = 2; \dfrac{y_{E'}}{y_E} = \dfrac{2}{1} = 2$ | $\dfrac{x_{F'}}{x_F} = \dfrac{4}{2} = 2; \dfrac{y_{F'}}{y_F} = \dfrac{-4}{-2} = 2$ |

Each vertex's preimage coordinate is multiplied by 2 to create the corresponding image vertex. Therefore, the common scale factor is $k = 2$.

4. Verify that corresponding vertices are collinear with the center of dilation, C.

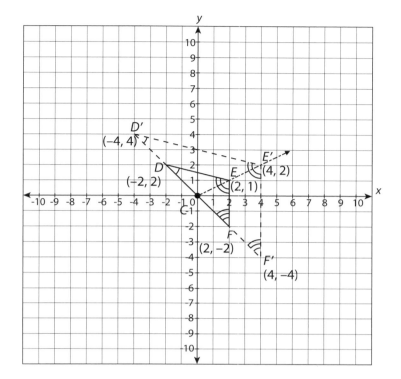

A straight line can be drawn connecting the center with the corresponding vertices. This means that the corresponding vertices are collinear with the center of dilation.

5. Draw conclusions.

The transformation is a dilation because the shape, orientation, and angle measures have been preserved. Additionally, the size has changed by a scale factor of 2. All corresponding sides are parallel, and the corresponding vertices are collinear with the center of dilation.

## Example 2

Is the following transformation a dilation? Justify your answer using the properties of dilations.

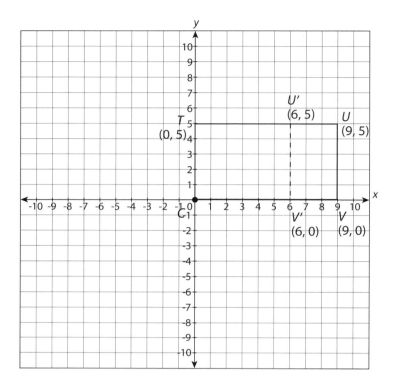

1. Verify that shape, orientation, and angles have been preserved from the preimage to the image.

   The preimage and image are both rectangles with the same orientation. The angle measures have been preserved since all angles are right angles.

2. Verify that the corresponding sides are parallel.

$\overline{TU'}$ is on the same line as $\overline{TU}$; therefore, $\overline{TU} \parallel \overline{TU'}$.

$\overline{CV'}$ is on the same line as $\overline{CV}$; therefore, $\overline{CV} \parallel \overline{CV'}$.

By inspection, $\overline{UV}$ and $\overline{U'V'}$ are vertical; therefore, $\overline{UV} \parallel \overline{U'V'}$.

$\overline{TC}$ remains unchanged from the preimage to the image.

All corresponding sides are parallel.

3. Verify that the distances of the corresponding sides have changed by a common scale factor, $k$.

Since the segments of the figure are on a coordinate plane and are either horizontal or vertical, find the distance by counting.

In $\square TUVC$:              In $\square TU'V'C$:
$TU = VC = 9$              $TU' = V'C = 6$
$UV = CT = 5$              $U'V' = CT = 5$

The formula for calculating the scale factor is:

$$\text{scale factor} = \frac{\text{length of image side}}{\text{length of preimage side}}$$

Start with the horizontal sides of the rectangle.

$$\frac{TU'}{TU} = \frac{6}{9} = \frac{2}{3} \qquad\qquad \frac{V'C}{VC} = \frac{6}{9} = \frac{2}{3}$$

Both corresponding horizontal sides have a scale factor of $\dfrac{2}{3}$.

Next, calculate the scale factor of the vertical sides.

$$\frac{U'V'}{UV} = \frac{5}{5} = 1 \qquad\qquad \frac{CT}{CT} = \frac{5}{5} = 1$$

Both corresponding vertical sides have a scale factor of 1.

4. Draw conclusions.

The vertical corresponding sides have a scale factor that is not consistent with the scale factor of $\dfrac{2}{3}$ for the horizontal sides. Since all corresponding sides do not have the same common scale factor, the transformation is NOT a dilation. ✔

## Example 3

The following transformation represents a dilation. What is the scale factor? Does this indicate enlargement, reduction, or congruence?

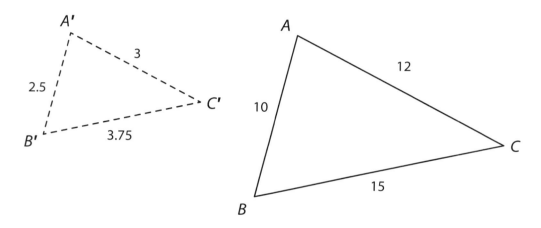

1. Determine the scale factor.

Start with the ratio of one set of corresponding sides.

$$\text{scale factor} = \frac{\text{length of image side}}{\text{length of preimage side}}$$

$$\frac{A'B'}{AB} = \frac{2.5}{10} = \frac{1}{4}$$

The scale factor appears to be $\dfrac{1}{4}$.

2. Verify that the other sides maintain the same scale factor.

$$\frac{B'C'}{BC} = \frac{3.75}{15} = \frac{1}{4} \text{ and } \frac{C'A'}{CA} = \frac{3}{12} = \frac{1}{4}. \text{ Therefore,}$$

$$\frac{A'B'}{AB} = \frac{B'C'}{BC} = \frac{C'A'}{CA} = \frac{1}{4} \text{ and the scale factor, } k, \text{ is } \frac{1}{4}.$$

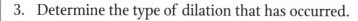

3. Determine the type of dilation that has occurred.

If $k > 1$, then the dilation is an enlargement.

If $0 < k < 1$, then the dilation is a reduction.

If $k = 1$, then the dilation is a congruency transformation.

Since $k = \frac{1}{4}$, $k$ is between 0 and 1, or $0 < k < 1$.

The dilation is a reduction.

## Practice 5.2.1: Investigating Properties of Parallelism and the Center

Determine whether each of the following transformations represents a dilation. Justify your answer using the properties of dilations.

1. Compare $\triangle STC$ to $\triangle S'T'C$.

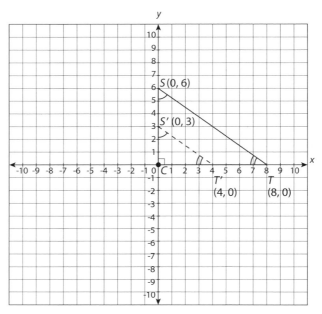

2. Compare quadrilateral $STUV$ to quadrilateral $S'T'U'V'$.

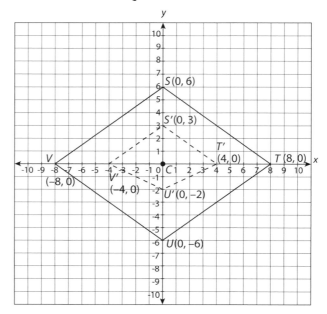

*continued*

# UNIT 5 • SIMILARITY, RIGHT TRIANGLE TRIGONOMETRY, AND PROOF
## Lesson 2: Investigating Properties of Dilations

3. Compare □CPQR to □CPQ'R'.

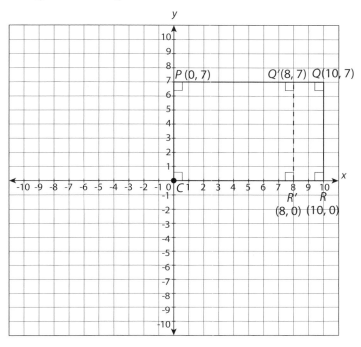

4. Compare □CTUV to □CT'U'V'.

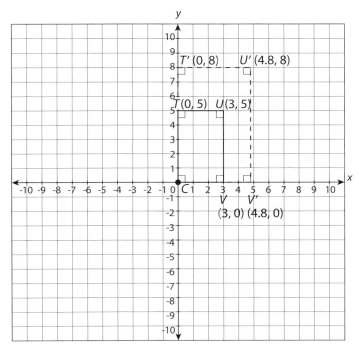

For problems 5 and 6, the following transformations represent dilations. Determine the scale factor and whether the dilation is an enlargement, a reduction, or a congruency transformation.

5.

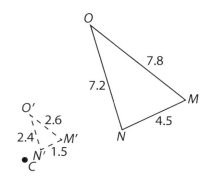

6.

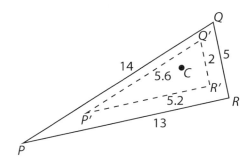

Use the given information in each problem that follows to answer the questions.

7. A triangle with vertices $D$, $E$, and $F$ has side lengths as follows: $DE = 12.2$,

$EF = 7.6$, and $FD = 8.4$. If the image is dilated through the center $C\,(0, 0)$ and

now has side lengths of $D'E' = \dfrac{61}{5}$, $E'F' = \dfrac{38}{5}$, and $F'D' = \dfrac{42}{5}$, what is the scale

factor? Does this dilation indicate an enlargement, a reduction, or a congruency

transformation? Explain.

8.  A company makes triangular wedges used to install laminate flooring. Customers have complained that the wedge is too small. The company's designers propose dilating the wedge. The drawing below shows the side views of the original wedge and the dilated wedge. What is the scale factor? Does the scale factor represent an enlargement, a reduction, or a congruency transformation? Explain.

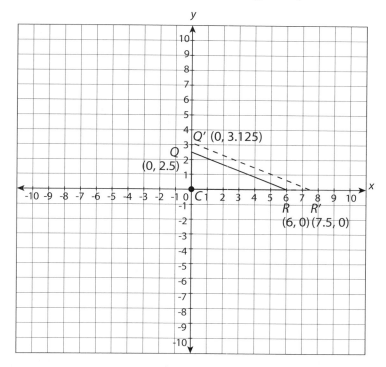

continued

9. The laminate flooring designers proposed another wedge design, shown below. Does this design represent a dilation? Explain.

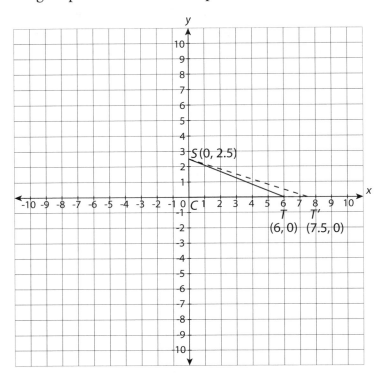

10. A neighborhood committee is planning a new community pool. The committee has proposed a design for the pool. The design consists of two rectangles. The inner rectangle is the pool, and has been dilated about $C(0, 0)$ to create the concrete walkway that will border the pool. The vertices of the pool are $P(-2, 4)$, $Q(2, 4)$, $R(2, -4)$, and $S(-2, -4)$. The vertices of the outside edge of the concrete walkway are $P'(-3, 6)$, $Q'(3, 6)$, $R'(3, -6)$, and $S'(-3, -6)$. What is the scale factor? Does this represent an enlargement, a reduction, or a congruency transformation? Explain.

# Lesson 5.2.2: Investigating Scale Factors

## Introduction

A figure is dilated if the preimage can be mapped to the image using a scale factor through a center point, usually the origin. You have been determining if figures have been dilated, but how do you create a dilation? If the dilation is centered about the origin, use the scale factor and multiply each coordinate in the figure by that scale factor. If a distance is given, multiply the distance by the scale factor.

## Key Concepts

- The notation is as follows: $D_k(x,y) = (kx, ky)$.

- Multiply each coordinate of the figure by the scale factor when the center is at $(0, 0)$.

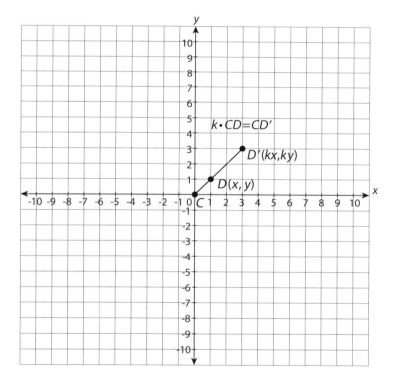

- The lengths of each side in a figure also are multiplied by the scale factor.

- If you know the lengths of the preimage figure and the scale factor, you can calculate the lengths of the image by multiplying the preimage lengths by the scale factor.

- Remember that the dilation is an enlargement if $k > 1$, a reduction if $0 < k < 1$, and a congruency transformation if $k = 1$.

# Guided Practice 5.2.2

## Example 1

If $\overline{AB}$ has a length of 3 units and is dilated by a scale factor of 2.25, what is the length of $\overline{A'B'}$? Does this represent an enlargement or a reduction?

1. To determine the length of $\overline{A'B'}$, multiply the scale factor by the length of the segment.

   $AB = 3; k = 2.25$

   $A'B' = k \bullet AB$

   $A'B' = 2.25 \bullet 3 = 6.75$

   $\overline{A'B'}$ is 6.75 units long.

2. Determine the type of dilation.

   Since the scale factor is greater than 1, the dilation is an enlargement.

## Example 2

A triangle has vertices $G$ (2, –3), $H$ (–6, 2), and $J$ (0, 4). If the triangle is dilated by a scale factor of 0.5 through center $C$ (0, 0), what are the image vertices? Draw the preimage and image on the coordinate plane.

1. Start with one vertex and multiply each coordinate by the scale factor, $k$.

   $D_k = (kx, ky)$

   $G' = D_{0.5}[G\,(2, -3)] = D_{0.5}(0.5 \bullet 2, 0.5 \bullet -3) = (1, -1.5)$

2. Repeat the process with another vertex. Multiply each coordinate of the vertex by the scale factor.

   $H' = D_{0.5}[H\,(-6, 2)] = D_{0.5}(0.5 \bullet -6, 0.5 \bullet 2) = (-3, 1)$

3. Repeat the process for the last vertex. Multiply each coordinate of the vertex by the scale factor.

$$J' = D_{0.5}[J(0, 4)] = D_{0.5}(0.5 \bullet 0, 0.5 \bullet 4) = (0, 2)$$

4. List the image vertices.

$G'(1, -1.5)$

$H'(-3, 1)$

$J'(0, 2)$

5. Draw the preimage and image on the coordinate plane.

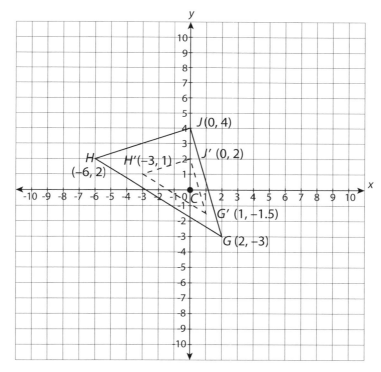

## Example 3

What are the side lengths of $\triangle D'E'F'$ with a scale factor of 2.5 given the preimage and image below and the information that $DE = 1$, $EF = 9.2$, and $FD = 8.6$?

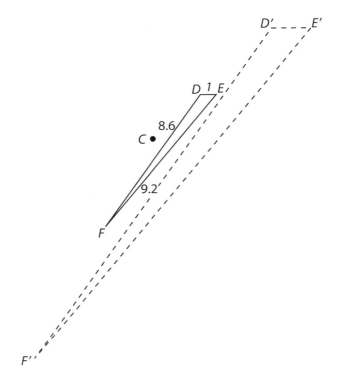

1. Choose a side to start with and multiply the scale factor ($k$) by that side length.

$DE = 1; k = 2.5$

$D'E' = k \bullet DE$

$D'E' = 2.5 \bullet 1 = 2.5$

2. Choose a second side and multiply the scale factor by that side length.

$EF = 9.2; k = 2.5$

$E'F' = k \bullet EF$

$E'F' = 2.5 \bullet 9.2 = 23$

3. Choose the last side and multiply the scale factor by that side length.

   $FD = 8.6; k = 2.5$

   $F'D' = k \bullet FD$

   $F'D' = 2.5 \bullet 8.6 = 21.5$

4. Label the figure with the side lengths.

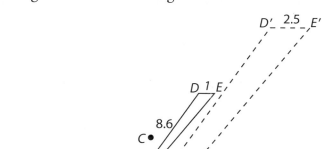

## Practice 5.2.2: Investigating Scale Factors

Determine the lengths of the dilated segments given the preimage length and the scale factor.

1. $\overline{BC}$ is 13.5 units long and the segment is dilated by a scale factor of $k = 0.75$.

2. $\overline{FG}$ is 19 units long and the segment is dilated by a scale factor of $k = 1.5$.

3. $\overline{QR}$ is 5.8 units long and the segment is dilated by a scale factor of 80%.

4. $\overline{VW}$ is $\dfrac{27}{5}$ units long and the segment is dilated by a scale factor of $\dfrac{1}{9}$.

Determine the image vertices of the dilations given a center and scale factor.

5. $\triangle TUV$ has the following vertices: $T(-9, -3)$, $U(-6, -6)$, and $V(-2, -3)$. What are the vertices under a dilation with a center at $(0, 0)$ and a scale factor of $\dfrac{1}{3}$?

6. $\triangle BDE$ has the following vertices: $B(-1, 0)$, $D(-5, -6)$, and $E(3, -4)$. What are the vertices under a dilation with a center at $(0, 0)$ and a scale factor of 2?

7. $\triangle NOP$ has the following vertices: $N(-6, -2)$, $O(3, 5)$, and $P(4, -8)$. What are the vertices under a dilation with a center at $(0, 0)$ and a scale factor of 160%?

8. $\triangle EFG$ has the following vertices: $E(4, 9)$, $F(5, 3)$, and $G(9, 10)$. What are the vertices under a dilation with a center at $(0, 0)$ and a scale factor of 30%?

9. $\triangle IJK$ has the following vertices: $I(6, 5)$, $J(2, 2)$, and $K(-3, 4)$. What are the final vertices after 2 successive dilations with a center at $(0, 0)$ and a scale factor of $\dfrac{3}{4}$? What is the scale factor from $\triangle IJK$ to $\triangle I''J''K''$?

10. Jenelle is sophomore class president. She's creating a poster for spirit week. First, she drew the design on graph paper. Then she projected the design onto a wall where she'd taped a giant sheet of poster paper. The projector increased the image by 960%. If the original poster design is 7.5 inches by 10 inches, what are the dimensions of the full-size poster?

# Lesson 3: Defining and Applying Similarity

## Common Core State Standards

**G–SRT.2**   Given two figures, use the definition of similarity in terms of similarity transformations to decide if they are similar; explain using similarity transformations the meaning of similarity for triangles as the equality of all corresponding pairs of angles and the proportionality of all corresponding pairs of sides.

**G–SRT.3**   Use the properties of similarity transformations to establish the AA criterion for two triangles to be similar.

## Essential Questions

1. What does it mean for two triangles to be similar?

2. How can you prove that two triangles are similar?

3. How can you use similar triangles to solve problems?

## WORDS TO KNOW

| | |
|---|---|
| **Angle-Angle (AA) Similarity Statement** | If two angles of one triangle are congruent to two angles of another triangle, then the triangles are similar. |
| **proportional** | having a constant ratio to another quantity |
| **ratio of similitude** | a ratio of corresponding sides; also known as the scale factor |
| **similar** | two figures that are the same shape but not necessarily the same size; the symbol for representing similarity between figures is $\sim$ |
| **similarity transformation** | a rigid motion followed by a dilation; a transformation that results in the position and size of a figure changing, but not the shape |

# Recommended Resources

- Analyzemath.com. "Similar Triangles Examples."

  http://www.walch.com/rr/00021

  This site provides examples and illustrations of similarity criteria.

- Math Open Reference. "Similar Triangles."

  http://www.walch.com/rr/00022

  This site includes a summary of similarity as well as links to tests of similarity.

- Math.com. "Similar Figures."

  http://www.walch.com/rr/00023

  This site provides a summary of similar figures and how to calculate lengths of sides of similar figures.

# Lesson 5.3.1: Defining Similarity

## Introduction

Congruent triangles have corresponding parts with angle measures that are the same and side lengths that are the same. If two triangles are congruent, they are also **similar**. Similar triangles have the same shape, but may be different in size. It is possible for two triangles to be similar but not congruent. Just like with determining congruency, it is possible to determine similarity based on the angle measures and lengths of the sides of the triangles.

## Key Concepts

- To determine whether two triangles are similar, observe the angle measures and the side lengths of the triangles.

- When a triangle is transformed by a **similarity transformation** (a rigid motion [reflection, translation, or rotation] followed by a dilation), the result is a triangle with a different position and size, but the same shape.

- If two triangles are similar, then their corresponding angles are congruent and the measures of their corresponding sides are **proportional**, or have a constant ratio.

- The ratio of corresponding sides is known as the **ratio of similitude**.

- The scale factor of the dilation is equal to the ratio of similitude.

- Similar triangles with a scale factor of 1 are congruent triangles.

- Like with congruent triangles, corresponding angles and sides can be determined by the order of the letters.

- If $\triangle ABC$ is similar to $\triangle DEF$, the vertices of the two triangles correspond in the same order as they are named.

- The symbol $\rightarrow$ shows that parts are corresponding.

    $\angle A \rightarrow \angle D$; they are equivalent.

    $\angle B \rightarrow \angle E$; they are equivalent.

    $\angle C \rightarrow \angle F$; they are equivalent.

- The corresponding angles are used to name the corresponding sides.

$$\overline{AB} \rightarrow \overline{DE}$$
$$\overline{BC} \rightarrow \overline{EF}$$
$$\overline{AC} \rightarrow \overline{DF}$$

$$\frac{AB}{DE} = \frac{BC}{EF} = \frac{AC}{DF}$$

- Observe the diagrams of $\triangle ABC$ and $\triangle DEF$.

- The symbol for similarity ($\sim$) is used to show that figures are similar.

$\triangle ABC \sim \triangle DEF$

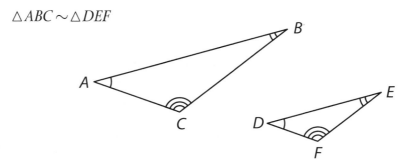

$$\angle A \cong \angle D$$
$$\angle B \cong \angle E$$
$$\angle C \cong \angle F$$

$$\frac{AB}{DE} = \frac{BC}{EF} = \frac{AC}{DF}$$

# Guided Practice 5.3.1

## Example 1

Use the definition of similarity in terms of similarity transformations to determine whether the two figures are similar. Explain your answer.

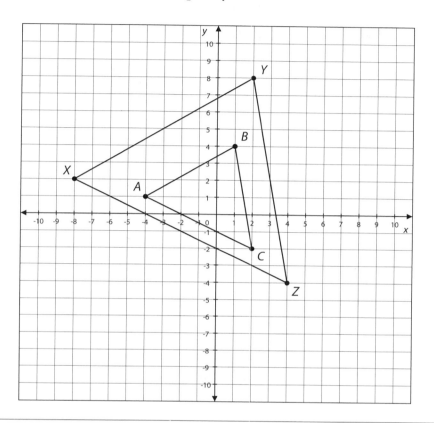

1. Examine the orientation of the triangles.

| △*ABC* | | △*XYZ* | |
|---|---|---|---|
| **Side** | **Orientation** | **Side** | **Orientation** |
| $\overline{AB}$ | Top left side of triangle | $\overline{XY}$ | Top left side of triangle |
| $\overline{AC}$ | Bottom left side of triangle | $\overline{XZ}$ | Bottom left side of triangle |
| $\overline{BC}$ | Right side of triangle | $\overline{YZ}$ | Right side of triangle |

The orientation of the triangles has remained the same, indicating translation, dilation, stretch, or compression.

2. Determine whether a dilation has taken place by calculating the scale factor.

First, identify the vertices of each triangle.

$A$ (−4, 1), $B$ (1, 4), and $C$ (2, −2)

$X$ (−8, 2), $Y$ (2, 8), and $Z$ (4, −4)

Then, find the length of each side of $\triangle ABC$ and $\triangle XYZ$ using the distance formula, $d = \sqrt{(x_2 - x_1)^2 + (y_2 - y_1)^2}$.

Calculate the distance of $\overline{AB}$.

$d = \sqrt{(x_2 - x_1)^2 + (y_2 - y_1)^2}$ 　　　Distance formula

$d = \sqrt{[(1)-(-4)]^2 + [(4)-(1)]^2}$ 　　　Substitute (−4, 1) and (1, 4) for $(x_1, y_1)$ and $(x_2, y_2)$.

$d = \sqrt{(5)^2 + (3)^2}$ 　　　Simplify.

$d = \sqrt{25+9}$

$d = \sqrt{34}$

The distance of $\overline{AB}$ is $\sqrt{34}$ units.

Calculate the distance of $\overline{BC}$.

$d = \sqrt{(x_2 - x_1)^2 + (y_2 - y_1)^2}$ 　　　Distance formula

$d = \sqrt{[(2)-(1)]^2 + [(-2)-(4)]^2}$ 　　　Substitute (1, 4) and (2, −2) for $(x_1, y_1)$ and $(x_2, y_2)$.

$d = \sqrt{(1)^2 + (-6)^2}$ 　　　Simplify.

$d = \sqrt{1+36}$

$d = \sqrt{37}$

The distance of $\overline{BC}$ is $\sqrt{37}$ units.

(*continued*)

Calculate the distance of $\overline{AC}$.

$$d = \sqrt{(x_2 - x_1)^2 + (y_2 - y_1)^2}$$   Distance formula

$$d = \sqrt{[(2) - (-4)]^2 + [(-2) - (1)]^2}$$   Substitute (–4, 1) and (2, –2) for $(x_1, y_1)$ and $(x_2, y_2)$.

$$d = \sqrt{(6)^2 + (-3)^2}$$   Simplify.

$$d = \sqrt{36 + 9}$$

$$d = \sqrt{45} = \sqrt{9 \cdot 5} = 3\sqrt{5}$$

The distance of $\overline{AC}$ is $3\sqrt{5}$ units.

Calculate the distance of $\overline{XY}$.

$$d = \sqrt{(x_2 - x_1)^2 + (y_2 - y_1)^2}$$   Distance formula

$$d = \sqrt{[(2) - (-8)]^2 + [(8) - (2)]^2}$$   Substitute (–8, 2) and (2, 8) for $(x_1, y_1)$ and $(x_2, y_2)$.

$$d = \sqrt{(10)^2 + (6)^2}$$   Simplify.

$$d = \sqrt{100 + 36}$$

$$d = \sqrt{136} = \sqrt{4 \cdot 34} = 2\sqrt{34}$$

The distance of $\overline{XY}$ is $2\sqrt{34}$ units.

(*continued*)

Calculate the distance of $\overline{YZ}$.

$$d = \sqrt{(x_2 - x_1)^2 + (y_2 - y_1)^2}$$ 　　　Distance formula

$$d = \sqrt{[(4)-(2)]^2 + [(-4)-(8)]^2}$$ 　　　Substitute (2, 8) and (4, −4) for $(x_1, y_1)$ and $(x_2, y_2)$.

$$d = \sqrt{(2)^2 + (-12)^2}$$ 　　　Simplify.

$$d = \sqrt{4 + 144}$$

$$d = \sqrt{148} = \sqrt{4 \cdot 37} = 2\sqrt{37}$$

The distance of $\overline{YZ}$ is $2\sqrt{37}$ units.

Calculate the distance of $\overline{XZ}$.

$$d = \sqrt{(x_2 - x_1)^2 + (y_2 - y_1)^2}$$ 　　　Distance formula

$$d = \sqrt{[(4)-(-8)]^2 + [(-4)-(2)]^2}$$ 　　　Substitute (−8, 2) and (4, −4) for $(x_1, y_1)$ and $(x_2, y_2)$.

$$d = \sqrt{(12)^2 + (-6)^2}$$ 　　　Simplify.

$$d = \sqrt{144 + 36}$$

$$d = \sqrt{180} = \sqrt{36 \cdot 5} = 6\sqrt{5}$$

The distance of $\overline{XZ}$ is $6\sqrt{5}$ units.

3. Calculate the scale factor of the changes in the side lengths.

   Divide the side lengths of $\triangle XYZ$ by the side lengths of $\triangle ABC$.

   $$\frac{XY}{AB} = \frac{2\sqrt{34}}{\sqrt{34}} = 2$$

   $$\frac{YZ}{BC} = \frac{2\sqrt{37}}{\sqrt{37}} = 2$$

   $$\frac{XZ}{AC} = \frac{6\sqrt{5}}{3\sqrt{5}} = 2$$

   The scale factor is constant between each pair of corresponding sides.

4. Determine if another transformation has taken place.

   Multiply the coordinate of each vertex of the preimage by the scale factor, $k$.

   $D_k(x, y) = (kx, ky)$                 Dilation by a scale factor of $k$

   $D_2(-4, 1) = [2(-4), 2(1)] = (-8, 2)$

   $D_2(1, 4) = [2(1), 2(4)] = (2, 8)$

   $D_2(2, -2) = [2(2), 2(-2)] = (4, -4)$

   You can map $\triangle ABC$ onto $\triangle XYZ$ by the dilation with a scale factor of 2.

5. State your conclusion.

   A dilation is a similarity transformation; therefore, $\triangle ABC$ and $\triangle XYZ$ are similar. The ratio of similitude is 2.

## Example 2

Use the definition of similarity in terms of similarity transformations to determine whether the two figures are similar. Explain your answer.

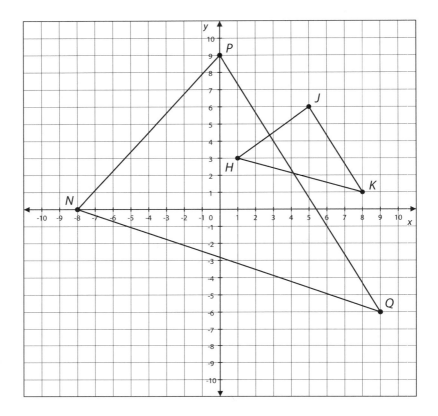

1. Examine the angle measures of the triangles.

   Use a protractor or construction methods to determine if corresponding angles are congruent.

   None of the angles of $\triangle HJK$ are congruent to the angles of $\triangle NPQ$.

2. Summarize your findings.

   Similarity transformations preserve angle measure.

   The angles of $\triangle HJK$ and $\triangle NPQ$ are not congruent.

   There are no sequences of transformations that will map $\triangle HJK$ onto $\triangle NPQ$.

   $\triangle HJK$ and $\triangle NPQ$ are not similar triangles.

## Example 3

A dilation of $\triangle TUV$ centered at point $P$ with a scale factor of 2 is then reflected over the line $\ell$. Determine if $\triangle TUV$ is similar to $\triangle DEF$. If possible, find the unknown angle measures and lengths in $\triangle DEF$.

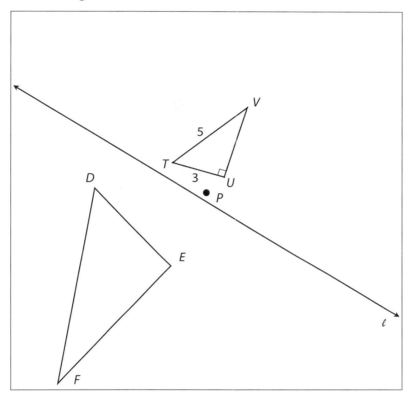

1. Determine if $\triangle TUV$ and $\triangle DEF$ are similar.

   The transformations performed on $\triangle TUV$ are dilation and reflection.

   The sequence of dilating and reflecting a figure is a similarity transformation; therefore, $\triangle TUV \sim \triangle DEF$.

2. Identify the angle measures of $\triangle DEF$.

Corresponding angles of similar triangles are congruent.

$$\angle T \cong \angle D$$

$$\angle U \cong \angle E$$

$$\angle V \cong \angle F$$

Since $\angle U$ is marked as a right angle, $\angle E$ must also be a right angle.

3. Identify the known lengths of $\triangle DEF$.

Corresponding sides of similar triangles are proportional.

The ratio of similitude is equal to the scale factor used in the dilation of the figure.

$$\frac{DE}{TU} = \frac{EF}{UV} = \frac{DF}{TV} = 2$$

Since the length of $\overline{TU}$ is 3 units, the length of the corresponding side $\overline{DE}$ can be found using the ratio of similitude.

$$\frac{DE}{3} = 2$$

$$DE = 6$$

$\overline{DE}$ is 6 units long.

Since the length of $\overline{TV}$ is 5 units, the length of the corresponding side $\overline{DF}$ can be found.

$$\frac{DF}{5} = 2$$

$$DF = 10$$

$\overline{DF}$ is 10 units long.

## Practice 5.3.1: Defining Similarity

Find all the angle measures and side lengths for each triangle of the given similar pairs.

1. $\triangle ABC \sim \triangle DEF$

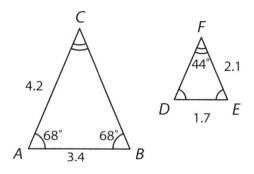

2. $\triangle JKL \sim \triangle MNP$

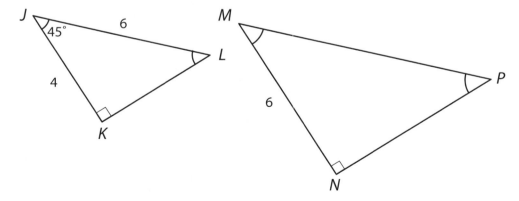

*continued*

# UNIT 5 • SIMILARITY, RIGHT TRIANGLE TRIGONOMETRY, AND PROOF
## Lesson 3: Defining and Applying Similarity

Determine if the two given triangles are similar. Use the definition of similarity in terms of similarity transformations to explain your answer.

3.

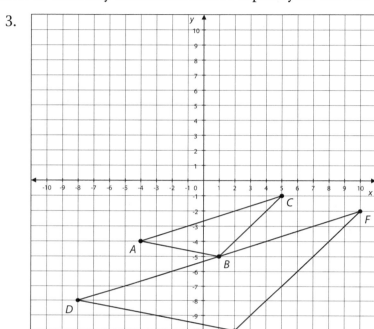

4.

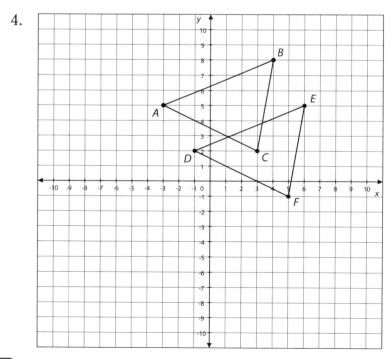

*continued*

# UNIT 5 • SIMILARITY, RIGHT TRIANGLE TRIGONOMETRY, AND PROOF
## Lesson 3: Defining and Applying Similarity

5.

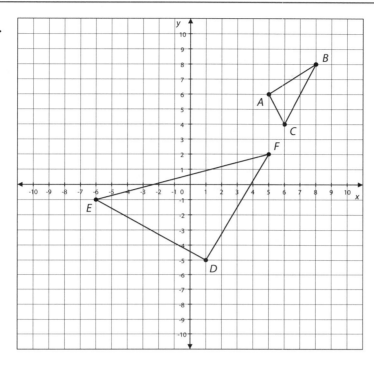

6.

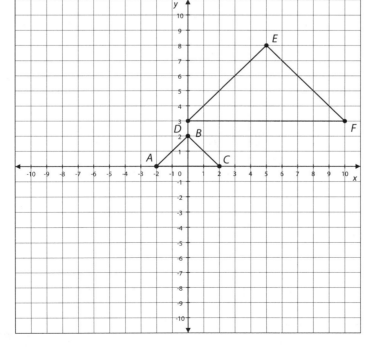

# UNIT 5 • SIMILARITY, RIGHT TRIANGLE TRIGONOMETRY, AND PROOF
## Lesson 3: Defining and Applying Similarity

7.

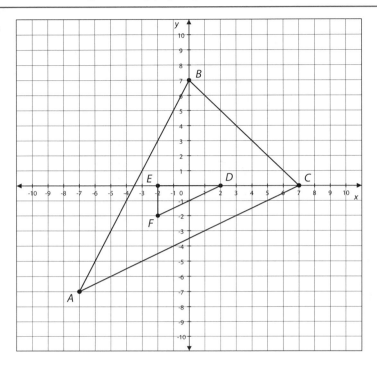

8.

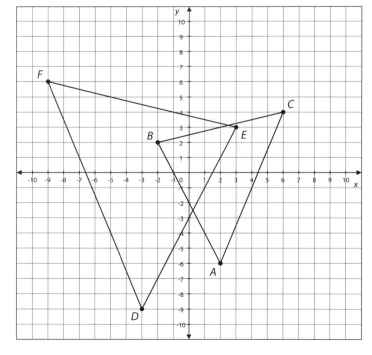

*continued*

# UNIT 5 • SIMILARITY, RIGHT TRIANGLE TRIGONOMETRY, AND PROOF
## Lesson 3: Defining and Applying Similarity

9.

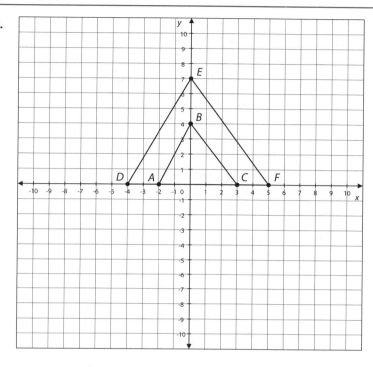

10.

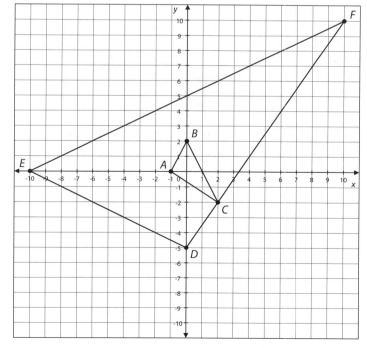

# Lesson 5.3.2: Applying Similarity Using the Angle-Angle (AA) Criterion

## Introduction

When a series of similarity transformations are performed on a triangle, the result is a similar triangle. When triangles are similar, the corresponding angles are congruent and the corresponding sides are of the same proportion. It is possible to determine if triangles are similar by measuring and comparing each angle and side, but this can take time. There exists a set of similarity statements, similar to the congruence statements, that let us determine with less information whether triangles are similar.

## Key Concepts

- The **Angle-Angle (AA) Similarity Statement** is one statement that allows us to prove triangles are similar.

- The AA Similarity Statement allows that if two angles of one triangle are congruent to two angles of another triangle, then the triangles are similar.

  $\triangle ABC \sim \triangle XYZ$

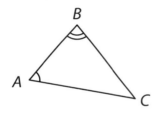 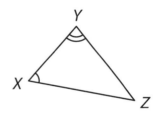

- Notice that it is not necessary to show that the third pair of angles is congruent because the sum of the angles must equal $180°$.

- Similar triangles have corresponding sides that are proportional.

- The Angle-Angle Similarity Statement can be used to solve various problems, including those that involve indirect measurement, such as using shadows to find the height of tall structures.

# Guided Practice 5.3.2

## Example 1

Explain why the triangles are similar and write a similarity statement.

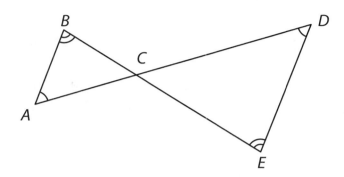

1. Identify the given information.

   According to the diagram, $\angle A \cong \angle D$ and $\angle B \cong \angle E$.

2. State your conclusion.

   $\triangle ABC \sim \triangle DEC$ by the Angle-Angle (AA) Similarity Statement. ✔

## Example 2

Explain why $\triangle ABC \sim \triangle DEF$, and then find the length of $\overline{DF}$.

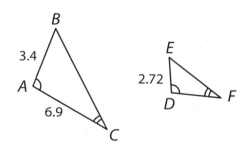

1. Show that the triangles are similar.

   According to the diagram, $\angle A \cong \angle D$ and $\angle C \cong \angle F$.

   $\triangle ABC \sim \triangle DEF$ by the Angle-Angle (AA) Similarity Statement.

2. Find the length of $\overline{DF}$.

Corresponding sides of similar triangles are proportional.

Create and solve a proportion to find the length of $\overline{DF}$.

$$\frac{AB}{DE} = \frac{AC}{DF}$$ Corresponding sides are proportional.

$$\frac{3.4}{2.72} = \frac{6.9}{x}$$ Substitute known values. Let $x$ represent the length of $\overline{DF}$.

$(2.72)(6.9) = (3.4)(x)$  Solve for $x$.

$18.768 = 3.4x$

$x = 5.52$

The length of $\overline{DF}$ is 5.52 units.

## Example 3

Identify the similar triangles. Find $x$ and the measures of the indicated sides.

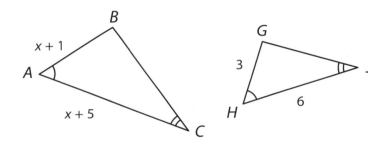

1. Show that the triangles are similar.

According to the diagram, $\angle A \cong \angle H$ and $\angle C \cong \angle J$.

$\triangle ABC \sim \triangle HGJ$ by the Angle-Angle (AA) Similarity Statement.

2. Use the definition of similar triangles to find the value of $x$.

Corresponding sides of similar triangles are proportional.

Create and solve a proportion to find the value of $x$.

$$\frac{AB}{HG} = \frac{AC}{HJ}$$   Corresponding sides are proportional.

$$\frac{x+1}{3} = \frac{x+5}{6}$$   Substitute known values.

$(x + 1)(6) = (3)(x + 5)$   Solve for $x$.

$6x + 6 = 3x + 15$

$3x = 9$

$x = 3$

3. Find the unknown side lengths.

Use the value of $x$ to find the unknown lengths of the triangles.

$AB = x + 1$

$= 3 + 1$

$= 4$

$AC = x + 5$

$= 3 + 5$

$= 8$

The length of $\overline{AB}$ is 4 units.

The length of $\overline{AC}$ is 8 units.

## Example 4

Suppose a person 5 feet 10 inches tall casts a shadow that is 3 feet 6 inches long. At the same time of day, a flagpole casts a shadow that is 12 feet long. To the nearest foot, how tall is the flagpole?

1. Identify the known information.

   The height of a person and the length of the shadow cast create a right angle.

   The height of the flagpole and the length of the shadow cast create a second right angle.

   You can use this information to create two triangles.

   Draw a picture to help understand the information.

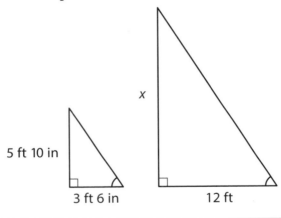

2. Determine if the triangles are similar.

   Two pairs of angles are congruent.

   According to the Angle-Angle (AA) Similarity Statement, the triangles are similar.

   Corresponding sides of similar triangles are proportional.

3. Find the height of the flagpole.

   Create and solve a proportion to find the height of the flagpole.

   $$\frac{5\frac{10}{12}}{x}=\frac{3\frac{6}{12}}{12}$$   Corresponding sides are proportional. Let $x$ represent the height of the flagpole.

   $$\frac{5\frac{5}{6}}{x}=\frac{3\frac{1}{2}}{12}$$   Simplify.

   $$\left(5\frac{5}{6}\right)(12)=\left(3\frac{1}{2}\right)(x)$$   Solve for $x$.

   $$70=\left(3\frac{1}{2}\right)(x)$$

   $$x=20$$

   The flagpole is 20 feet tall.

### Practice 5.3.2: Applying Similarity Using the Angle-Angle (AA) Criterion
Decide whether each pair of triangles is similar. Explain your answer.

1.

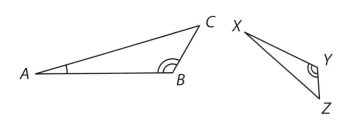

2.

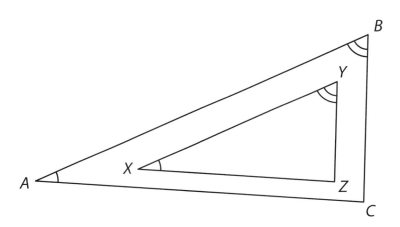

3.

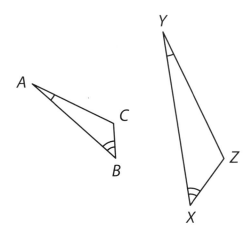

*continued*

# UNIT 5 • SIMILARITY, RIGHT TRIANGLE TRIGONOMETRY, AND PROOF
## Lesson 3: Defining and Applying Similarity

Identify the similar triangles. Find $x$ and the measure of the indicated sides.

4.

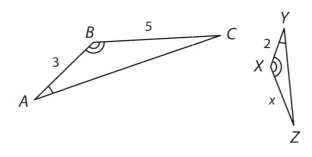

5.

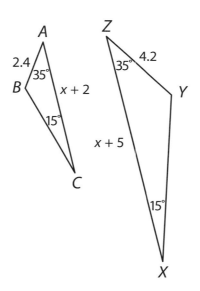

*continued*

6.

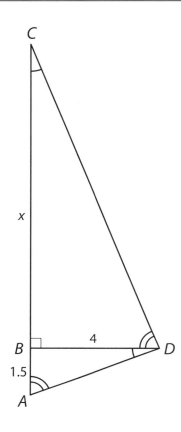

*continued*

# UNIT 5 • SIMILARITY, RIGHT TRIANGLE TRIGONOMETRY, AND PROOF
## Lesson 3: Defining and Applying Similarity

Use the definition of similarity to solve each problem.

7. A telephone pole that is 40 feet tall casts a shadow that is 16 feet long. Find the height of a mailbox that casts a 1.2-foot shadow.

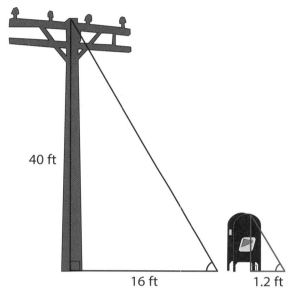

40 ft

16 ft            1.2 ft

8. A 25-foot flagpole casts a shadow that is 37.5 feet long. A man standing near the flagpole is 6 feet tall. At the same time of day, how long is his shadow?

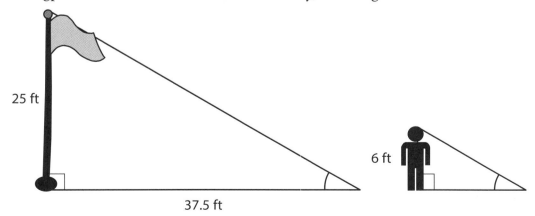

25 ft

6 ft

37.5 ft

*continued*

# UNIT 5 • SIMILARITY, RIGHT TRIANGLE TRIGONOMETRY, AND PROOF
## Lesson 3: Defining and Applying Similarity

9. A tree on a tree farm casts a shadow 9 meters long. A shrub near the tree casts a shadow 2.5 meters long. If the shrub is 0.6 meters high, how tall is the tree?

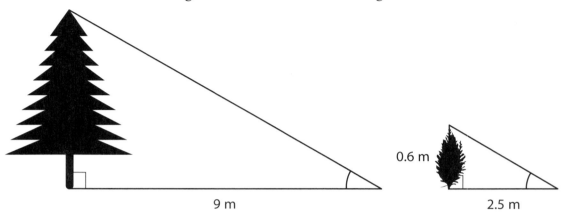

0.6 m

9 m          2.5 m

10. The support beams of truss bridges are triangles. Jeremiah made a model of a truss bridge with a scale of 1 inch = 5 feet. If the height of the tallest triangle on the model is 12 inches, what is the height of the tallest triangle on the actual bridge?

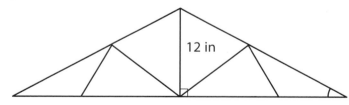

12 in

# Lesson 4: Proving Similarity

## Common Core State Standards

**G–SRT.4**  Prove theorems about triangles. *Theorems include: a line parallel to one side of a triangle divides the other two sides proportionally, and conversely; the Pythagorean Theorem proved using triangle similarity.*

**G–SRT.5**  Use congruence and similarity criteria for triangles to solve problems and to prove relationships in geometric figures.

## Essential Questions

1.  How can you prove that two triangles are similar?

2.  How does a line parallel to one side of a triangle divide the second side of the triangle?

3.  How can you use triangle similarity to prove the Pythagorean Theorem?

4.  How can you use similar triangles to solve problems?

5.  How can you use similarity and congruence to solve problems?

## WORDS TO KNOW

| | |
|---|---|
| **altitude** | the perpendicular line from a vertex of a figure to its opposite side; height |
| **angle bisector** | a ray that divides an angle into two congruent angles |
| **converse of the Pythagorean Theorem** | If the sum of the squares of the measures of two sides of a triangle equals the square of the measure of the longest side, then the triangle is a right triangle. |
| **flow proof** | a graphical method of presenting the logical steps used to show an argument. In a flow proof, the logical statements are written in boxes and the reason for each statement is written below the box. |
| **paragraph proof** | statements written out in complete sentences in a logical order to show an argument |

| | |
|---|---|
| **parallel lines** | lines in a plane that either do not share any points and never intersect, or share all points; written as $\overleftrightarrow{AB} \parallel \overleftrightarrow{PQ}$ |
| **proof** | a set of justified statements organized to form a convincing argument that a given statement is true |
| **Reflexive Property of Congruent Segments** | a segment is congruent to itself; $\overline{AB} \cong \overline{AB}$ |
| **Segment Addition Postulate** | If $B$ is between $A$ and $C$, then $AB + BC = AC$. Conversely, if $AB + BC = AC$, then $B$ is between $A$ and $C$. |
| **Side-Angle-Side (SAS) Similarity Statement** | If the measures of two sides of a triangle are proportional to the measures of two corresponding sides of another triangle and the included angles are congruent, then the triangles are similar. |
| **Side-Side-Side (SSS) Similarity Statement** | If the measures of the corresponding sides of two triangles are proportional, then the triangles are similar. |
| **Symmetric Property of Congruent Segments** | If $\overline{AB} \cong \overline{CD}$, then $\overline{CD} \cong \overline{AB}$. |
| **theorem** | a statement that is shown to be true |
| **Transitive Property of Congruent Segments** | If $\overline{AB} \cong \overline{CD}$, and $\overline{CD} \cong \overline{EF}$, then $\overline{AB} \cong \overline{EF}$. |
| **two-column proof** | numbered statements and corresponding reasons that show the argument in a logical order |

# Recommended Resources

- Learn Zillion. "Prove the Pythagorean Theorem."

  http://www.walch.com/rr/00024

  This site offers a video explaining the Pythagorean Theorem through similar triangles as well as links to practice questions and questions to support understanding.

- Math Open Reference. "Similar Triangles."

  http://www.walch.com/rr/00025

  This site includes a summary of similarity and links to tests of similarity.

- Math Warehouse. "Triangle Angle Bisector Theorem."

  http://www.walch.com/rr/00026

  This site includes a summary of the Angle Bisector Theorem in addition to illustrated examples.

# Lesson 5.4.1: Proving Triangle Similarity Using Side-Angle-Side (SAS) and Side-Side-Side (SSS) Similarity

## Introduction

There are many ways to show that two triangles are similar, just as there are many ways to show that two triangles are congruent. The Angle-Angle (AA) Similarity Statement is one of them. The Side-Angle-Side (SAS) and Side-Side-Side (SSS) similarity statements are two more ways to show that triangles are similar. In this lesson, we will prove that triangles are similar using the similarity statements.

## Key Concepts

- The **Side-Angle-Side (SAS) Similarity Statement** asserts that if the measures of two sides of a triangle are proportional to the measures of two corresponding sides of another triangle and the included angles are congruent, then the triangles are similar.

- Similarity statements identify corresponding parts just like congruence statements do.

$$\triangle ABC \sim \triangle DEF$$

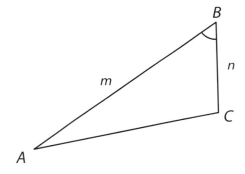
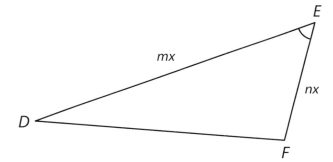

$$\angle B \cong \angle E$$

$$DE = (x)AB$$

$$EF = (x)BC$$

- The **Side-Side-Side (SSS) Similarity Statement** asserts that if the measures of the corresponding sides of two triangles are proportional, then the triangles are similar.

$\triangle ABC \sim \triangle DEF$

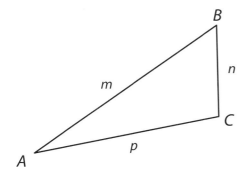 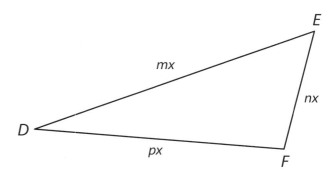

$DE = (x)AB$

$EF = (x)BC$

$DF = (x)AC$

- It is important to note that while both similarity and congruence statements include an SSS and an SAS statement, the statements do not mean the same thing.

- Similar triangles have corresponding sides that are proportional, whereas congruent triangles have corresponding sides that are of the same length.

- Like with the Angle-Angle Similarity Statement, both the Side-Angle-Side and the Side-Side-Side similarity statements can be used to solve various problems.

- The ability to prove that triangles are similar is essential to solving many problems.

- A **proof** is a set of justified statements organized to form a convincing argument that a given statement is true.

- Definitions, algebraic properties, and previously proven statements can be used to prove a given statement.

- There are several types of proofs, such as paragraph proofs, two-column proofs, and flow diagrams.

- Every good proof includes the following:

  - a statement of what is to be proven

  - a list of the given information

  - if possible, a diagram including the given information

  - step-by-step statements that support your reasoning

# Guided Practice 5.4.1

## Example 1

Prove $\triangle ABC \sim \triangle DEC$.

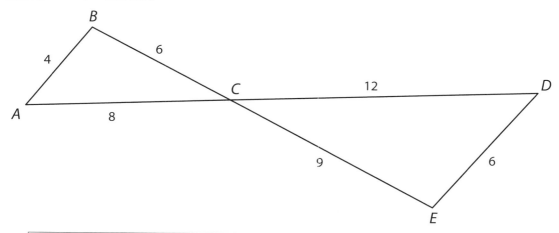

1. Identify the given information.

   Lengths for each side of both triangles are given.

   | | |
   |---|---|
   | $AB = 4$ | $DE = 6$ |
   | $BC = 6$ | $EC = 9$ |
   | $AC = 8$ | $DC = 12$ |

2. Compare the side lengths of both triangles.

   Pair the lengths of the sides of $\triangle ABC$ with the corresponding lengths of the sides of $\triangle DEC$ to determine if there is a common ratio.

   $$\frac{AB}{DE} = \frac{4}{6} = \frac{2}{3} \qquad \frac{BC}{EC} = \frac{6}{9} = \frac{2}{3} \qquad \frac{AC}{DC} = \frac{8}{12} = \frac{2}{3}$$

   Notice the common ratio, $\frac{2}{3}$; the side lengths are proportional.

3. State your conclusion.

   Similar triangles must have side lengths that are proportional.

   $\triangle ABC \sim \triangle DEC$ by the Side-Side-Side (SSS) Similarity Statement.

## Example 2

Determine whether the triangles are similar. Explain your reasoning.

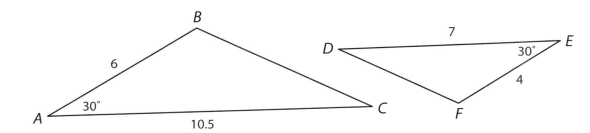

1. Identify the given information.

   According to the diagram, $\angle A \cong \angle E$ .

   Given the side lengths, both $\angle A$ and $\angle E$ are included angles.

2. Compare the given side lengths of both triangles.

   If the triangles are similar, then the corresponding sides are proportional.

   $$\frac{AB}{EF} = \frac{6}{4} = \frac{3}{2} \qquad \frac{AC}{ED} = \frac{10.5}{7} = \frac{3}{2}$$

   The side lengths are proportional.

3. State your conclusion.

   The measures of two sides of $\triangle ABC$ are proportional to the measures of two corresponding sides of $\triangle EFD$ , and the included angles are congruent.

   $\triangle ABC \sim \triangle EFD$ by the Side-Angle-Side (SAS) Similarity Statement.

# Example 3

Determine whether the triangles are similar. Explain your reasoning.

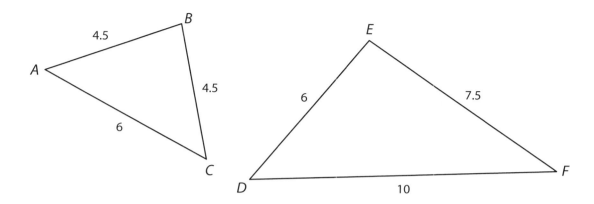

1. Identify the given information.

   The measures of each side of both triangles are given.

2. Compare the side lengths of both triangles.

   Pair the lengths of the sides of $\triangle ABC$ with the corresponding lengths of the sides of $\triangle DEF$ to determine if there is a common ratio.

$$\frac{AB}{DE} = \frac{4.5}{6} = \frac{3}{4} \qquad \frac{BC}{EF} = \frac{4.5}{7.5} = \frac{3}{5} \qquad \frac{AC}{DF} = \frac{6}{10} = \frac{3}{5}$$

   Notice there is not a common ratio; therefore, the side lengths are not proportional.

3. State your conclusion.

   Similar triangles must have side lengths that are proportional.

   $\triangle ABC$ is not similar to $\triangle DEF$.

# Example 4

$\triangle ABE \sim \triangle DCF$, $\overline{AB}$ and $\overline{DC}$ are corresponding sides, and $\overline{AE}$ and $\overline{DF}$ are corresponding sides. Find the value of $x$.

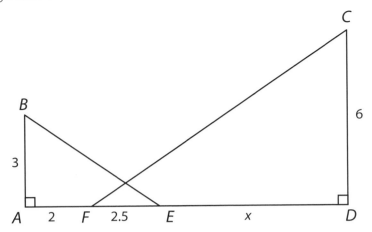

1. Determine the scale factor of the triangle sides.

$$\frac{AB}{DC} = \frac{3}{6} = \frac{1}{2}$$

The scale factor is $\frac{1}{2}$.

2. Find the length of $x$.

$$\frac{AE}{DF} = \frac{2+2.5}{x+2.5} = \frac{4.5}{x+2.5} = \frac{1}{2}$$

Solve the proportion $\dfrac{4.5}{x+2.5} = \dfrac{1}{2}$ for $x$.

$(4.5)(2) = (1)(x + 2.5)$    Find the cross products.

$9 = x + 2.5$             Simplify.

$x = 6.5$                Solve for $x$.

The length of $x$ is 6.5 units.

### Practice 5.4.1: Proving Triangle Similarity Using Side-Angle-Side (SAS) and Side-Side-Side (SSS) Similarity

Prove that the triangles are similar.

1.

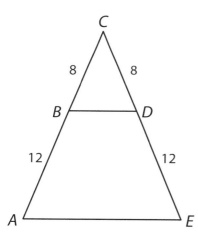

2.

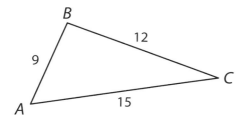

3.

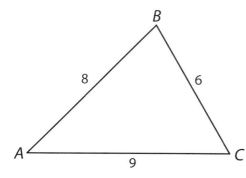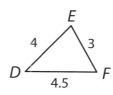

*continued*

# UNIT 5 • SIMILARITY, RIGHT TRIANGLE TRIGONOMETRY, AND PROOF
## Lesson 4: Proving Similarity

Determine whether the triangles are similar. If the triangles are similar, write a similarity statement.

4.

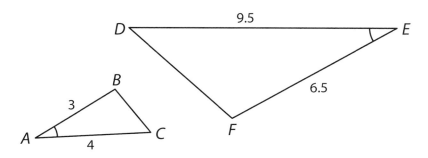

5.

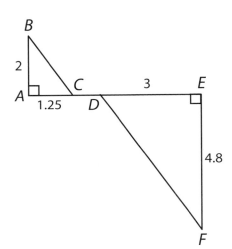

6.

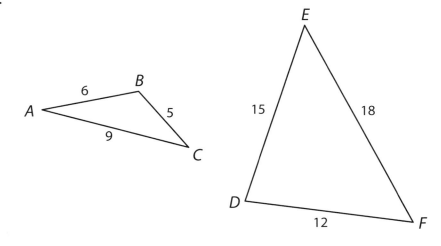

*continued*

7.

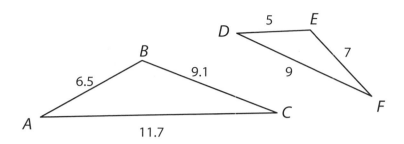

For problems 8–10, find $x$.

8.

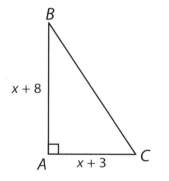

*continued*

9.

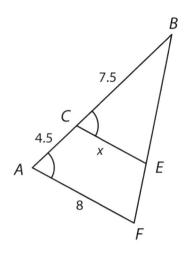

10.

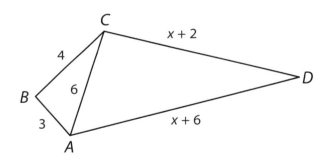

# Lesson 5.4.2: Working with Ratio Segments

## Introduction

Archaeologists, among others, rely on the Angle-Angle (AA), Side-Angle-Side (SAS), and Side-Side-Side (SSS) similarity statements to determine actual distances and locations created by similar triangles. Many engineers, surveyors, and designers use these statements along with other properties of similar triangles in their daily work. Having the ability to determine if two triangles are similar allows us to solve many problems where it is necessary to find segment lengths of triangles.

## Key Concepts

- **Parallel lines** are lines in a plane that either do not share any points and never intersect, or share all points.

- If a line parallel to one side of a triangle intersects the other two sides of the triangle, then the parallel line divides these two sides proportionally.

- This is known as the Triangle Proportionality Theorem.

| Theorem |
| --- |
| **Triangle Proportionality Theorem** |
| If a line parallel to one side of a triangle intersects the other two sides of the triangle, then the parallel line divides these two sides proportionally. 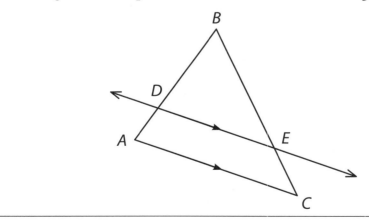 |

- In the previous figure, $\overline{AC} \parallel \overline{DE}$; therefore, $\dfrac{AD}{DB} = \dfrac{CE}{EB}$.

- Notice the arrows in the middle of $\overline{DE}$ and $\overline{AC}$, which indicate the segments are parallel.

- This theorem can be used to find the lengths of various sides or portions of sides of a triangle.

- $\triangle ABC \sim \triangle DBE$ because of the Side-Angle-Side (SAS) Similarity Statement.

- It is also true that if a line divides two sides of a triangle proportionally, then the line is parallel to the third side.

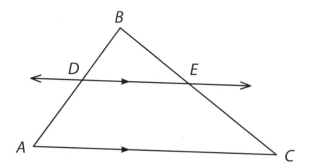

- In the figure above, $\dfrac{AD}{DB} = \dfrac{CE}{EB}$; therefore, $\overline{AC} \parallel \overline{DE}$.

- This is helpful when determining if two lines or segments are parallel.

- It is possible to determine the lengths of the sides of triangles because of the **Segment Addition Postulate**.

- This postulate states that if $B$ is between $A$ and $C$, then $AB + BC = AC$.

- It is also true that if $AB + BC = AC$, then $B$ is between $A$ and $C$.

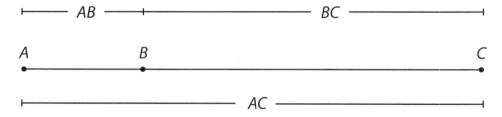

- Segment congruence is also helpful when determining the lengths of sides of triangles.

- The **Reflexive Property of Congruent Segments** means that a segment is congruent to itself, so $\overline{AB} \cong \overline{AB}$.

- According to the **Symmetric Property of Congruent Segments**, if $\overline{AB} \cong \overline{CD}$, then $\overline{CD} \cong \overline{AB}$.

- The **Transitive Property of Congruent Segments** allows that if $\overline{AB} \cong \overline{CD}$ and $\overline{CD} \cong \overline{EF}$, then $\overline{AB} \cong \overline{EF}$.

- This information is also helpful when determining segment lengths and proving statements.

- If one angle of a triangle is bisected, or cut in half, then the **angle bisector** of the triangle divides the opposite side of the triangle into two segments that are proportional to the other two sides of the triangle.

- This is known as the Triangle Angle Bisector Theorem.

---

**Theorem**

**Triangle Angle Bisector Theorem**

If one angle of a triangle is bisected, or cut in half, then the angle bisector of the triangle divides the opposite side of the triangle into two segments that are proportional to the other two sides of the triangle.

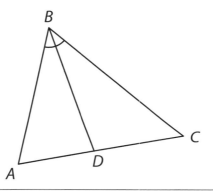

---

- In the figure above, $\angle ABD \cong \angle DBC$; therefore, $\dfrac{AD}{DC} = \dfrac{BA}{BC}$.

- These theorems can be used to determine segment lengths as well as verify that lines or segments are parallel.

# Guided Practice 5.4.2

**Example 1**

Find the length of $\overline{BE}$.

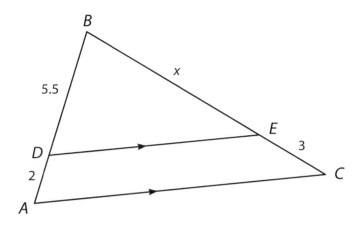

---

1. Identify the given information.

   According to the diagram, $\overline{AC} \parallel \overline{DE}$.

---

2. Find the length of $\overline{BE}$.

   Use the Triangle Proportionality Theorem to find the length of $\overline{BE}$.

   $\dfrac{BD}{DA} = \dfrac{BE}{EC}$      Create a proportion.

   $\dfrac{5.5}{2} = \dfrac{x}{3}$      Substitute the known lengths of each segment.

   $(3)(5.5) = (2)(x)$      Find the cross products.

   $16.5 = 2x$      Solve for $x$.

   $x = 8.25$

   The length of $\overline{BE}$ is 8.25 units.

## Example 2

Using two different methods, find the length of $\overline{CA}$.

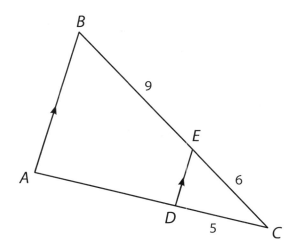

## Method 1

1. Identify the given information.

   According to the diagram, $\overline{AB}\|\overline{DE}$.

2. Find the length of $\overline{CA}$.

   Use the Triangle Proportionality Theorem to find the length of $\overline{CA}$.

   $\dfrac{CA}{CD}=\dfrac{CB}{CE}$      Create a proportion.

   $\dfrac{CA}{5}=\dfrac{9+6}{6}$      Substitute the known lengths of each segment.

   $(6)(CA) = (5)(9 + 6)$   Find the cross products.

   $(6)(CA) = (5)(15)$     Solve for $CA$.

   $(6)(CA) = 75$

   $CA = 12.5$

   The length of $\overline{CA}$ is 12.5 units.

## Method 2

1. Identify the given information.

   According to the diagram, $\overline{AB} \| \overline{DE}$.

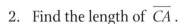

2. Find the length of $\overline{CA}$.

   Use the Triangle Proportionality Theorem to find the length of $\overline{CA}$.

   An alternative method for finding the length of $\overline{CA}$ is to first find the length of $\overline{DA}$.

   $\dfrac{CD}{DA} = \dfrac{CE}{EA}$       Create a proportion.

   $\dfrac{5}{x} = \dfrac{6}{9}$       Substitute the known lengths of each segment.

   $(5)(9) = (6)(x)$       Find the cross products.

   $45 = 6x$       Solve for $x$.

   $x = 7.5$

   The length of $\overline{CA}$ is equal to the sum of $\overline{CD}$ and $\overline{DA}$.

   $CD + DA = CA$

   $5 + 7.5 = 12.5$

   The length of $\overline{CA}$ is 12.5 units.

**Example 3**

Prove that $\overline{DE} \parallel \overline{AC}$.

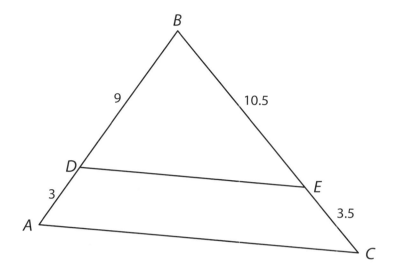

1. Determine if $\overline{DE}$ divides $\overline{BA}$ and $\overline{BC}$ proportionally.

$$\frac{BD}{DA} = \frac{9}{3} = 3$$

$$\frac{BE}{EC} = \frac{10.5}{3.5} = 3$$

2. State your conclusion.

$\dfrac{BD}{DA} = \dfrac{BE}{EC} = 3$; therefore, $\overline{DE} \parallel \overline{AC}$ because of the Triangle Proportionality Theorem.

## Example 4

Is $\overline{DE} \parallel \overline{AC}$ ?

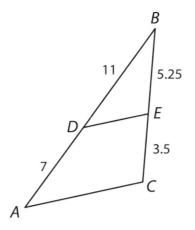

1. Determine if $\overline{DE}$ divides $\overline{BA}$ and $\overline{BC}$ proportionally.

$$\frac{BD}{DA} = \frac{11}{7}$$

$$\frac{BE}{EC} = \frac{5.25}{3.5} = \frac{3}{2}$$

2. State your conclusion.

$$\frac{11}{7} \neq \frac{3}{2}$$

$\frac{BD}{DA} \neq \frac{BE}{EC}$; therefore, $\overline{DE}$ is not parallel to $\overline{AC}$ because of the Triangle Proportionality Theorem.

**Example 5**

Find the lengths of $\overline{BD}$ and $\overline{DC}$.

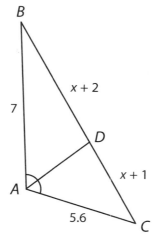

1. Identify the given information.

   $\angle BAD \cong \angle DAC$

   $\dfrac{BD}{DC} = \dfrac{BA}{AC}$ because of the Triangle Angle Bisector Theorem.

2. Determine the lengths of $\overline{BD}$ and $\overline{DC}$.

   $\dfrac{BD}{DC} = \dfrac{BA}{AC}$      Create a proportion.

   $\dfrac{x+2}{x+1} = \dfrac{7}{5.6}$      Substitute the known lengths of each segment.

   $(x+2)(5.6) = (x+1)(7)$    Find the cross products.

   $5.6x + 11.2 = 7x + 7$     Solve for $x$.

   $4.2 = 1.4x$

   $x = 3$

   $BD = x + 2 = 3 + 2 = 5$

   $DC = x + 1 = 3 + 1 = 4$

3. State your conclusion.

   The length of $\overline{BD}$ is 5 units.

   The length of $\overline{DC}$ is 4 units.

## Practice 5.4.2: Working with Ratio Segments

Use the Triangle Proportionality Theorem and the Triangle Angle Bisector Theorem to find the unknown lengths of the given segments.

1. $\overline{CD}$

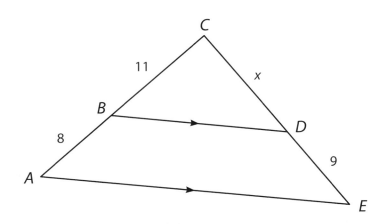

2. $\overline{BC}$

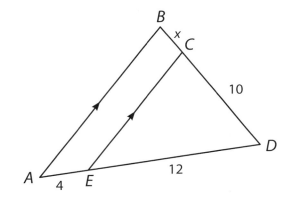

3. $\overline{DE}$

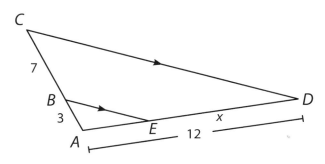

*continued*

4. $\overline{CD}$

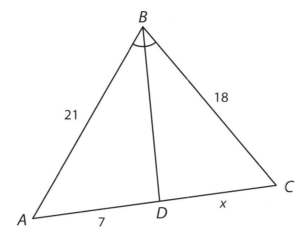

5. $\overline{BC}$ ; $\overline{CD}$

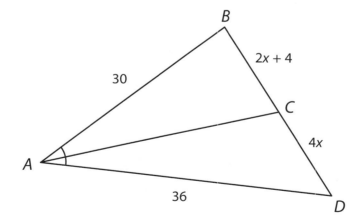

*continued*

6. $\overline{CB}$ ; $\overline{CD}$

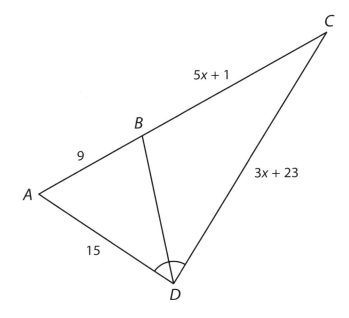

Use the Triangle Proportionality Theorem to determine if the given segments are parallel. Explain your reasoning.

7. Is $\overline{AB} \| \overline{EC}$ ?

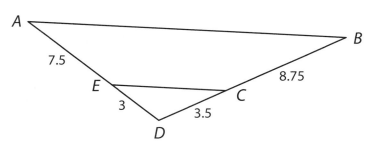

*continued*

8.  Is $\overline{AE} \parallel \overline{BD}$?

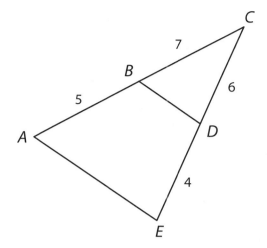

9.  If $AC = 22$ units and $AD = 27$ units, is $\overline{BE} \parallel \overline{CD}$?

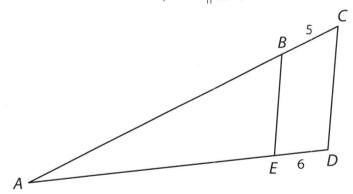

10.  If $AC = 10$ units and $EC = 14$ units, is $\overline{BD} \parallel \overline{AE}$?

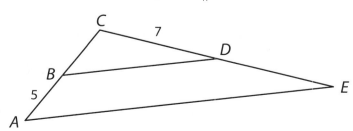

# Lesson 5.4.3: Proving the Pythagorean Theorem Using Similarity

## Introduction

Geometry includes many definitions and statements. Once a statement has been shown to be true, it is called a **theorem**. Theorems, like definitions, can be used to show other statements are true. One of the most well known theorems of geometry is the Pythagorean Theorem, which relates the length of the hypotenuse of a right triangle to the lengths of its legs. The theorem states that the sum of the squares of the lengths of the legs ($a$ and $b$) of a right triangle is equal to the square of the length of the hypotenuse ($c$). This can be written algebraically as $a^2 + b^2 = c^2$. The Pythagorean Theorem has many applications and can be very helpful when solving real-world problems. There are several ways to prove the Pythagorean Theorem; one way is by using similar triangles and similarity statements.

## Key Concepts

### The Pythagorean Theorem

- The Pythagorean Theorem is often used to find the lengths of the sides of a right triangle, a triangle that includes one 90° angle.

| Theorem |
| --- |
| **Pythagorean Theorem** |
| The sum of the squares of the lengths of the legs ($a$ and $b$) of a right triangle is equal to the square of the length of the hypotenuse ($c$). 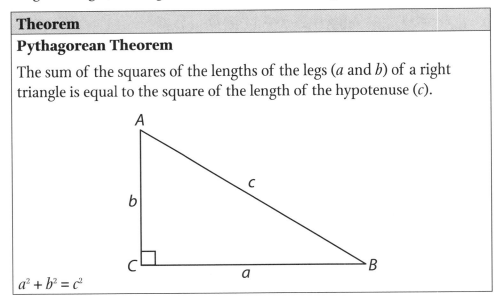 $a^2 + b^2 = c^2$ |

- In the triangle on the previous page, angle $C$ is 90°, as shown by the square.

- The longest side of the right triangle, $c$, is called the hypotenuse and is always located across from the right angle.

- The legs of the right triangle, $a$ and $b$, are the two shorter sides.

- It is also true that if the sum of the squares of the measures of two sides of a triangle equals the square of the measure of the longest side, then the triangle is a right triangle.

- This is known as the **converse of the Pythagorean Theorem**.

- To prove the Pythagorean Theorem using similar triangles, you must first identify the similar triangles.

- In this example, there is only one triangle given.

- Begin by drawing the **altitude,** the segment from angle $C$ that is perpendicular to the line containing the opposite side, $c$.

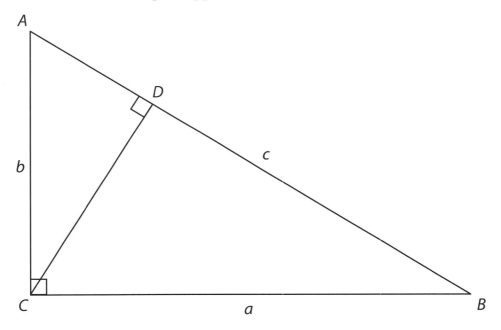

- Notice that by creating the altitude $\overline{CD}$, we have created two smaller right triangles, $\triangle ADC$ and $\triangle BDC$, within the larger given right triangle, $\triangle ACB$.

- $\angle ACB$ and $\angle ADC$ are 90° and are therefore congruent.

- $\angle A$ of $\triangle ADC$ is congruent to $\angle A$ of $\triangle ACB$ because of the Reflexive Property of Congruence.

- According to the Angle-Angle (AA) Similarity Statement, if two angles of one triangle are congruent to two angles of another triangle, then the triangles are similar; therefore, $\triangle ADC \sim \triangle ACB$.

- $\angle ACB$ and $\angle BDC$ are 90° and are therefore congruent.

- $\angle B$ of $\triangle BDC$ is congruent to $\angle B$ of $\triangle ACB$ because of the Reflexive Property of Congruence.

- Two angles in $\triangle BDC$ are congruent to two angles in $\triangle ACB$; therefore, $\triangle BDC \sim \triangle ACB$.

- Similarity is transitive. Since $\triangle ADC \sim \triangle ACB$ and $\triangle BDC \sim \triangle ACB$, then $\triangle ADC \sim \triangle BDC$.

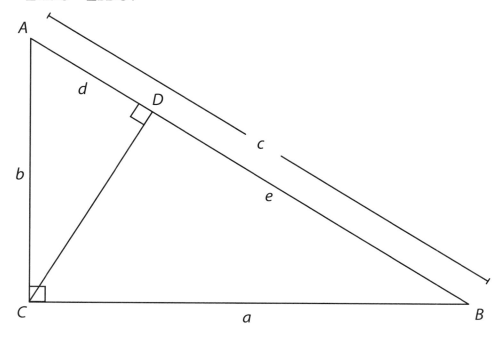

- Corresponding sides of similar triangles are proportional; therefore, $\dfrac{c}{b} = \dfrac{b}{d}$ and $\dfrac{c}{a} = \dfrac{a}{e}$.

- Determining the cross products of each proportion leads to the Pythagorean Theorem.

$$\frac{c}{b} = \frac{b}{d}$$
$$cd = b^2$$

$$\frac{c}{a} = \frac{a}{e}$$
$$ce = a^2$$

| | |
|---|---|
| $cd + ce = a^2 + b^2$ | Add both equations. |
| $c(e + d) = a^2 + b^2$ | Factor. |
| $c^2 = a^2 + b^2$ | $(e + d)$ is equal to $c$ because of segment addition. |

- The converse of the Pythagorean Theorem can be useful when proving right triangles using similar triangles.

## Types of Proofs

- **Paragraph proofs** are statements written out in complete sentences in a logical order to show an argument.

- **Flow proofs** are a graphical method of presenting the logical steps used to show an argument.

- In a flow proof, the logical statements are written in boxes and the reason for each statement is written below the box.

- Another accepted form of proof is a **two-column proof**.

- Two-column proofs include numbered statements and corresponding reasons that show the argument in a logical order.

- Two-column proofs appear in the Guided Practice examples that follow.

# Guided Practice 5.4.3

## Example 1

Write a two-column proof to prove the Pythagorean Theorem using similar triangles.

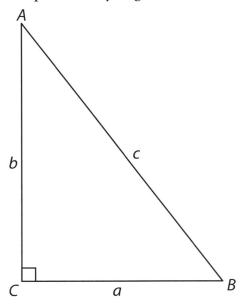

1. Draw in helpful information.

   Draw the altitude from $\angle C$ and label the point of intersection on $\overline{AB}$ as $D$.

   Label $\overline{AD}$ as $e$.

   Label $\overline{DB}$ as $f$.

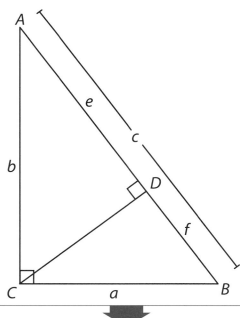

2.  Identify the similar triangles.

    It is often helpful to redraw the triangles.

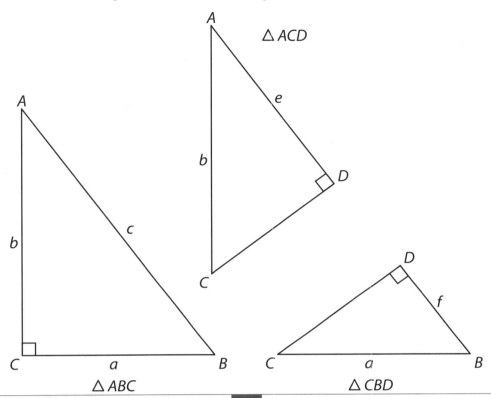

3.  Create the two-column proof.

| Statements | Reasons |
|---|---|
| 1.  $\triangle ABC$ with right $\angle C$ | 1.  Given |
| 2.  $\triangle ABC \sim \triangle ACD$<br>$\triangle ABC \sim \triangle CBD$ | 2.  If the altitude is drawn to the hypotenuse of a right triangle, then the two triangles formed are similar to the original triangle and each other. |
| 3.  $\dfrac{c}{a} = \dfrac{a}{f}$; $\dfrac{c}{b} = \dfrac{b}{e}$ | 3.  Definition of similar triangles; corresponding sides are proportional. |
| 4.  $cf = a^2$; $ce = b^2$ | 4.  Multiplication Property of Equality |
| 5.  $cf + ce = a^2 + b^2$ | 5.  Addition Property of Equality |
| 6.  $c(f + e) = a^2 + b^2$ | 6.  Distributive Property of Equality |
| 7.  $e + f = c$ | 7.  Segment Addition Postulate |
| 8.  $c(c) = a^2 + b^2$ or $c^2 = a^2 + b^2$ | 8.  Substitution Property |

## Example 2

Find the length of the altitude, $x$, of $\triangle ABC$.

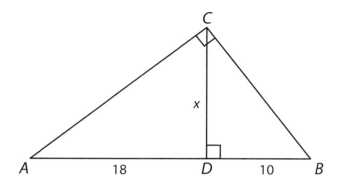

1.  Identify the similar triangles.

    $\triangle ABC$ is a right triangle.

    The altitude of $\triangle ABC$ is drawn from right $\angle ACB$ to the opposite side, creating two smaller similar triangles.

    $\triangle ABC \sim \triangle ACD \sim \triangle CBD$

2.  Use corresponding sides to write a proportion containing $x$.

    $$\frac{\text{shorter leg of } \triangle ACD}{\text{shorter leg of } \triangle CBD} = \frac{\text{longer leg of } \triangle ACD}{\text{longer leg of } \triangle CBD}$$

    $\dfrac{x}{10} = \dfrac{18}{x}$      Substitute values for each side.

    $(x)(x) = (10)(18)$      Find the cross products.

    $x^2 = 180$      Simplify.

    $x = 6\sqrt{5} \approx 13.4$      Take the positive square root of each side.

3.  Summarize your findings.

    The length of the altitude, $x$, of $\triangle ABC$ is $6\sqrt{5}$ units, or approximately 13.4 units.

## Example 3

Find the unknown values in the figure.

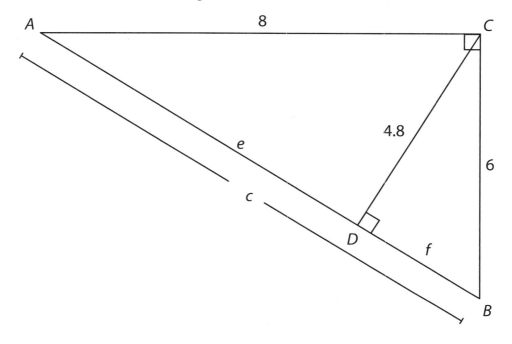

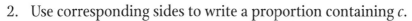

1. Identify the similar triangles.

   $\triangle ABC$ is a right triangle.

   The altitude of $\triangle ABC$ is drawn from right $\angle ACB$ to the opposite side, creating two smaller similar triangles.

   $\triangle ABC \sim \triangle ACD \sim \triangle CBD$

2. Use corresponding sides to write a proportion containing $c$.

   $$\frac{\text{hypotenuse of } \triangle ACD}{\text{hypotenuse of } \triangle ABC} = \frac{\text{shorter leg of } \triangle ACD}{\text{shorter leg of } \triangle ABC}$$

   | | |
   |---|---|
   | $\dfrac{8}{c} = \dfrac{4.8}{6}$ | Substitute values for each side. |
   | $(8)(6) = (c)(4.8)$ | Find the cross products. |
   | $48 = 4.8c$ | Simplify. |
   | $c = 10$ | Solve for $c$. |

3. Use corresponding sides to write a proportion containing $e$.

$$\frac{\text{longer leg of } \triangle ACD}{\text{longer leg of } \triangle ABC} = \frac{\text{shorter leg of } \triangle ACD}{\text{shorter leg of } \triangle ABC}$$

$\dfrac{e}{8} = \dfrac{4.8}{6}$      Substitute values for each side.

$(e)(6) = (8)(4.8)$      Find the cross products.

$6e = 38.4$      Simplify.

$e = 6.4$      Solve for $e$.

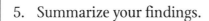

4. Use corresponding sides to write a proportion containing $f$.

$$\frac{\text{longer leg of } \triangle CBD}{\text{longer leg of } \triangle ABC} = \frac{\text{shorter leg of } \triangle CBD}{\text{shorter leg of } \triangle ABC}$$

$\dfrac{4.8}{8} = \dfrac{f}{6}$      Substitute values for each side.

$(4.8)(6) = (8)(f)$      Find the cross products.

$28.8 = 8f$      Simplify.

$f = 3.6$      Solve for $f$.

5. Summarize your findings.

The length of $c$ is 10 units.

The length of $e$ is 6.4 units.

The length of $f$ is 3.6 units.

### Practice 5.4.3: Proving the Pythagorean Theorem Using Similarity

Find the unknown length(s) in each figure.

1.

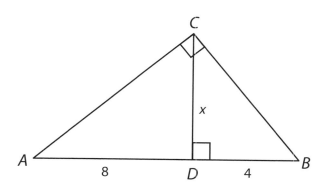

2.

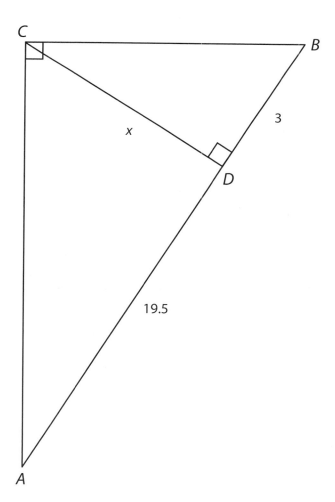

*continued*

3.

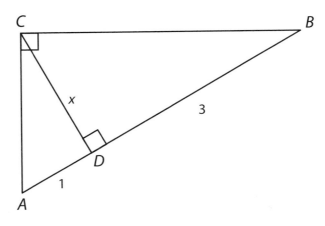

4.

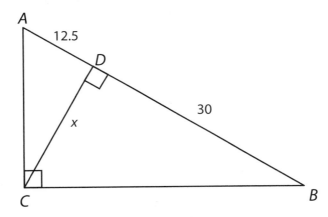

5.

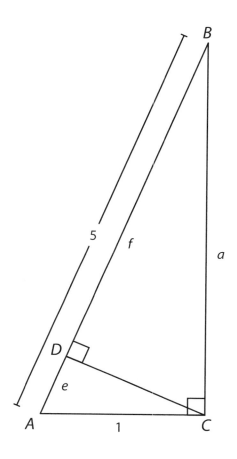

6.

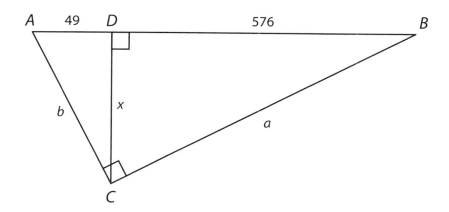

*continued*

7.

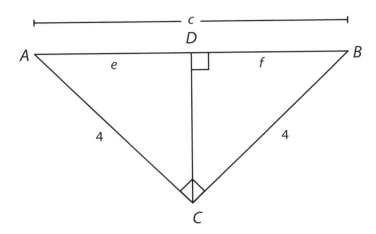

8.

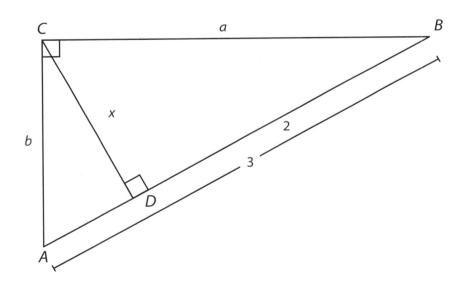

*continued*

9.

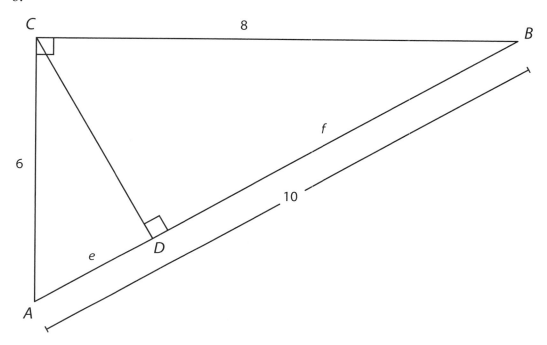

10. Using similar triangles, write a paragraph proof of the converse of the Pythagorean Theorem.

Given: $\triangle ABC$, with $c^2 = a^2 + b^2$

Prove: $\triangle ABC$ is a right triangle.

# Lesson 5.4.4: Solving Problems Using Similarity and Congruence

## Introduction

Design, architecture, carpentry, surveillance, and many other fields rely on an understanding of the properties of similar triangles. Being able to determine if triangles are similar and understanding their properties can help you solve real-world problems.

## Key Concepts

### Similarity

- Similarity statements include Angle-Angle (AA), Side-Angle-Side (SAS), and Side-Side-Side (SSS).

- These statements allow us to prove triangles are similar.

- Similar triangles have corresponding sides that are proportional.

- It is important to note that while both similarity and congruence statements include an SSS and an SAS statement, the statements do not mean the same thing.

- Similar triangles have corresponding sides that are proportional, whereas congruent triangles have corresponding sides that are of the same length.

### Triangle Theorems

- The Triangle Proportionality Theorem states that if a line parallel to one side of a triangle intersects the other two sides of the triangle, then the parallel line divides these two sides proportionally.

- This theorem can be used to find the lengths of various sides or portions of sides of a triangle.

- It is also true that if a line divides two sides of a triangle proportionally, then the line is parallel to the third side.

- The Triangle Angle Bisector Theorem states if one angle of a triangle is bisected, or cut in half, then the angle bisector of the triangle divides the opposite side of the triangle into two segments that are proportional to the other two sides of the triangle.

- The Pythagorean Theorem, written symbolically as $a^2 + b^2 = c^2$, is often used to find the lengths of the sides of a right triangle, which is a triangle that includes one $90°$ angle.

- Drawing the altitude, the segment from the right angle perpendicular to the line containing the opposite side, creates two smaller right triangles that are similar.

# Guided Practice 5.4.4

## Example 1

A meterstick casts a shadow 65 centimeters long. At the same time, a tree casts a shadow 2.6 meters long. How tall is the tree?

1. Draw a picture to understand the information.

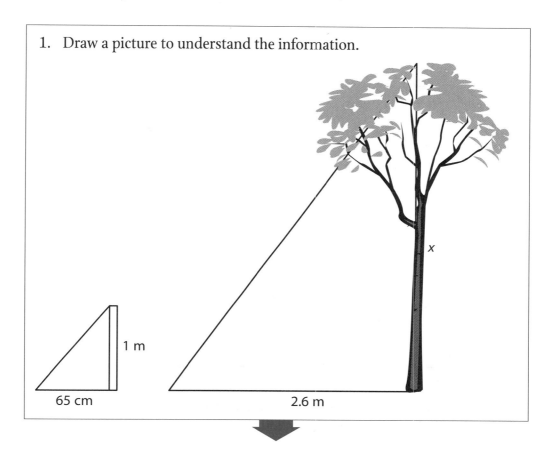

2. Determine if the triangles are similar.

The rays of the sun create the shadows, which are considered to be parallel.

Right angles are formed between the ground and the meterstick as well as the ground and the tree.

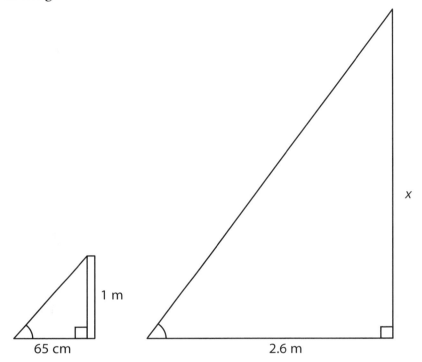

Two angles of the triangles are congruent; therefore, by Angle-Angle Similarity, the triangles are similar.

3. Solve the problem.

   Convert all measurements to the same units.

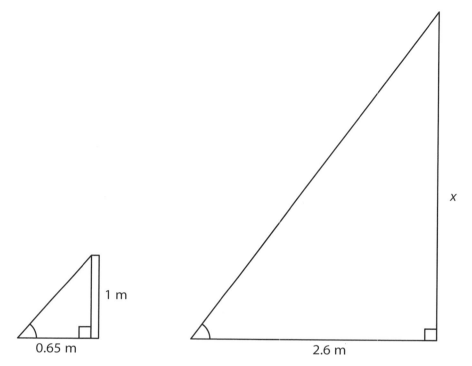

1 m

0.65 m

2.6 m

   Similar triangles have proportional sides.

   Create a proportion to find the height of the tree.

$$\frac{\text{height of stick}}{\text{height of tree}} = \frac{\text{length of stick's shadow}}{\text{length of tree's shadow}}$$   Create a proportion.

$$\frac{1}{x} = \frac{0.65}{2.6}$$   Substitute known values.

$(1)(2.6) = (0.65)(x)$   Find the cross products.

$2.6 = 0.65x$   Simplify.

$x = 4$   Solve for $x$.

   The height of the tree is 4 meters.

## Example 2

Finding the distance across a canyon can often be difficult. A drawing of similar triangles can be used to make this task easier. Use the diagram to determine $\overline{AR}$, the distance across the canyon.

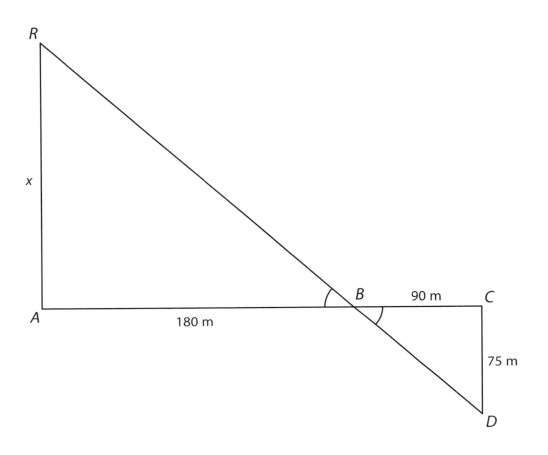

1.  Interpret the given information.

    A person standing at point $A$ can sight a rock across the canyon at point $R$.

    Point $C$ is selected so that $\overline{CA}$ is perpendicular to $\overline{AR}$, the distance across the canyon.

    Point $D$ is selected so that $\overline{CD}$ is perpendicular to $\overline{CA}$ and can be easily measured.

    The point of intersection of $\overline{RD}$ and $\overline{CA}$, point $B$, can then be found.

2. Determine if the triangles are similar.

$\angle A$ and $\angle C$ both measure 90° and are congruent.

$\angle RBA \cong \angle DBC$

By the Angle-Angle Similarity Statement, $\triangle RBA \sim \triangle DBC$.

3. Solve the problem.

Similar triangles have proportional sides.

Create a proportion to find the distance across the canyon.

$\dfrac{AB}{BC} = \dfrac{AR}{CD}$      Create a proportion.

$\dfrac{180}{90} = \dfrac{x}{75}$      Substitute known values.

$(180)(75) = (90)(x)$      Find the cross products.

$13{,}500 = 90x$      Simplify.

$x = 150$      Solve for $x$.

The distance across the canyon is 150 meters.

## Example 3

To find the distance across a pond, Rita climbs a 30-foot observation tower on the shore of the pond and locates points $A$ and $B$ so that $\overline{AC}$ is perpendicular to $\overline{CB}$. She then finds the measure of $\overline{DB}$ to be 12 feet. What is the measure of $\overline{AD}$, the distance across the pond?

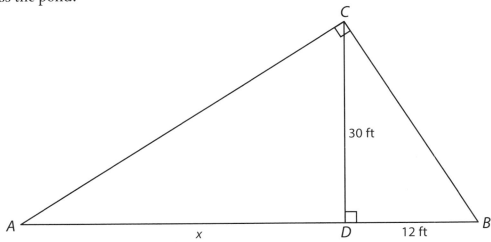

1. Determine if the triangles are similar.

   $\triangle ABC$ is a right triangle with $\angle C$ the right angle.

   $\overline{CD}$ is the altitude of $\triangle ABC$, creating two similar triangles, $\triangle ACD$ and $\triangle CBD$.

   $$\triangle ABC \sim \triangle ACD \sim \triangle CBD$$

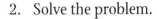

2. Solve the problem.

   Similar triangles have proportional sides.

   Create a proportion to find the distance across the pond.

   $\dfrac{BD}{CD} = \dfrac{CD}{AD}$      Create a proportion.

   $\dfrac{12}{30} = \dfrac{30}{x}$      Substitute known values.

   $(12)(x) = (30)(30)$      Find the cross products.

   $12x = 900$      Simplify.

   $x = 75$      Solve for $x$.

   The distance across the pond is 75 feet.

## Example 4

To estimate the height of an overhang, a surveyor positions herself so that her line of sight to the top of the overhang and her line of sight to the bottom form a right angle. What is the height of the overhang to the nearest tenth of a meter?

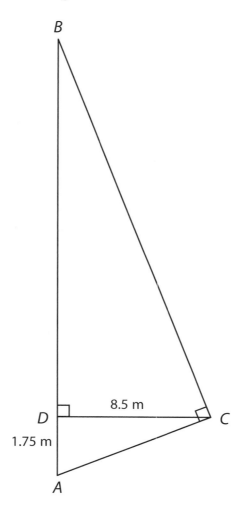

1. Determine if the triangles are similar.

   $\triangle ABC$ is a right triangle with $\angle C$ the right angle.

   $\overline{CD}$ is the altitude of $\triangle ABC$, creating two similar triangles, $\triangle ACD$ and $\triangle CBD$.

   $\triangle ABC \sim \triangle ACD \sim \triangle CBD$

2. Solve the problem.

Similar triangles have proportional sides.

Create a proportion to find the height of the overhang.

$$\dfrac{AD}{CD} = \dfrac{CD}{BD}$$     Create a proportion.

$$\dfrac{1.75}{8.5} = \dfrac{8.5}{x}$$     Substitute known values.

$(1.75)(x) = (8.5)(8.5)$     Find the cross products.

$1.75x = 72.25$     Simplify.

$x \approx 41.3$     Solve for $x$.

The length of $\overline{BD}$ is approximately 41.3 meters; however, the measure of the overhang is represented by $\overline{AB}$.

Find the length of $\overline{AB}$.

$41.3 + 1.75 = 43.05$

The height of the overhang is approximately 43.1 meters.

# UNIT 5 • SIMILARITY, RIGHT TRIANGLE TRIGONOMETRY, AND PROOF
## Lesson 4: Proving Similarity

## Practice 5.4.4: Solving Problems Using Similarity and Congruence

Use what you have learned about similar triangles to solve each problem.

1. A flat-roofed building casts a shadow that is 38 feet long. At the same time, a 6-foot-tall street sign casts a shadow that is 7 feet long. What is the height of the building?

2. A 20-foot statue casts a shadow that is 8 feet long. At the same time, a tree casts a shadow that is 3.5 feet long. What is the height of the tree?

For problems 3–10, use the information and the diagrams to solve each problem.

3. A piece of decorative trim is added to an asymmetrical roofline. What is the length of the roof from the peak to the decorative trim, $\overline{BD}$?

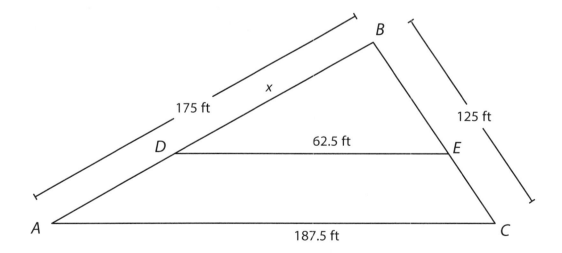

*continued*

4. A right-of-way parallel to Waterhouse Road is to be constructed on a triangular plot of land. What is the length of the plot of land along Elm Street between the right-of-way and Waterhouse Road?

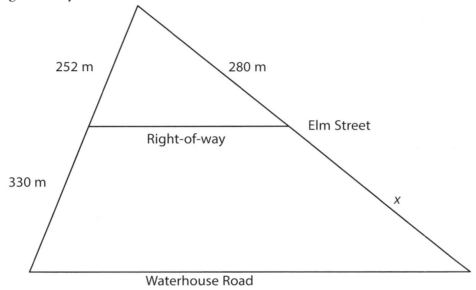

5. To measure $\overline{BC}$, the distance across a lake, a surveyor stands at point $A$ and locates points $B$, $C$, $D$, and $E$. To the nearest meter, what is the distance across the lake?

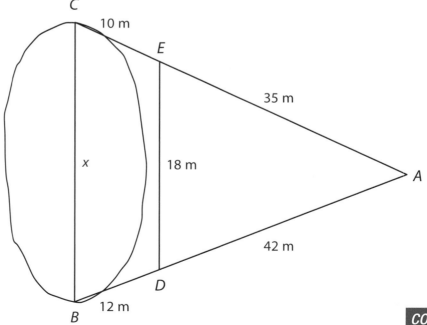

*continued*

6. To measure $\overline{BC}$, the distance across a sinkhole, an engineer stands at point $A$ and locates points $B$, $C$, $D$, and $E$. What is the distance across the sinkhole?

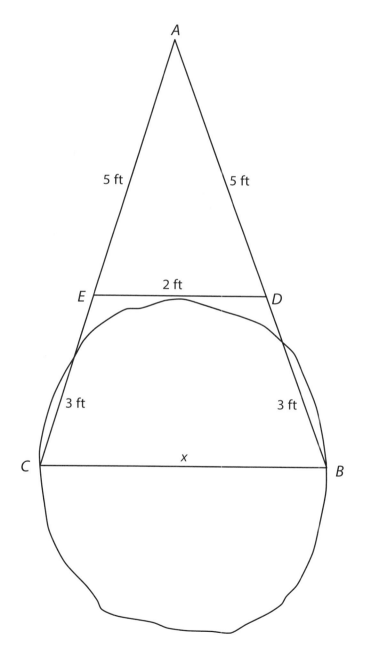

*continued*

7. To estimate the height of his school, a student positions himself so that his line of sight to the top of the school and his line of sight to the bottom form a right angle. What is the height of the school?

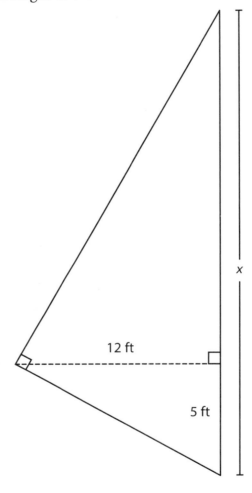

8. To estimate the height of a statue, Garrick positions himself so that his line of sight to the top of the statue and his line of sight to the bottom form a right angle. What is the height of the statue to the nearest tenth of a meter?

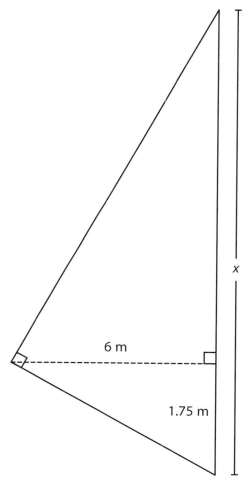

6 m

1.75 m

$x$

9. The height of a ramp at a point 2.0 meters from its bottom edge is 1.9 meters. If the ramp runs for 8.2 meters along the ground, what is its height at its highest point, to the nearest tenth of a meter?

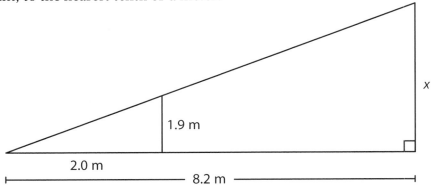

10. A geographer completed the following diagram to map a canyon's width. Determine $\overline{CD}$, the distance across the canyon.

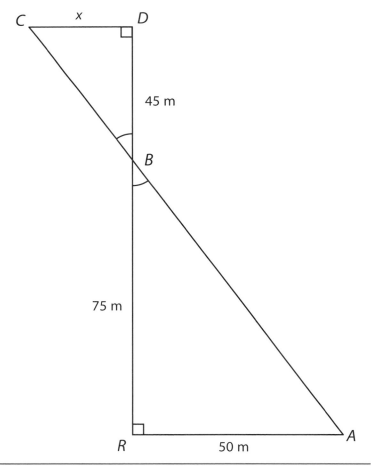

# Lesson 5: Proving Theorems About Lines and Angles

## Common Core State Standard

**G–CO.9**    Prove theorems about lines and angles. *Theorems include: vertical angles are congruent; when a transversal crosses parallel lines, alternate interior angles are congruent and corresponding angles are congruent; points on a perpendicular bisector of a line segment are exactly those equidistant from the segment's endpoints.*

## Essential Questions

1. How do angle relationships work together in two pairs of intersecting, opposite rays?

2. How do angle relationships work together in a set of parallel lines intersected by a transversal?

3. How are angle relationships important in the real world?

4. How do proofs apply to situations outside of mathematics?

## WORDS TO KNOW

| | |
|---|---|
| **adjacent angles** | angles that lie in the same plane and share a vertex and a common side. They have no common interior points. |
| **alternate exterior angles** | angles that are on opposite sides of the transversal and lie on the exterior of the two lines that the transversal intersects |
| **alternate interior angles** | angles that are on opposite sides of the transversal and lie within the interior of the two lines that the transversal intersects |
| **complementary angles** | two angles whose sum is 90° |
| **corresponding angles** | angles in the same relative position with respect to the transversal and the intersecting lines |
| **equidistant** | the same distance from a reference point |
| **exterior angles** | angles that lie outside a pair of parallel lines |

| | |
|---|---|
| **interior angles** | angles that lie between a pair of parallel lines |
| **linear pair** | a pair of adjacent angles whose non-shared sides form a straight angle |
| **nonadjacent angles** | angles that have no common vertex or common side, or have shared interior points |
| **perpendicular bisector** | a line that intersects a segment at its midpoint at a right angle |
| **perpendicular lines** | two lines that intersect at a right angle (90˚). The lines form four adjacent and congruent right angles. |
| **plane** | a flat, two-dimensional figure without depth that has at least three non-collinear points and extends infinitely in all directions |
| **postulate** | a true statement that does not require a proof |
| **proof** | a set of justified statements organized to form a convincing argument that a given statement is true |
| **right angle** | an angle measuring 90˚ |
| **same-side exterior angles** | angles that lie on the same side of the transversal and are outside the lines that the transversal intersects; sometimes called consecutive exterior angles |
| **same-side interior angles** | angles that lie on the same side of the transversal and are in between the lines that the transversal intersects; sometimes called consecutive interior angles |
| **straight angle** | an angle with rays in opposite directions; i.e., a straight line |
| **supplementary angles** | two angles whose sum is 180° |
| **transversal** | a line that intersects a system of two or more lines |
| **vertical angles** | nonadjacent angles formed by two pairs of opposite rays |

# Recommended Resources

- Interactivate. "Angles."

  http://www.walch.com/rr/00027

  This website generates a set of parallel lines intersected by a transversal and prompts users to identify the angle relationships. The site provides immediate feedback.

- IXL Learning. "Geometry: Angles: Identify complementary, supplementary, vertical, adjacent, and congruent angles."

  http://www.walch.com/rr/00028

  This online quiz allows users to receive immediate feedback about their answers. If the answer is incorrect, the program explains how to solve the problem correctly. This site deals with complementary, supplementary, vertical, adjacent, and congruent angles.

- IXL Learning. "Geometry: Parallel and perpendicular lines: transversals of parallel lines: find angle measures."

  http://www.walch.com/rr/00029

  This online quiz deals with angle relationships in a set of parallel lines intersected by a transversal, and provides immediate feedback. For incorrect answers, the program explains how to solve the problem correctly.

- Math Is Fun. "Vertically Opposite Angles."

  http://www.walch.com/rr/00030

  This website gives a brief explanation of vertical angles and provides a manipulative so users can investigate how angle measures change as the positions of the intersecting lines change. There is a short quiz at the end of the lesson, as well as links to other sites on angle relationships.

- Math-Play.com. "Angles Jeopardy Game."

  http://www.walch.com/rr/00031

  This online activity is provided in a game-show format that allows users to compete in teams or individually. The multiple-choice quiz questions pertain to angle relationships, and are worth points according to difficulty. Players receive immediate feedback.

# Lesson 5.5.1: Proving the Vertical Angles Theorem

## Introduction

Think about crossing a pair of chopsticks and the angles that are created when they are opened at various positions. How many angles are formed? What are the relationships among those angles? This lesson explores angle relationships. We will be examining the relationships of angles that lie in the same plane. A **plane** is a two-dimensional figure, meaning it is a flat surface, and it extends infinitely in all directions. Planes require at least three non-collinear points. Planes are named using those points or a capital script letter. Since they are flat, planes have no depth.

## Key Concepts

- Angles can be labeled with one point at the vertex, three points with the vertex point in the middle, or with numbers. See the examples that follow.

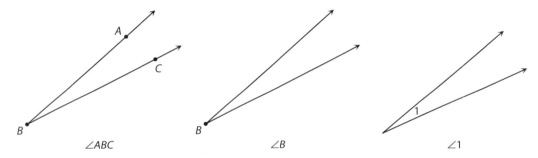

- Be careful when using one vertex point to name the angle, as this can lead to confusion.

- If the vertex point serves as the vertex for more than one angle, three points or a number must be used to name the angle.

- **Straight angles** are angles with rays in opposite directions—in other words, straight angles are straight lines.

| Straight angle | Not a straight angle |
|---|---|
| $\angle BCD$ is a straight angle. Points $B$, $C$, and $D$ lie on the same line. | $\angle PQR$ is not a straight angle. Points $P$, $Q$, and $R$ do not lie on the same line. |

- **Adjacent angles** are angles that lie in the same plane and share a vertex and a common side. They have no common interior points.

- **Nonadjacent angles** have no common vertex or common side, or have shared interior points.

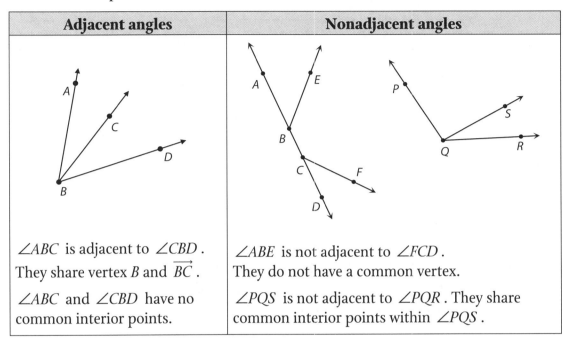

| Adjacent angles | Nonadjacent angles |
|---|---|
| $\angle ABC$ is adjacent to $\angle CBD$. They share vertex $B$ and $\overrightarrow{BC}$.<br><br>$\angle ABC$ and $\angle CBD$ have no common interior points. | $\angle ABE$ is not adjacent to $\angle FCD$. They do not have a common vertex.<br><br>$\angle PQS$ is not adjacent to $\angle PQR$. They share common interior points within $\angle PQS$. |

- **Linear pairs** are pairs of adjacent angles whose non-shared sides form a straight angle.

| Linear pair | Not a linear pair |
|---|---|
| $\angle ABC$ and $\angle CBD$ are a linear pair. They are adjacent angles with non-shared sides, creating a straight angle. | $\angle ABE$ and $\angle FCD$ are not a linear pair. They are not adjacent angles. |

- **Vertical angles** are nonadjacent angles formed by two pairs of opposite rays.

| Theorem |
| --- |
| **Vertical Angles Theorem** |
| Vertical angles are congruent. |

| Vertical angles | Not vertical angles |
| --- | --- |
| 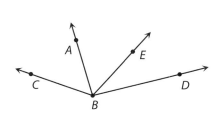 | |
| $\angle ABC$ and $\angle EBD$ are vertical angles. | $\angle ABC$ and $\angle EBD$ are not vertical angles. |
| $\angle ABC \cong \angle EBD$ | $\overrightarrow{BC}$ and $\overrightarrow{BD}$ are not opposite rays. |
| $\angle ABE$ and $\angle CBD$ are vertical angles. | They do not form one straight line. |
| $\angle ABE \cong \angle CBD$ | |

| Postulate |
| --- |
| **Angle Addition Postulate** |
| If $D$ is in the interior of $\angle ABC$, then $m\angle ABD + m\angle DBC = m\angle ABC$. |
| If $m\angle ABD + m\angle DBC = m\angle ABC$, then $D$ is in the interior of $\angle ABC$. |
| 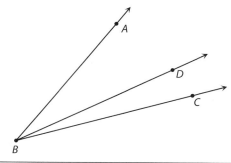 |

- Informally, the Angle Addition Postulate means that the measure of the larger angle is made up of the sum of the two smaller angles inside it. **Postulates** are true statements that don't need proofs.

- **Supplementary angles** are two angles whose sum is 180°.

- Supplementary angles can form a linear pair or be nonadjacent.

- In the following diagram, the angles form a linear pair.

    $m\angle ABD + m\angle DBC = 180$

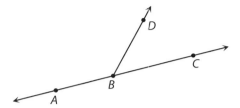

- The next diagram shows a pair of supplementary angles that are nonadjacent.

    $m\angle PQR + m\angle TUV = 180$

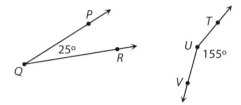

| Theorem |
| --- |
| **Supplement Theorem** |
| If two angles form a linear pair, then they are supplementary. |

- Angles have the same congruence properties that segments do.

| Theorem |
| --- |
| Congruence of angles is reflexive, symmetric, and transitive. |
|     •  Reflexive Property: $\angle 1 \cong \angle 1$ |
|     •  Symmetric Property: If $\angle 1 \cong \angle 2$, then $\angle 2 \cong \angle 1$. |
|     •  Transitive Property: If $\angle 1 \cong \angle 2$ and $\angle 2 \cong \angle 3$, then $\angle 1 \cong \angle 3$. |

| Theorem |
| --- |
| Angles supplementary to the same angle or to congruent angles are congruent. |
| If $m\angle 1 + m\angle 2 = 180$ and $m\angle 2 + m\angle 3 = 180$, then $\angle 1 \cong \angle 3$. |

- **Perpendicular lines** form four adjacent and congruent **right angles,** or 90° angles.

| Theorem |
| --- |
| If two congruent angles form a linear pair, then they are right angles. |
| If two angles are congruent and supplementary, then each angle is a right angle. |

- The symbol for indicating perpendicular lines in a diagram is a box at one of the right angles, as shown below.

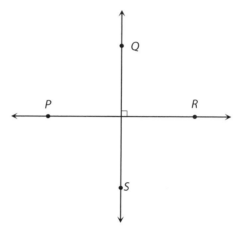

- The symbol for writing perpendicular lines is ⊥ , and is read as "is perpendicular to."

- In the diagram, $\overleftrightarrow{SQ} \perp \overleftrightarrow{PR}$.

- Rays and segments can also be perpendicular.

- In a pair of perpendicular lines, rays, or segments, only one right angle box is needed to indicate perpendicular lines.

- **Perpendicular bisectors** are lines that intersect a segment at its midpoint at a right angle; they are perpendicular to the segment.

- Any point along the perpendicular bisector is **equidistant,** or the same distance, from the endpoints of the segment that it bisects.

## Theorem

### Perpendicular Bisector Theorem

If a point lies on the perpendicular bisector of a segment, then that point is equidistant from the endpoints of the segment.

If a point is equidistant from the endpoints of a segment, then the point lies on the perpendicular bisector of the segment.

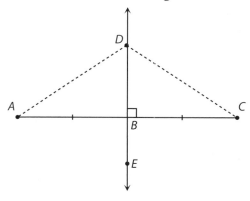

If $\overleftrightarrow{DE}$ is the perpendicular bisector of $\overline{AC}$, then $DA = DC$.

If $DA = DC$, then $\overleftrightarrow{DE}$ is the perpendicular bisector of $\overline{AC}$.

- **Complementary angles** are two angles whose sum is 90°.

- Complementary angles can form a right angle or be nonadjacent.

- The following diagram shows a pair of nonadjacent complementary angles.

$m\angle B + m\angle E = 90$

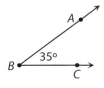 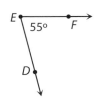

- The next diagram shows a pair of adjacent complementary angles labeled with numbers.

$$m\angle 1 + m\angle 2 = 90$$

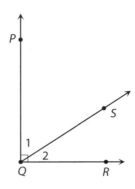

| Theorem |
| --- |
| **Complement Theorem** |
| If the non-shared sides of two adjacent angles form a right angle, then the angles are complementary. |
| Angles complementary to the same angle or to congruent angles are congruent. |

# Guided Practice 5.5.1

## Example 1

Look at the following diagram. List pairs of supplementary angles, pairs of vertical angles, and a pair of opposite rays.

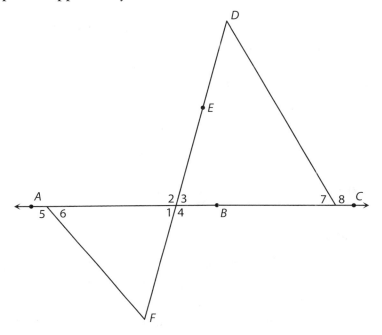

1.  List pairs of supplementary angles.

    Supplementary angles have a sum of 180°.

    ∠5 and ∠6 are adjacent supplementary angles. They form a linear pair.

    ∠1 and ∠4 are adjacent supplementary angles. They form a linear pair.

    ∠2 and ∠3 are adjacent supplementary angles. They form a linear pair.

    ∠7 and ∠8 are adjacent supplementary angles. They form a linear pair.

    ∠1 and ∠2 are adjacent supplementary angles. They form a linear pair.

    ∠3 and ∠4 are adjacent supplementary angles. They form a linear pair.

2. List the vertical angles.

   Vertical angles are nonadjacent angles that are formed by a pair of intersecting lines.

   $\angle 1$ and $\angle 3$ are vertical angles. They are formed by the intersecting segments of $\overleftrightarrow{AC}$ and $\overleftrightarrow{DF}$.

   $\angle 2$ and $\angle 4$ are vertical angles. They are formed by the intersecting segments of $\overleftrightarrow{AC}$ and $\overleftrightarrow{DF}$.

3. List a pair of opposite rays.

   Opposite rays form a straight angle.

   $\overrightarrow{BA}$ and $\overrightarrow{BC}$ are opposite rays.

   Also, $\overrightarrow{EF}$ and $\overrightarrow{ED}$ are opposite rays. This can be misleading since what is pictured represents segments, but remember that segments are just parts of lines and the line extends in both directions infinitely. From the line, any number of rays can be named.

## Example 2

Prove the theorem that angles complementary to congruent angles are congruent using the given information.

In the figure below, prove that $\angle 1$ is congruent to $\angle 4$, given that $\overleftrightarrow{AC}$ is perpendicular to $\overrightarrow{CD}$ and $\angle 2$ is congruent to $\angle 3$.

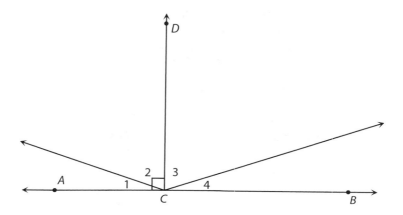

1.  Start by writing the given statements and the proof statement.

    Given: $\overleftrightarrow{AC} \perp \overrightarrow{CD}$; $\angle 2 \cong \angle 3$

    Prove: $\angle 1 \cong \angle 4$

2.  Start writing what you know about perpendicular lines and complementary angles.

    Perpendicular lines form four adjacent and congruent right angles.

    Complementary angles have a sum of 90°, which is a right angle.

3. Determine where the right angles are located and use the Complement Theorem.

$\angle ACD$ is a right angle because of the given information that $\overleftrightarrow{AC} \perp \overrightarrow{CD}$. $\angle ACD$ is made up of two adjacent complementary angles, $\angle 1$ and $\angle 2$. Therefore, $m\angle 1 + m\angle 2 = 90$.

$\angle BCD$ is a right angle because of the given information that $\overleftrightarrow{AC} \perp \overrightarrow{CD}$. $\angle BCD$ is made up of two adjacent complementary angles, $\angle 3$ and $\angle 4$. Therefore, $m\angle 3 + m\angle 4 = 90$.

4. Use the definition of congruence.

Since $\angle 2 \cong \angle 3$, $m\angle 2 = m\angle 3$. The definition of congruence states that if two angles are congruent, then the measures of their angles are equal.

5. Use substitution.

Since $m\angle 1 + m\angle 2 = 90$ and $m\angle 2 = m\angle 3$, $m\angle 1 + m\angle 3 = 90$. Notice that $m\angle 3$ was substituted in for $m\angle 2$.

Also, as stated in step 3, $m\angle 3 + m\angle 4 = 90$. Since two expressions ($m\angle 1 + m\angle 3$ and $m\angle 3 + m\angle 4$) both equal 90, set those two expressions equal to each other.

$m\angle 1 + m\angle 3 = m\angle 3 + m\angle 4$

6. Use the Reflexive Property.

$m\angle 3 = m\angle 3$

7. Use the Subtraction Property.

$m\angle 1 + m\angle 3 = m\angle 3 + m\angle 4$  Set the expressions equal to each other.

$m\angle 1 = m\angle 4$  Subtract $m\angle 3$ from both sides of the equation.

8. Use the definition of congruent angles.

$m\angle 1 = m\angle 4$

$\angle 1 \cong \angle 4$

9. Organize the information into a paragraph proof.

From the given information, 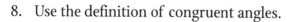 $\overleftrightarrow{AC}$ is perpendicular to $\overrightarrow{CD}$. By the definition of perpendicular lines, these perpendicular lines create four right angles. Two of the right angles are $\angle ACD$ and $\angle BCD$. Each of the angles is made up of two smaller angles. By the Complement Theorem, $m\angle 1 + m\angle 2 = 90$ and $m\angle 3 + m\angle 4 = 90$. Since $\angle 2 \cong \angle 3$, the measures of $\angle 2$ and $\angle 3$ are equal according to the definition of congruence. $m\angle 3$ can be substituted into the first complementary angle equation for $m\angle 2$ so that $m\angle 1 + m\angle 3 = 90$. Since two expressions are set equal to 90, they are equal to each other; therefore, $m\angle 1 + m\angle 3 = m\angle 3 + m\angle 4$. Congruence of angles is reflexive, meaning that $m\angle 3 = m\angle 3$. This angle can be subtracted from both sides of the equation, leaving $m\angle 1 = m\angle 4$. By the definition of congruent angles, $\angle 1 \cong \angle 4$.

**Example 3**

In the diagram below, $\overleftrightarrow{AC}$ and $\overrightarrow{BD}$ are intersecting lines. If $m\angle 1 = 3x+14$ and $m\angle 2 = 9x+22$, find $m\angle 3$ and $m\angle 4$.

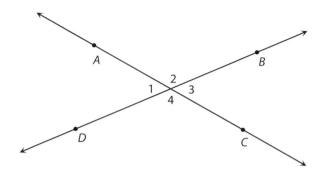

1. Use the Supplement Theorem.

   Since $\overleftrightarrow{BD}$ is a straight line, $m\angle 1 + m\angle 2 = 180$.

2. Use substitution to find the value of $x$.

   Substitute the measures of $\angle 1$ and $\angle 2$ into the equation $m\angle 1 + m\angle 2 = 180$.

   $m\angle 1 = 3x+14$

   $m\angle 2 = 9x+22$

   | | |
   |---|---|
   | $m\angle 1 + m\angle 2 = 180$ | Supplement Theorem |
   | $(3x + 14) + (9x + 22) = 180$ | Substitute $3x + 14$ and $9x + 22$ for $m\angle 1$ and $m\angle 2$. |
   | $12x + 36 = 180$ | Combine like terms. |
   | $12x = 144$ | Subtract 36 from both sides. |
   | $x = 12$ | Divide both sides by 12. |

3. Use substitution to find $m\angle 1$.

$m\angle 1 = 3x + 14$ and $x = 12$    Given

$m\angle 1 = 3(12) + 14$    Substitute 12 for $x$.

$m\angle 1 = 36 + 14$    Multiply.

$m\angle 1 = 50$    Add.

4. Use substitution to find $m\angle 2$.

$m\angle 2 = 9x + 22$ and $x = 12$    Given

$m\angle 2 = 9(12) + 22$    Substitute 12 for $x$.

$m\angle 2 = 108 + 22$    Multiply.

$m\angle 2 = 130$    Add.

5. Use the Vertical Angles Theorem to find $m\angle 3$ and $m\angle 4$.

$\angle 1$ and $\angle 3$ are vertical angles.

$\angle 1 \cong \angle 3$    Vertical Angles Theorem

$m\angle 1 = m\angle 3$    Definition of congruent angles

$50 = m\angle 3$    Substitute 50 for $m\angle 1$.

$\angle 2$ and $\angle 4$ are vertical angles.

$\angle 2 \cong \angle 4$    Vertical Angles Theorem

$m\angle 2 = m\angle 4$    Definition of congruent angles

$130 = m\angle 4$    Substitute 130 for $m\angle 2$.

$m\angle 3 = 50$; $m\angle 4 = 130$

The measure of $\angle 3$ is 50° and the measure of $\angle 4$ is 130°.

## Example 4

Prove that vertical angles are congruent given a pair of intersecting lines, $\overleftrightarrow{AC}$ and $\overleftrightarrow{BD}$.

1. Draw a diagram and label three adjacent angles.

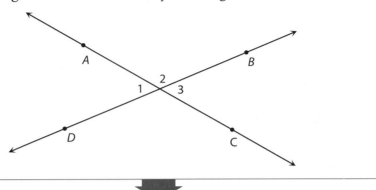

2. Start with the Supplement Theorem.

   Supplementary angles add up to 180°.

   $m\angle 1 + m\angle 2 = 180$

   $m\angle 2 + m\angle 3 = 180$

3. Use substitution.

   Both expressions are equal to 180, so they are equal to each other. Rewrite the first equation, substituting $m\angle 2 + m\angle 3$ in for 180.

   $m\angle 1 + m\angle 2 = m\angle 2 + m\angle 3$

4. Use the Reflexive Property.

   $m\angle 2 = m\angle 2$

5. Use the Subtraction Property.

Since $m\angle2 = m\angle2$, these measures can be subtracted out of the equation $m\angle1 + m\angle2 = m\angle2 + m\angle3$.

This leaves $m\angle1 = m\angle3$.

6. Use the definition of congruence.

Since $m\angle1 = m\angle3$, by the definition of congruence, $\angle1 \cong \angle3$.

$\angle1$ and $\angle3$ are vertical angles and they are congruent. This proof also shows that angles supplementary to the same angle are congruent.

## Example 5

In the diagram below, $\overleftrightarrow{DB}$ is the perpendicular bisector of $\overline{AC}$. If $AD = 4x - 1$ and $DC = x + 11$, what are the values of $AD$ and $DC$?

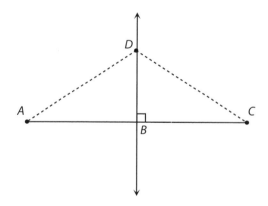

1. Use the Perpendicular Bisector Theorem to determine the values of $AD$ and $DC$.

If a point is on the perpendicular bisector of a segment, then that point is equidistant from the endpoints of the segment being bisected. That means $AD = DC$.

2. Use substitution to solve for $x$.

| | |
|---|---|
| $AD = 4x - 1$ and $DC = x + 11$ | Given equations |
| $AD = DC$ | Perpendicular Bisector Theorem |
| $4x - 1 = x + 11$ | Substitute $4x - 1$ for $AD$ and $x + 11$ for $DC$. |
| $3x = 12$ | Combine like terms. |
| $x = 4$ | Divide both sides of the equation by 3. |

3. Substitute the value of $x$ into the given equations to determine the values of $AD$ and $DC$.

$AD = 4x - 1$ $\qquad\qquad$ $DC = x + 11$

$AD = 4(4) - 1$ $\qquad\qquad$ $DC = (4) + 11$

$AD = 15$ $\qquad\qquad$ $DC = 15$

$AD$ and $DC$ are each 15 units long.

## Practice 5.5.1: Proving the Vertical Angles Theorem

Use the following diagram to solve problems 1–4.

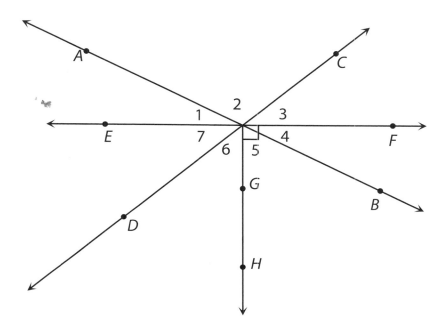

1. List two pairs of adjacent angles and two pairs of nonadjacent angles.

2. List three angles that altogether are supplementary angles. Write a statement about those angles using the Supplement Theorem.

3. List a pair of vertical angles. Write a statement about those angles using the Vertical Angles Theorem.

4. List a pair of complementary angles. Write a statement about those angles using the Complement Theorem.

In the diagram that follows, $\overleftrightarrow{AC}$ and $\overleftrightarrow{BD}$ intersect. Use this information to solve for the measures of the unknown angles in problems 5 and 6. Show and justify your work.

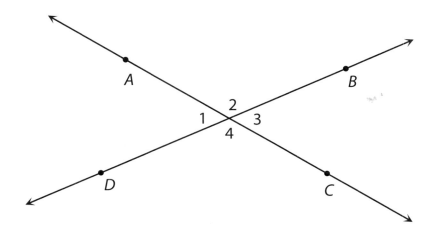

5. Find $m\angle 4$ if $m\angle 2 = 3x + 74$ and $m\angle 3 = 2x + 11$.

6. Find $m\angle 3$ if $m\angle 1 = 11x - 9$ and $m\angle 3 = 7x + 23$.

*continued*

# UNIT 5 • SIMILARITY, RIGHT TRIANGLE TRIGONOMETRY, AND PROOF
## Lesson 5: Proving Theorems About Lines and Angles

Use the diagram that follows to solve problems 7 and 8.

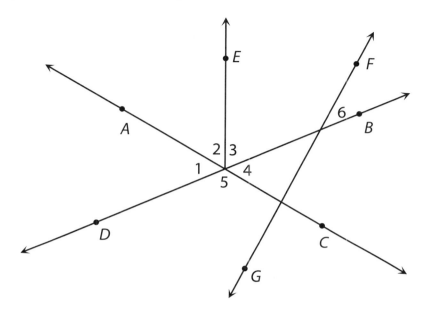

7. Find $m\angle5$ if $m\angle2=3x-6$, $m\angle3=5x-4$, and $m\angle5=7x+4$.

8. Find $m\angle1$ if $\angle4$ and $\angle6$ are complementary, $m\angle4=2x-8$, and $m\angle6=2x-14$.

*continued*

# UNIT 5 • SIMILARITY, RIGHT TRIANGLE TRIGONOMETRY, AND PROOF
## Lesson 5: Proving Theorems About Lines and Angles

Use the diagram that follows to solve problems 9 and 10.

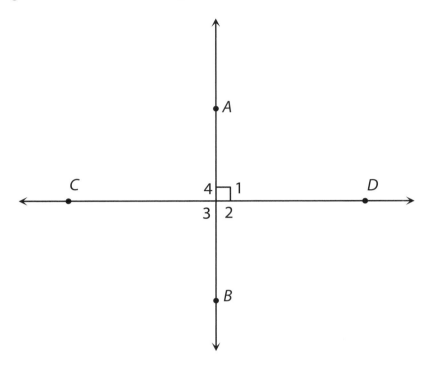

9. Given that $\overleftrightarrow{AB} \perp \overleftrightarrow{CD}$, prove that $\angle 2$, $\angle 3$, and $\angle 4$ are right angles.

10. Given that $\overleftrightarrow{AB}$ is the perpendicular bisector of $\overline{CD}$, $AC = 10x - 21$, and $AD = 7x + 18$, find the value of $x$.

# Lesson 5.5.2: Proving Theorems About Angles in Parallel Lines Cut by a Transversal

## Introduction

Think about all the angles formed by parallel lines intersected by a transversal. What are the relationships among those angles? In this lesson, we will prove those angle relationships. First, look at a diagram of a pair of parallel lines and notice the interior angles versus the exterior angles. The **interior angles** lie between the parallel lines and the **exterior angles** lie outside the pair of parallel lines. In the following diagram, line $k$ is the transversal. A **transversal** is a line that intersects a system of two or more lines. Lines $\ell$ and $m$ are parallel. The exterior angles are $\angle 1$, $\angle 2$, $\angle 7$, and $\angle 8$. The interior angles are $\angle 3$, $\angle 4$, $\angle 5$, and $\angle 6$.

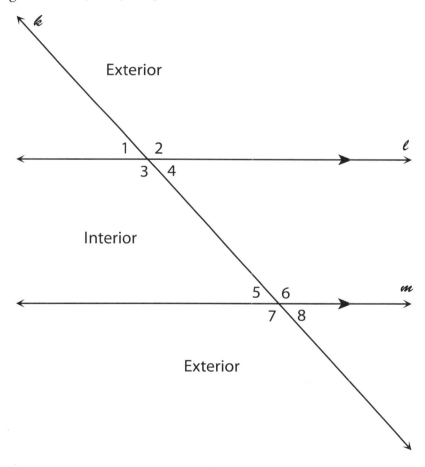

## Key Concepts

- A straight line has a constant slope and parallel lines have the same slope.

- If a line crosses a set of parallel lines, then the angles in the same relative position have the same measures.

- Angles in the same relative position with respect to the transversal and the intersecting lines are **corresponding angles**.

- If the lines that the transversal intersects are parallel, then corresponding angles are congruent.

---

**Postulate**

**Corresponding Angles Postulate**

If two parallel lines are cut by a transversal, then corresponding angles are congruent.

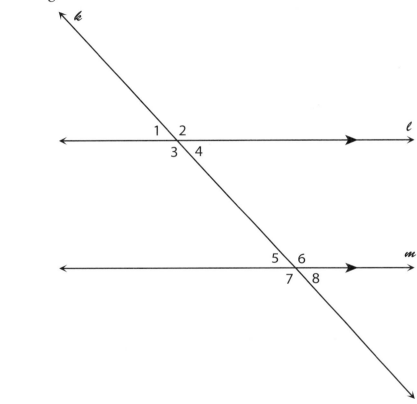

Corresponding angles:

$$\angle 1 \cong \angle 5, \ \angle 2 \cong \angle 6, \ \angle 3 \cong \angle 7, \ \angle 4 \cong \angle 8$$

The converse is also true. If corresponding angles of lines that are intersected by a transversal are congruent, then the lines are parallel.

---

- **Alternate interior angles** are angles that are on opposite sides of the transversal and lie on the interior of the two lines that the transversal intersects.

- If the two lines that the transversal intersects are parallel, then alternate interior angles are congruent.

---

**Theorem**

**Alternate Interior Angles Theorem**

If two parallel lines are intersected by a transversal, then alternate interior angles are congruent.

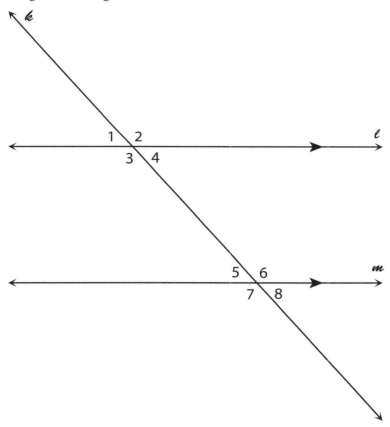

Alternate interior angles:

$\angle 3 \cong \angle 6$, $\angle 4 \cong \angle 5$

The converse is also true. If alternate interior angles of lines that are intersected by a transversal are congruent, then the lines are parallel.

---

- **Same-side interior angles** are angles that lie on the same side of the transversal and are in between the lines that the transversal intersects.

- If the lines that the transversal intersects are parallel, then same-side interior angles are supplementary.

- Same-side interior angles are sometimes called consecutive interior angles.

---

**Theorem**

**Same-Side Interior Angles Theorem**

If two parallel lines are intersected by a transversal, then same-side interior angles are supplementary.

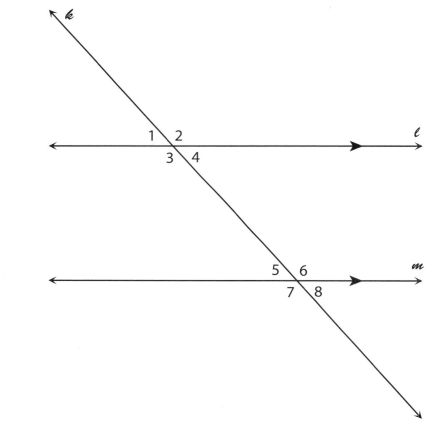

Same-side interior angles:

$$m\angle 3 + m\angle 5 = 180$$

$$m\angle 4 + m\angle 6 = 180$$

The converse is also true. If same-side interior angles of lines that are intersected by a transversal are supplementary, then the lines are parallel.

---

- **Alternate exterior angles** are angles that are on opposite sides of the transversal and lie on the exterior (outside) of the two lines that the transversal intersects.

- If the two lines that the transversal intersects are parallel, then alternate exterior angles are congruent.

---

**Theorem**

**Alternate Exterior Angles Theorem**

If parallel lines are intersected by a transversal, then alternate exterior angles are congruent.

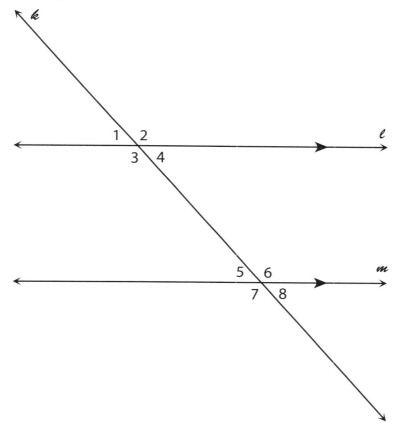

Alternate exterior angles:

$$\angle 1 \cong \angle 8, \ \angle 2 \cong \angle 7$$

The converse is also true. If alternate exterior angles of lines that are intersected by a transversal are congruent, then the lines are parallel.

---

- **Same-side exterior angles** are angles that lie on the same side of the transversal and are outside the lines that the transversal intersects.

- If the lines that the transversal intersects are parallel, then same-side exterior angles are supplementary.

- Same-side exterior angles are sometimes called consecutive exterior angles.

---

**Theorem**

**Same-Side Exterior Angles Theorem**

If two parallel lines are intersected by a transversal, then same-side exterior angles are supplementary.

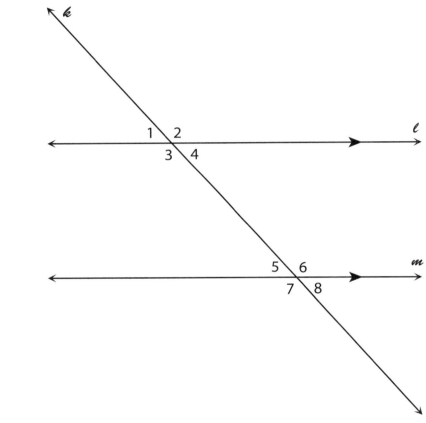

Same-side exterior angles:

$$m\angle 1 + m\angle 7 = 180$$
$$m\angle 2 + m\angle 8 = 180$$

The converse is also true. If same-side exterior angles of lines that are intersected by a transversal are supplementary, then the lines are parallel.

---

- When the lines that the transversal intersects are parallel and perpendicular to the transversal, then all the interior and exterior angles are congruent right angles.

---

**Theorem**

**Perpendicular Transversal Theorem**

If a line is perpendicular to one line that is parallel to another, then the line is perpendicular to the second parallel line.

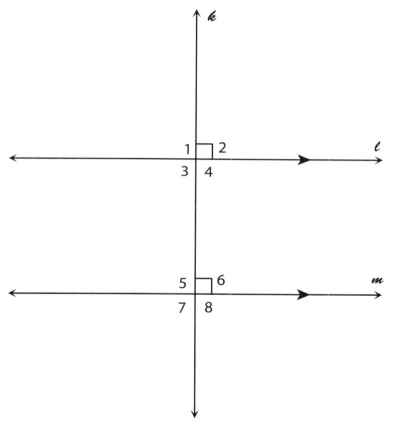

The converse is also true. If a line intersects two lines and is perpendicular to both lines, then the two lines are parallel.

# Guided Practice 5.5.2

## Example 1

Given $\overline{AB} \| \overline{DE}$, prove that $\triangle ABC \sim \triangle DEC$.

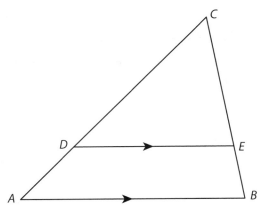

1. State the given information.

   $\overline{AB} \| \overline{DE}$

2. Extend the lines in the figure to show the transversals.

   Indicate the corresponding angles and mark the congruence of the corresponding angles with arcs.

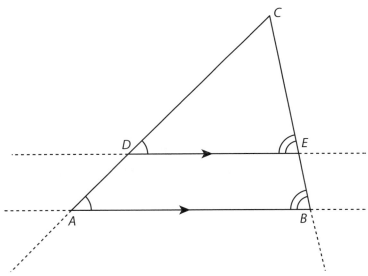

   $\angle CAB \cong \angle CDE$ and $\angle CBA \cong \angle CED$ because each pair is a set of corresponding angles.

3. Use the AA (angle-angle) criteria.

When two pairs of corresponding angles of a triangle are congruent, the angles are similar.

In this case, we actually know that all three pairs of corresponding angles are congruent because $\angle C \cong \angle C$ by the Reflexive Property.

4. Write the information in a two-column proof.

| Statements | Reasons |
|---|---|
| 1. $\overline{AB} \parallel \overline{DE}$ | 1. Given |
| 2. $\angle CAB \cong \angle CDE$, $\angle CBA \cong \angle CED$ | 2. Corresponding Angles Postulate |
| 3. $\triangle ABC \sim \triangle DEC$ | 3. AA Postulate |

## Example 2

Given two parallel lines and a transversal, prove that alternate interior angles are congruent. In the following diagram, lines $\ell$ and $m$ are parallel. Line $k$ is the transversal.

Given: $\ell \parallel m$, and line $k$ is a transversal.

Prove: $\angle 3 \cong \angle 6$

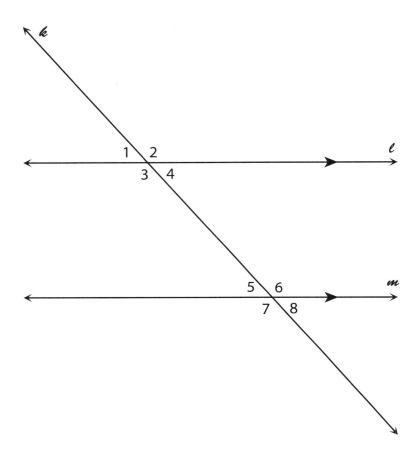

1. State the given information.

   $\ell \parallel m$, and line $k$ is a transversal.

2. Use the Corresponding Angles Postulate.

   Corresponding angles are angles that lie in the same relative position with respect to the transversal and the lines the transversal intersects. If the lines that the transversal intersects are parallel, then corresponding angles are congruent. $\angle 3$ and $\angle 7$ are corresponding angles because they are both below the parallel lines and on the left side of the transversal.

   $\angle 3 \cong \angle 7$ because they are corresponding angles.

3. Use the Vertical Angles Theorem.

   Vertical angles are formed when a pair of lines intersect. Vertical angles are the nonadjacent angles formed by these intersecting lines. Vertical angles are congruent.

   $\angle 7 \cong \angle 6$ because they are vertical angles.

4. Use the Transitive Property.

   Since $\angle 3 \cong \angle 7$ and $\angle 7 \cong \angle 6$, $\angle 3 \cong \angle 6$.

5. Write the information in a flow proof.

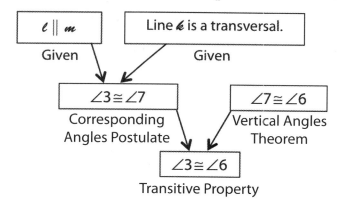

## Example 3

In the following diagram, $\overleftrightarrow{AB} \parallel \overleftrightarrow{CD}$ and $\overleftrightarrow{AC} \parallel \overleftrightarrow{BD}$. If $m\angle 1 = 3(x+15)$, $m\angle 2 = 2x+55$, and $m\angle 3 = 4y+9$, find the measures of the unknown angles and the values of $x$ and $y$.

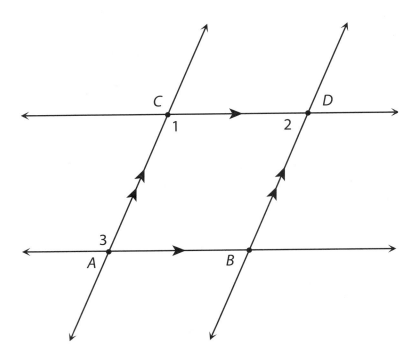

1. Find the relationship between two angles that have the same variable.

   $\angle 1$ and $\angle 2$ are same-side interior angles and are both expressed in terms of $x$.

2. Use the Same-Side Interior Angles Theorem.

   Same-side interior angles are supplementary. Therefore, $m\angle 1 + m\angle 2 = 180$.

3.  Use substitution and solve for $x$.

$m\angle 1 = 3(x+15)$ and $m\angle 2 = 2x+55$    Given

$m\angle 1 + m\angle 2 = 180$    Same-Side Interior Angles Theorem

$[3(x+15)] + (2x+55) = 180$    Substitute $3(x+15)$ for $m\angle 1$ and $2x+55$ for $m\angle 2$.

$(3x+45) + (2x+55) = 180$    Distribute.

$5x+100 = 180$    Combine like terms.

$5x = 80$    Subtract 100 from both sides of the equation.

$x = 16$    Divide both sides by 5.

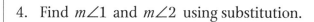

4.  Find $m\angle 1$ and $m\angle 2$ using substitution.

$m\angle 1 = 3(x+15)$; $x = 16$         $m\angle 2 = 2x+55$; $x = 16$

$m\angle 1 = 3[(16)+15]$              $m\angle 2 = 2(16)+55$

$m\angle 1 = 3(31)$                  $m\angle 2 = 32+55$

$m\angle 1 = 93$                     $m\angle 2 = 87$

After finding $m\angle 1$, to find $m\angle 2$ you could alternately use the Same-Side Interior Angles Theorem, which says that same-side interior angles are supplementary.

$m\angle 1 + m\angle 2 = 180$

$(93) + m\angle 2 = 180$

$m\angle 2 = 180 - 93$

$m\angle 2 = 87$

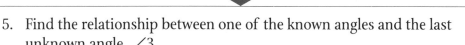

5.  Find the relationship between one of the known angles and the last unknown angle, $\angle 3$.

$\angle 1$ and $\angle 3$ lie on the opposite side of the transversal on the interior of the parallel lines. This means they are alternate interior angles.

6. Use the Alternate Interior Angles Theorem.

   The Alternate Interior Angles Theorem states that alternate interior angles are congruent if the transversal intersects a set of parallel lines. Therefore, $\angle 1 \cong \angle 3$.

7. Use the definition of congruence and substitution to find $m\angle 3$.

   $\angle 1 \cong \angle 3$, so $m\angle 1 = m\angle 3$.

   $m\angle 1 = 93$

   Using substitution, $93 = m\angle 3$.

8. Use substitution to solve for $y$.

   | | |
   |---|---|
   | $m\angle 3 = 4y + 9$ | Given |
   | $93 = 4y + 9$ | Substitute 93 for $m\angle 3$. |
   | $84 = 4y$ | Subtract 9 from both sides of the equation. |
   | $y = 21$ | Simplify. |

Unit 5: Similarity, Right Triangle Trigonometry, and Proof
5.5.2

## Example 4

In the following diagram, $\overleftrightarrow{AB} \| \overleftrightarrow{CD}$. If $m\angle 1 = 35$ and $m\angle 2 = 65$, find $m\angle EQF$.

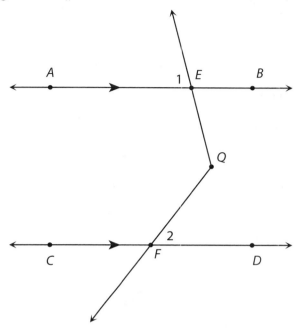

1. Draw a third parallel line that passes through point $Q$.

   Label a second point on the line as $P$. $\overleftrightarrow{PQ} \| \overleftrightarrow{AB} \| \overleftrightarrow{CD}$.

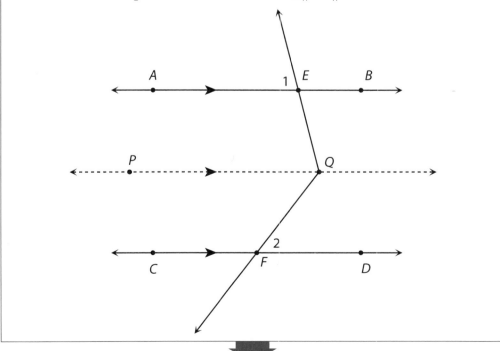

2. Use $\overrightarrow{QE}$ as a transversal to $\overleftrightarrow{AB}$ and $\overleftrightarrow{PQ}$ and identify angle relationships.

$\angle 1 \cong \angle BEQ$ because they are vertical angles.

$\angle BEQ \cong \angle EQP$ because they are alternate interior angles.

$\angle 1 \cong \angle EQP$ by the Transitive Property.

It was given that $m\angle 1 = 35$.

By substitution, $m\angle EQP = 35$.

3. Use $\overrightarrow{QF}$ as a transversal to $\overleftrightarrow{PQ}$ and $\overleftrightarrow{CD}$ and identify angle relationships.

$\angle 2 \cong \angle FQP$ because they are alternate interior angles.

It was given that $m\angle 2 = 65$.

By substitution, $m\angle FQP = 65$.

4. Use angle addition.

Notice that the angle measure we are looking for is made up of two smaller angle measures that we just found.

$m\angle EQF = m\angle EQP + m\angle FQP$

$m\angle EQF = 35 + 65$

$m\angle EQF = 100$

## Practice 5.5.2: Proving Theorems About Angles in Parallel Lines Cut by a Transversal

Use the following diagram to solve problems 1–5, given that $\overrightarrow{AB} \| \overleftrightarrow{CD}$ and line $\ell$ is the transversal. Justify your answers using angle relationships in parallel lines intersected by a transversal.

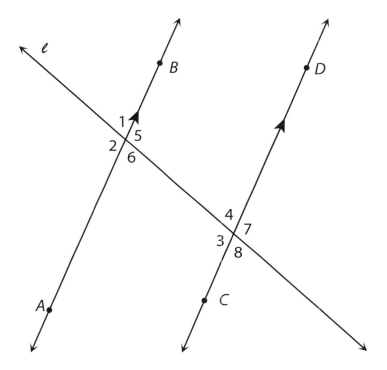

1.  Find $m\angle 8$ if $m\angle 1 = 2(x+38)$ and $m\angle 8 = 13x + 10$.

2.  Find $m\angle 3$ if $m\angle 3 = 9(x+5)$ and $m\angle 6 = 11x + 35$.

3.  Find $m\angle 5$ if $m\angle 5 = 6x + 62$ and $m\angle 3 = 2(7x + 15)$.

4.  Find $m\angle 1$ if $m\angle 1 = 3(x-4)$ and $m\angle 7 = 5x + 8$.

5.  Find $m\angle 2$ if $m\angle 2 = 4(x+18)$ and $m\angle 3 = 8x$.

Use the following diagram to solve problems 6 and 7. Given: $\overleftrightarrow{AB} \parallel \overleftrightarrow{CD}$.
Justify your reasoning.

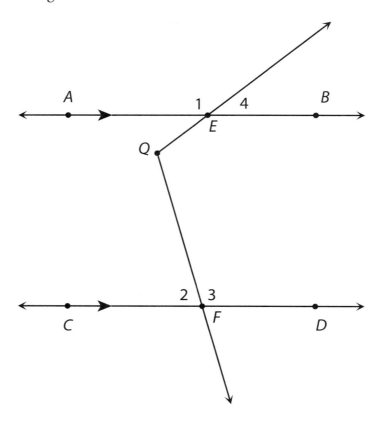

6. Find $m\angle EQF$ if $m\angle 4 = 46$ and $m\angle 3 = 115$.

7. Find $m\angle EQF$ if $m\angle 1 = 147$ and $m\angle 2 = 62$.

# UNIT 5 • SIMILARITY, RIGHT TRIANGLE TRIGONOMETRY, AND PROOF
## Lesson 5: Proving Theorems About Lines and Angles

Use the following diagram to solve problem 8. Given: $\overleftrightarrow{AF} \parallel \overleftrightarrow{BE}$, $\overleftrightarrow{HC} \parallel \overleftrightarrow{GD}$, $m\angle 1 = 4(3y-11)$, $m\angle 2 = 7x+3$, and $m\angle 3 = 5(x+5)$.

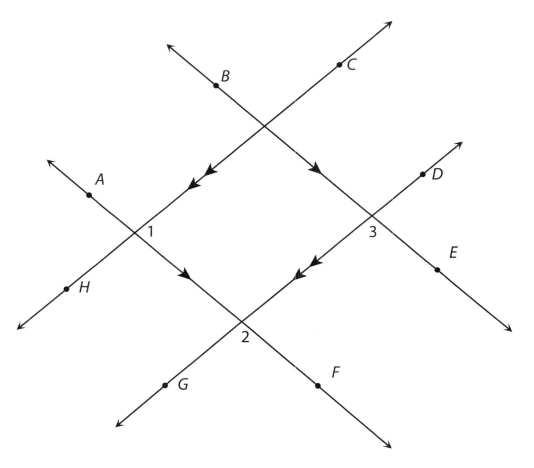

8. Find the measures of the numbered angles and the values of $x$ and $y$. Justify your reasoning.

For problem 9, prove that same-side exterior angles are supplementary using the given information and the diagram below.

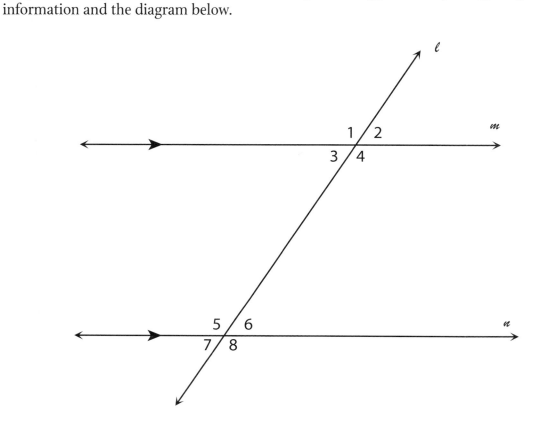

9. Given that $\ell$ is a transversal and lines $m$ and $n$ are parallel, prove that $\angle 2$ and $\angle 8$ are supplementary.

*continued*

# UNIT 5 • SIMILARITY, RIGHT TRIANGLE TRIGONOMETRY, AND PROOF
## Lesson 5: Proving Theorems About Lines and Angles

For problem 10, prove the Perpendicular Transversal Theorem using the given information and the diagram below.

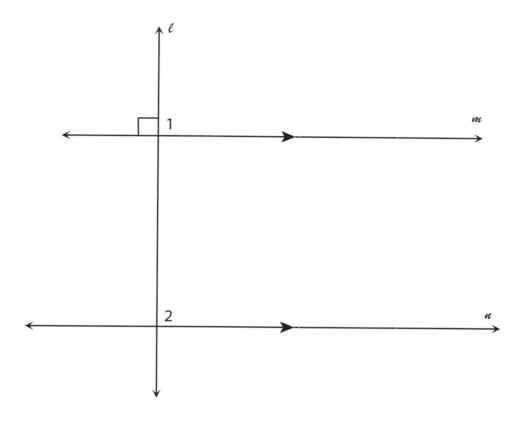

10. Given that $\ell$ is a transversal, lines $m$ and $n$ are parallel, and line $\ell$ is perpendicular to line $m$, prove that line $\ell$ is perpendicular to line $n$. Justify your answer in a proof.

# Lesson 6: Proving Theorems About Triangles

## Common Core State Standard

**G–CO.10** Prove theorems about triangles. *Theorems include: measures of interior angles of a triangle sum to 180°; base angles of isosceles triangles are congruent; the segment joining midpoints of two s ides of a triangle is parallel to the third side and half the length; the medians of a triangle meet at a point.*

## Essential Questions

1. What is the relationship between an interior and exterior angle at the same vertex?

2. What is the relationship between an exterior angle and the remote interior angles of a triangle?

3. How are properties of isosceles triangles used and applied?

4. What relationships exist between the midsegment and a triangle?

5. How can the point of concurrency be used to solve problems?

6. What are the similarities and differences among medians, altitudes, perpendicular bisectors, and angle bisectors of a triangle?

7. Is there only one center of a circle?

## WORDS TO KNOW

| | |
|---|---|
| **acute triangle** | a triangle in which all of the angles are acute (less than 90°) |
| **base** | the side that is opposite the vertex angle of an isosceles triangle |
| **base angle** | an angle formed by the base and one congruent side of an isosceles triangle |
| **centroid** | the intersection of the medians of a triangle |
| **circumcenter** | the intersection of the perpendicular bisectors of a triangle |
| **circumscribed circle** | a circle that contains all vertices of a polygon |

| | |
|---|---|
| **concurrent lines** | lines that intersect at one point |
| **coordinate proof** | a proof that involves calculations and makes reference to the coordinate plane |
| **equiangular** | having equal angles |
| **equilateral triangle** | a triangle with all three sides equal in length |
| **exterior angle of a polygon** | an angle formed by one side of a polygon and the extension of another side |
| **incenter** | the intersection of the angle bisectors of a triangle |
| **interior angle of a polygon** | an angle formed by two sides of a polygon |
| **inscribed circle** | a circle that contains one point from each side of a triangle |
| **isosceles triangle** | a triangle with at least two congruent sides |
| **legs** | congruent sides of an isosceles triangle |
| **median of a triangle** | the segment joining the vertex to the midpoint of the opposite side |
| **midpoint** | a point on a line segment that divides the segment into two equal parts |
| **midpoint formula** | a formula that states the midpoint of a segment created by connecting $(x_1, y_1)$ and $(x_2, y_2)$ is given by the formula $\left( \dfrac{x_1 + x_2}{2}, \dfrac{y_1 + y_2}{2} \right)$ |
| **midsegment** | a line segment joining the midpoints of two sides of a figure |
| **midsegment triangle** | the triangle formed when all three of the midsegments of a triangle are connected |
| **obtuse triangle** | a triangle with one angle that is obtuse (greater than 90°) |
| **orthocenter** | the intersection of the altitudes of a triangle |
| **point of concurrency** | a single point of intersection of three or more lines |
| **remote interior angles** | interior angles that are not adjacent to the exterior angle |
| **right triangle** | a triangle with one angle that measures 90° |
| **scalene triangle** | a triangle with no congruent sides |

| **supplementary angles** | two angles whose sum is 180° |
| **vertex angle** | angle formed by the legs of an isosceles triangle |

## Recommended Resources

- IXL Learning. "Triangles: Midsegments of triangles."

  http://www.walch.com/rr/00032

  This interactive website provides a series of problems related to midsegments of triangles and scores them immediately. If the user submits a wrong answer, a description and process for arriving at the correct answer are given.

- Math Open Reference. "Centroid of a Triangle."

  http://www.walch.com/rr/00033

  This website gives a brief explanation of the centroid of a triangle. An interactive applet allows users to change the size and shape of a triangle and observe the changes in the centroid. Also included are links to summaries of each of the triangle centers.

- Math Open Reference. "Isosceles Triangle."

  http://www.walch.com/rr/00034

  This website gives a brief explanation of the properties of isosceles triangles. Also included are links to finding the centers of triangles, as well as an interactive illustration demonstrating isosceles triangle properties.

- Math Warehouse. "Triangles."

  http://www.walch.com/rr/00035

  This website gives a brief explanation of the properties of triangles, including interior and exterior angles. The site also contains an interactive applet that allows users to change the measure of one angle of a triangle and observe the changes in the remaining angles.

- Mathwords.com. "Centers of a Triangle."

  http://www.walch.com/rr/00036

  This website contains a chart of the centers of a triangles and the lines used to find each center, as well as where the center is located on various triangles. Also included are links to interactive applets for each center.

# Lesson 5.6.1: Proving the Interior Angle Sum Theorem

## Introduction

Think of all the different kinds of triangles you can create. What are the similarities among the triangles? What are the differences? Are there properties that hold true for all triangles and others that only hold true for certain types of triangles? This lesson will explore angle relationships of triangles. We will examine the relationships of interior angles of triangles as well as the exterior angles of triangles, and how these relationships can be used to find unknown angle measures.

## Key Concepts

- There is more to a triangle than just three sides and three angles.

- Triangles can be classified by their angle measures or by their side lengths.

- Triangles classified by their angle measures can be acute, obtuse, or right triangles.

- All of the angles of an **acute triangle** are acute, or less than 90°.

- One angle of an **obtuse triangle** is obtuse, or greater than 90°.

- A **right triangle** has one angle that measures 90°.

| Acute triangle | Obtuse triangle | Right triangle |
|---|---|---|
| | | |
| All angles are less than 90°. | One angle is greater than 90°. | One angle measures 90°. |

- Triangles classified by the number of congruent sides can be scalene, isosceles, or equilateral.

- A **scalene triangle** has no congruent sides.

- An **isosceles triangle** has at least two congruent sides.

- An **equilateral triangle** has three congruent sides.

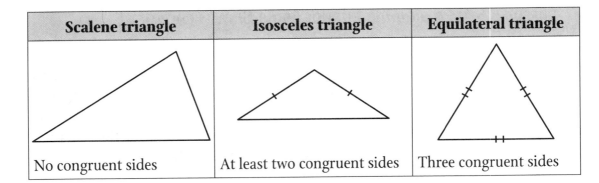

| Scalene triangle | Isosceles triangle | Equilateral triangle |
|---|---|---|
| No congruent sides | At least two congruent sides | Three congruent sides |

- It is possible to create many different triangles, but the sum of the angle measures of every triangle is 180°. This is known as the Triangle Sum Theorem.

---

**Theorem**

**Triangle Sum Theorem**

The sum of the angle measures of a triangle is 180°.

$$m\angle A + m\angle B + m\angle C = 180$$

---

- The Triangle Sum Theorem can be proven using the Parallel Postulate.
- The Parallel Postulate states that if a line can be created through a point not on a given line, then that line will be parallel to the given line.

- This postulate allows us to create a line parallel to one side of a triangle to prove angle relationships.

---

**Postulate**

**Parallel Postulate**

Given a line and a point not on it, there exists one and only one straight line that passes through that point and never intersects the first line.

---

- This theorem can be used to determine a missing angle measure by subtracting the known measures from $180°$.

- Most often, triangles are described by what is known as the **interior angles** of triangles (the angles formed by two sides of the triangle), but exterior angles also exist.

- In other words, interior angles are the angles inside the triangle.

- **Exterior angles** are angles formed by one side of the triangle and the extension of another side.

- The interior angles that are not adjacent to the exterior angle are called the **remote interior angles** of the exterior angle.

- The following illustration shows the differences among interior angles, exterior angles, and remote interior angles.

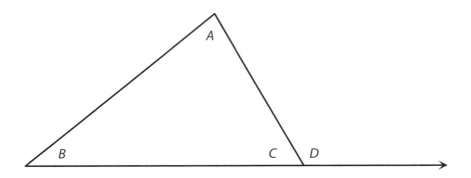

- Interior angles: $\angle A$, $\angle B$, and $\angle C$

- Exterior angle: $\angle D$

- Remote interior angles of $\angle D$: $\angle A$ and $\angle B$

- Notice that $\angle C$ and $\angle D$ are supplementary; that is, together they create a line and sum to $180°$.

- The measure of an exterior angle is equal to the sum of the measure of its remote interior angles. This is known as the Exterior Angle Theorem.

**Theorem**

**Exterior Angle Theorem**

The measure of an exterior angle of a triangle is equal to the sum of the measures of its remote interior angles.

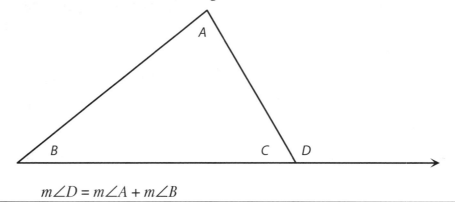

$$m\angle D = m\angle A + m\angle B$$

- This theorem can also be used to determine a missing angle measure of a triangle.

- The measure of an exterior angle will always be greater than either of the remote interior angles. This is known as the Exterior Angle Inequality Theorem.

| Theorem |
|---|
| **Exterior Angle Inequality Theorem** |

If an angle is an exterior angle of a triangle, then its measure is greater than the measure of either of its corresponding remote interior angles.

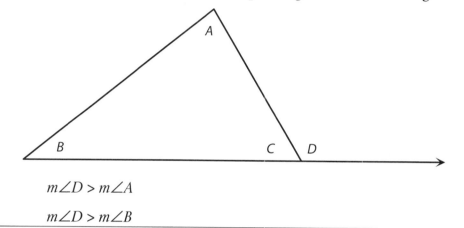

$$m\angle D > m\angle A$$
$$m\angle D > m\angle B$$

- The following theorems are also helpful when finding the measures of missing angles and side lengths.

| Theorem |
|---|
| If one side of a triangle is longer than another side, then the angle opposite the longer side has a greater measure than the angle opposite the shorter side. |

## Theorem

If one angle of a triangle has a greater measure than another angle, then the side opposite the greater angle is longer than the side opposite the lesser angle.

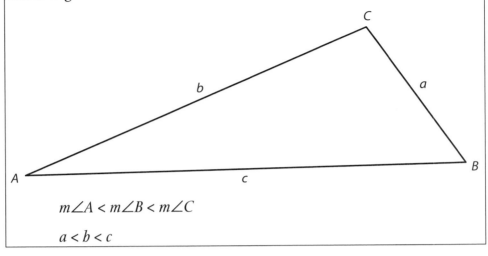

$$m\angle A < m\angle B < m\angle C$$

$$a < b < c$$

- The Triangle Sum Theorem and the Exterior Angle Theorem will be proven in this lesson.

# Guided Practice 5.6.1

**Example 1**

Find the measure of $\angle C$.

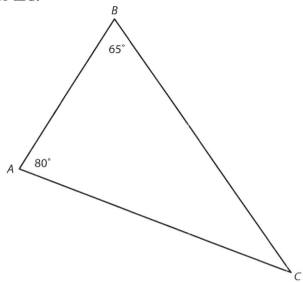

1. Identify the known information.

   Two measures of the three interior angles are given in the problem.

   $m\angle A = 80$

   $m\angle B = 65$

   The measure of $\angle C$ is unknown.

2. Calculate the measure of $\angle C$.

   The sum of the measures of the interior angles of a triangle is 180°.

   Create an equation to solve for the unknown measure of $\angle C$.

   | | |
   |---|---|
   | $m\angle A + m\angle B + m\angle C = 180$ | Triangle Sum Theorem |
   | $80 + 65 + m\angle C = 180$ | Substitute values for $m\angle A$ and $m\angle B$. |
   | $145 + m\angle C = 180$ | Simplify. |
   | $m\angle C = 35$ | Solve for $m\angle C$. |

3. State the answer.

   The measure of $\angle C$ is 35°.

## Example 2

Find the missing angle measures.

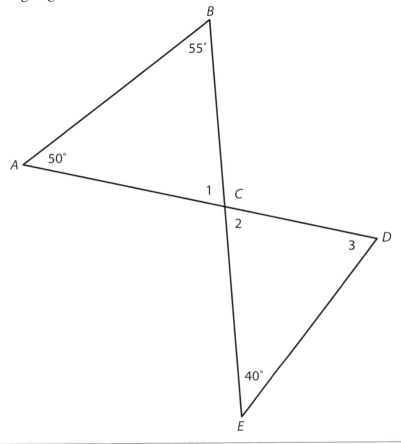

1. Identify the known information.

   The figure contains two triangles, $\triangle ABC$ and $\triangle CDE$.

   The measures of two of the three interior angles of $\triangle ABC$ are given in the problem.

   $m\angle A = 50$

   $m\angle B = 55$

   The measure of $\angle BCA$ is unknown.

   The measure of one of the three interior angles of $\triangle CDE$ is given in the problem.

   $m\angle E = 40$

   The measures of $\angle DCE$ and $\angle D$ are unknown.

2. Calculate the unknown measures.

The sum of the measures of the interior angles of a triangle is 180°.

Create an equation to solve for the unknown measure of $\angle BCA$.

$m\angle A + m\angle B + m\angle BCA = 180$    Triangle Sum Theorem

$50 + 55 + m\angle BCA = 180$         Substitute values for $m\angle A$ and $m\angle B$.

$105 + m\angle BCA = 180$            Simplify.

$m\angle BCA = 75$                Solve for $m\angle BCA$.

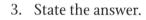

$\angle BCA$ and $\angle DCE$ are vertical angles and are congruent.

$m\angle DCE = m\angle BCA = 75$

Create an equation to solve for the unknown measure of $\angle D$.

$m\angle DCE + m\angle D + m\angle E = 180$    Triangle Sum Theorem

$75 + m\angle D + 40 = 180$         Substitute values for $m\angle DCE$ and $m\angle E$.

$115 + m\angle D = 180$            Simplify.

$m\angle D = 65$                Solve for $m\angle D$.

3. State the answer.

The measure of $\angle BCA$ is 75°.

The measure of $\angle DCE$ is 75°.

The measure of $\angle D$ is 65°.

## Example 3

Find the missing angle measures.

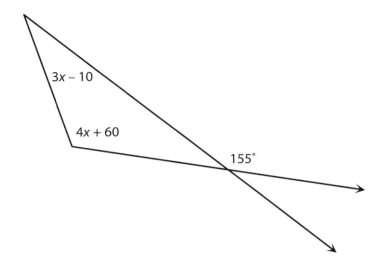

1. Identify the known information.

   One exterior angle measures 155°.

   The measures of the remote interior angles are stated as expressions.

   The value of $x$ is unknown.

2. Calculate the unknown measures.

   The measure of an exterior angle of a triangle is equal to the sum of the measures of its remote interior angles.

   Create an equation to solve for the unknown value of $x$.

   | | |
   |---|---|
   | $155 = (3x - 10) + (4x + 60)$ | Exterior Angle Theorem |
   | $155 = 7x + 50$ | Simplify. |
   | $105 = 7x$ | Solve for $x$. |
   | $x = 15$ | |

3. Determine the unknown measures using the value of $x$.

| | |
|---|---|
| $3x - 10$ | Unknown measure |
| $= 3(15) - 10$ | Substitute 15 for $x$. |
| $= 35$ | Simplify. |

| | |
|---|---|
| $4x + 60$ | Unknown measure |
| $= 4(15) + 60$ | Substitute 15 for $x$. |
| $= 120$ | Simplify. |

Check that the measures are correct.

| | |
|---|---|
| $155 = (3x - 10) + (4x + 60)$ | Original equation |
| $155 = 35 + 120$ | Substitute calculated values. |
| $155 = 155$ | Simplify. |

4. State the answer.

The measures of the remote interior angles are 35° and 120°.

## Example 4

The Triangle Sum Theorem states that the sum of the angle measures of a triangle is 180°. Write a two-column proof of this theorem.

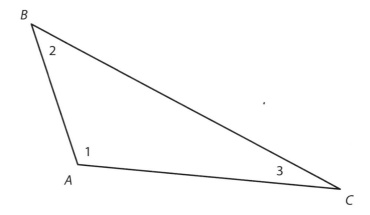

1. State the given information.

   Given: $\triangle ABC$

2. Draw a line, $\ell$, through point $B$ that is parallel to $\overline{AC}$ to aid in proving this theorem.

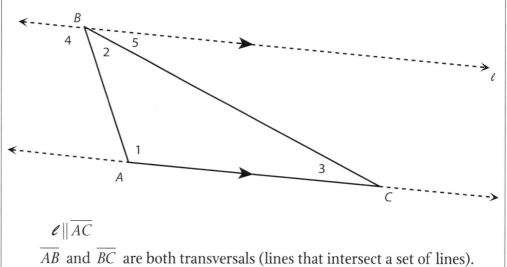

   $\ell \parallel \overline{AC}$

   $\overline{AB}$ and $\overline{BC}$ are both transversals (lines that intersect a set of lines).

3. State known information about angles created by parallel lines cut by a transversal.

   Alternate interior angles are congruent.

   $\angle 1$ and $\angle 4$ are alternate interior angles and are congruent.

   $\angle 3$ and $\angle 5$ are alternate interior angles and are congruent.

4. Identify known information about congruent angles.

   Congruent angles have the same measure.

   $m\angle 1 = m\angle 4$

   $m\angle 3 = m\angle 5$

5. Write the information in a two-column proof.

| Statements | Reasons |
|---|---|
| 1. $\triangle ABC$ | 1. Given |
| 2. Draw line $\ell$ through $B$ parallel to $\overline{AC}$. | 2. Parallel Postulate |
| 3. $\angle 1 \cong \angle 4$ | 3. Alternate Interior Angles Theorem |
| 4. $\angle 3 \cong \angle 5$ | 4. Alternate Interior Angles Theorem |
| 5. $m\angle 1 = m\angle 4$ | 5. Definition of congruent angles |
| 6. $m\angle 3 = m\angle 5$ | 6. Definition of congruent angles |
| 7. $m\angle 4 + m\angle 2 + m\angle 5 = 180$ | 7. Angle Addition Postulate and the definition of a straight angle |
| 8. $m\angle 1 + m\angle 2 + m\angle 3 = 180$ | 8. Substitution |

# UNIT 5 • SIMILARITY, RIGHT TRIANGLE TRIGONOMETRY, AND PROOF
## Lesson 6: Proving Theorems About Triangles

### Practice 5.6.1: Proving the Interior Angle Sum Theorem

Use what you know about the sums of the interior and exterior angles of triangles to determine the measure of each identified angle.

1. Find $m\angle B$.

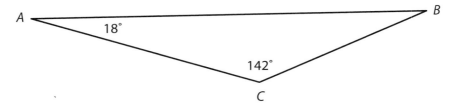

2. Find $m\angle B$.

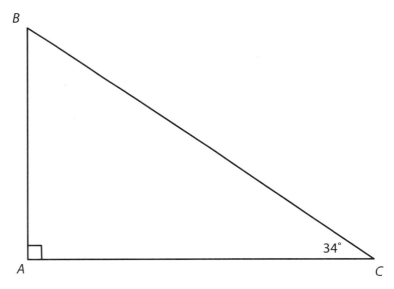

*continued*

3. Find $m\angle B$ and $m\angle C$.

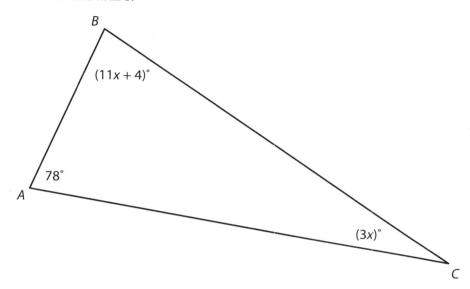

*B*

$(11x + 4)°$

$78°$

*A*

$(3x)°$

*C*

4. Find $m\angle A$, $m\angle B$, and $m\angle C$.

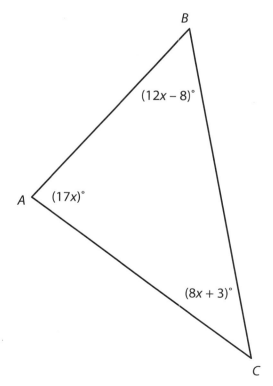

*B*

$(12x - 8)°$

*A* $(17x)°$

$(8x + 3)°$

*C*

*continued*

5.  Find $m\angle A$ and $m\angle B$.

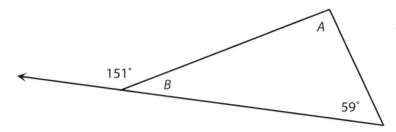

6.  Find $m\angle A$ and $m\angle B$.

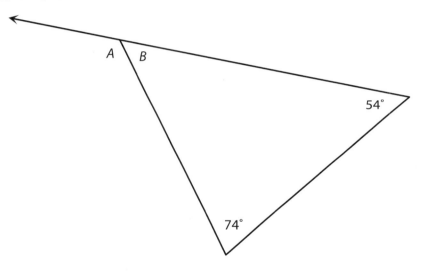

7.  Find $m\angle CAB$ and $m\angle ABC$.

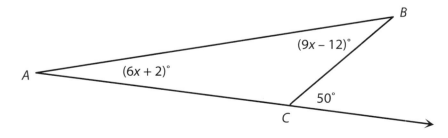

*continued*

8. Find $m\angle CAB$ and $m\angle ABC$.

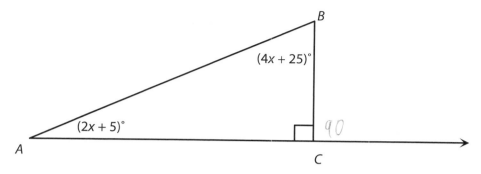

9. Find $m\angle CAB$ and $m\angle ABC$.

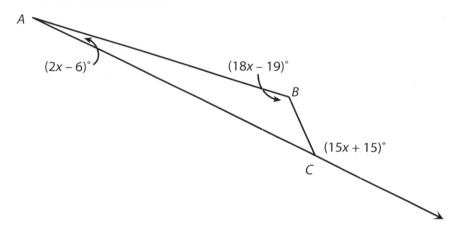

10. The Exterior Angle Theorem states that the measure of an exterior angle of a triangle is equal to the sum of the measures of its remote interior angles. Write a proof of this theorem, referring to the diagram below.

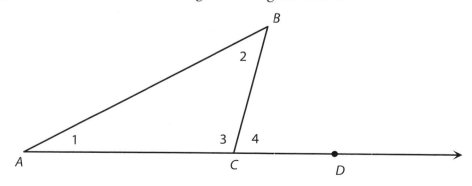

# Lesson 5.6.2: Proving Theorems About Isosceles Triangles

## Introduction

Isosceles triangles can be seen throughout our daily lives in structures, supports, architectural details, and even bicycle frames. Isosceles triangles are a distinct classification of triangles with unique characteristics and parts that have specific names. In this lesson, we will explore the qualities of isosceles triangles.

## Key Concepts

- Isosceles triangles have at least two congruent sides, called **legs**.
- The angle created by the intersection of the legs is called the **vertex angle**.
- Opposite the vertex angle is the **base** of the isosceles triangle.
- Each of the remaining angles is referred to as a **base angle**. The intersection of one leg and the base of the isosceles triangle creates a base angle.

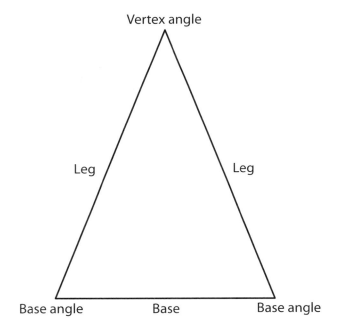

- The following theorem is true of every isosceles triangle.

---

**Theorem**

**Isosceles Triangle Theorem**

If two sides of a triangle are congruent, then the angles opposite the congruent sides are congruent.

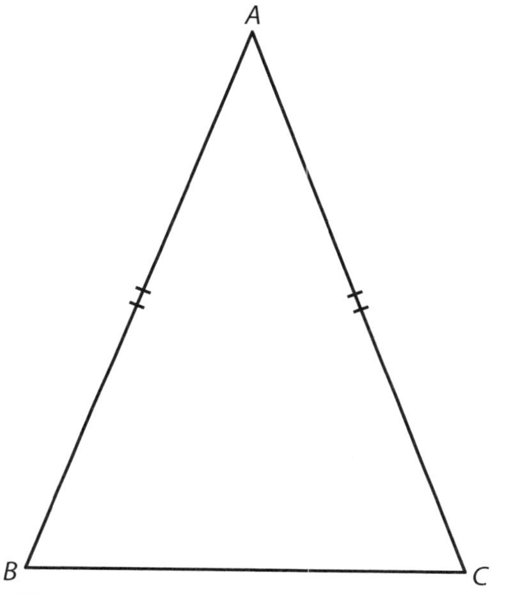

$m\angle B \cong m\angle C$

---

- If the Isosceles Triangle Theorem is reversed, then that statement is also true.

- This is known as the converse of the Isosceles Triangle Theorem.

---

**Theorem**

**Converse of the Isosceles Triangle Theorem**

If two angles of a triangle are congruent, then the sides opposite those angles are congruent.

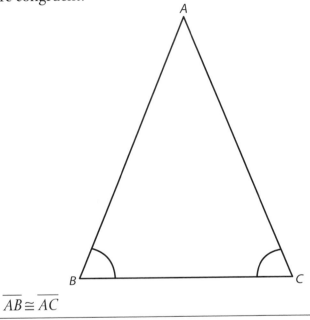

$$\overline{AB} \cong \overline{AC}$$

---

- If the vertex angle of an isosceles triangle is bisected, the bisector is perpendicular to the base, creating two right triangles.

- In the diagram that follows, $D$ is the midpoint of $\overline{BC}$.

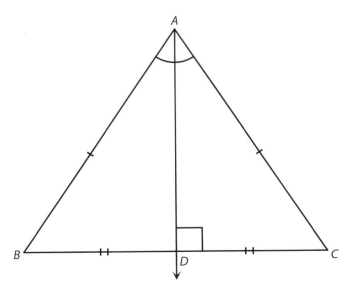

- Equilateral triangles are a special type of isosceles triangle, for which each side of the triangle is congruent.

- If all sides of a triangle are congruent, then all angles have the same measure.

---

**Theorem**

If a triangle is equilateral then it is **equiangular**, or has equal angles.

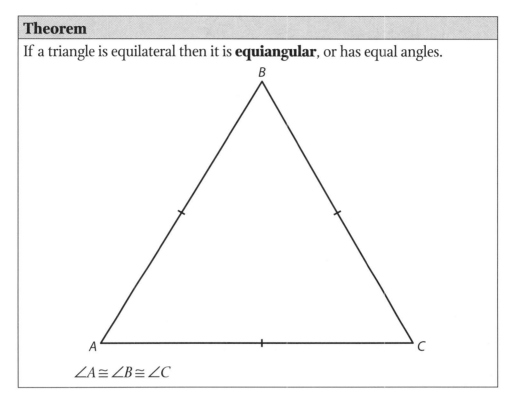

$\angle A \cong \angle B \cong \angle C$

---

- Each angle of an equilateral triangle measures $60°$ ($180 \div 3 = 60$).

- Conversely, if a triangle has equal angles, it is equilateral.

**Theorem**

If a triangle is equiangular, then it is equilateral.

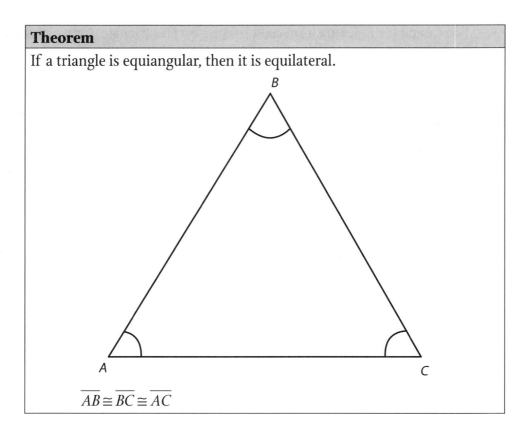

$$\overline{AB} \cong \overline{BC} \cong \overline{AC}$$

• These theorems and properties can be used to solve many triangle problems.

# Guided Practice 5.6.2

**Example 1**

Find the measure of each angle of $\triangle ABC$.

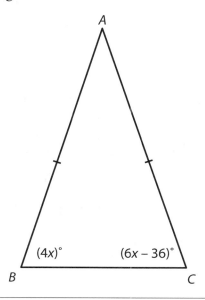

1. Identify the congruent angles.

   The legs of an isosceles triangle are congruent; therefore, $\overline{AB} \cong \overline{AC}$.

   The base of $\triangle ABC$ is $\overline{BC}$.

   $\angle B$ and $\angle C$ are base angles and are congruent.

2. Calculate the value of $x$.

   Congruent angles have the same measure.

   Create an equation.

   | | |
   |---|---|
   | $m\angle B = m\angle C$ | The measures of base angles of isosceles triangles are equal. |
   | $4x = 6x - 36$ | Substitute values for $m\angle B$ and $m\angle C$. |
   | $-2x = -36$ | Solve for $x$. |
   | $x = 18$ | |

3.  Calculate each angle measure.

$m\angle B = 4x = 4(18) = 72$      Substitute the value of $x$ into the expression for $m\angle B$.

$m\angle C = 6(18) - 36 = 72$      Substitute the value of $x$ into the expression for $m\angle C$.

$m\angle A + m\angle B + m\angle C = 180$      The sum of the angles of a triangle is $180°$.

$m\angle A + 72 + 72 = 180$      Substitute the known values.

$m\angle A = 36$      Solve for $m\angle A$.

4.  Summarize your findings.

$m\angle A = 36$

$m\angle B = 72$

$m\angle C = 72$

## Example 2

Determine whether $\triangle ABC$ with vertices $A$ (–4, 5), $B$ (–1, –4), and $C$ (5, 2) is an isosceles triangle. If it is isosceles, name a pair of congruent angles.

1. Use the distance formula to calculate the length of each side.

   Calculate the length of $\overline{AB}$.

   $$d = \sqrt{(x_2 - x_1)^2 + (y_2 - y_1)^2}$$

   $$AB = \sqrt{[(-1) - (-4)]^2 + [(-4) - (5)]^2}$$     Substitute (–4, 5) and (–1, –4) for $(x_1, y_1)$ and $(x_2, y_2)$.

   $$AB = \sqrt{(3)^2 + (-9)^2}$$     Simplify.

   $$AB = \sqrt{9 + 81}$$

   $$AB = \sqrt{90} = 3\sqrt{10}$$

   Calculate the length of $\overline{BC}$.

   $$d = \sqrt{(x_2 - x_1)^2 + (y_2 - y_1)^2}$$

   $$BC = \sqrt{[(5) - (-1)]^2 + [(2) - (-4)]^2}$$     Substitute (–1, –4) and (5, 2) for $(x_1, y_1)$ and $(x_2, y_2)$.

   $$BC = \sqrt{(6)^2 + (6)^2}$$     Simplify.

   $$BC = \sqrt{36 + 36}$$

   $$BC = \sqrt{72} = 6\sqrt{2}$$

   Calculate the length of $\overline{AC}$.

   $$d = \sqrt{(x_2 - x_1)^2 + (y_2 - y_1)^2}$$

   $$AC = \sqrt{[(5) - (-4)]^2 + [(2) - (5)]^2}$$     Substitute (–4, 5) and (5, 2) for $(x_1, y_1)$ and $(x_2, y_2)$.

   $$AC = \sqrt{(9)^2 + (-3)^2}$$     Simplify.

   $$AC = \sqrt{81 + 9}$$

   $$AC = \sqrt{90} = 3\sqrt{10}$$

2. Determine if the triangle is isosceles.

   A triangle with at least two congruent sides is an isosceles triangle.

   $\overline{AB} \cong \overline{AC}$, so $\triangle ABC$ is isosceles.

3. Identify congruent angles.

   If two sides of a triangle are congruent, then the angles opposite the sides are congruent.

   $\angle B \cong \angle C$

**Example 3**

Given $\overline{AB} \cong \overline{AC}$, prove that $\angle B \cong \angle C$.

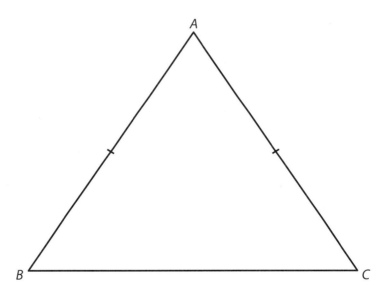

1. State the given information.

   $\overline{AB} \cong \overline{AC}$

2. Draw the angle bisector of $\angle A$ and extend it to $\overline{BC}$, creating the perpendicular bisector of $\overline{BC}$. Label the point of intersection $D$.

Indicate congruent sides.

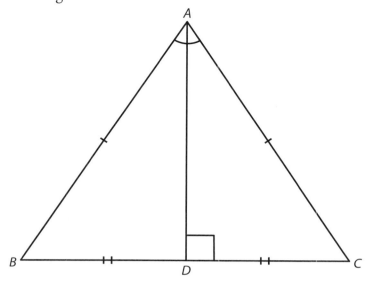

$\angle B$ and $\angle C$ are congruent corresponding parts.

3. Write the information in a two-column proof.

| Statements | Reasons |
|---|---|
| 1. $\overline{AB} \cong \overline{AC}$ | 1. Given |
| 2. Draw the angle bisector of $\angle A$ and extend it to $\overline{BC}$, creating a perpendicular bisector of $\overline{BC}$ and the midpoint of $\overline{BC}$. | 2. There is exactly one line through two points. |
| 3. $\overline{BD} \cong \overline{BC}$ | 3. Definition of midpoint |
| 4. $\overline{AD} \cong \overline{AD}$ | 4. Reflexive Property |
| 5. $\triangle ABD \cong \triangle ACD$ | 5. SSS Congruence Statement |
| 6. $\angle B \cong \angle C$ | 6. Corresponding Parts of Congruent Triangles are Congruent |

## Example 4

Find the values of $x$ and $y$.

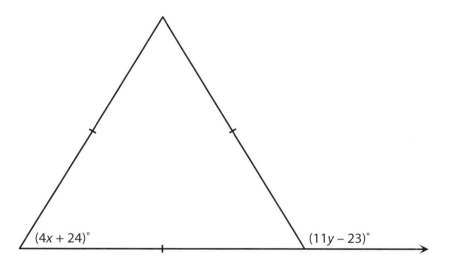

1. Make observations about the figure.

   The triangle in the diagram has three congruent sides.

   A triangle with three congruent sides is equilateral.

   Equilateral triangles are also equiangular.

   The measure of each angle of an equilateral triangle is 60°.

   An exterior angle is also included in the diagram.

   The measure of an exterior angle is the supplement of the adjacent interior angle.

2. Determine the value of $x$.

   The measure of each angle of an equilateral triangle is 60°.

   Create and solve an equation for $x$ using this information.

   | | |
   |---|---|
   | $4x + 24 = 60$ | Equation |
   | $4x = 36$ | Solve for $x$. |
   | $x = 9$ | |

   The value of $x$ is 9.

3. Determine the value of $y$.

   The exterior angle is the supplement to the interior angle.

   The interior angle is 60° by the properties of equilateral triangles.

   The sum of the measures of an exterior angle and interior angle pair equals 180.

   Create and solve an equation for $y$ using this information.

   | | |
   |---|---|
   | $11y - 23 + 60 = 180$ | Equation |
   | $11y + 37 = 180$ | Simplify. |
   | $11y = 143$ | Solve for $y$. |
   | $y = 13$ | |

   The value of $y$ is 13.

## Example 5

$\triangle ABC$ is equilateral. Prove that it is equiangular.

1. State the given information.

   $\triangle ABC$ is an equilateral triangle.

2. Plan the proof.

   Equilateral triangles are also isosceles triangles.

   Isosceles triangles have at least two congruent sides.

   $\overline{AB} \cong \overline{BC}$

   $\angle A$ and $\angle C$ are base angles in relation to $\overline{AB}$ and $\overline{BC}$.

   $\angle A \cong \angle C$ because of the Isosceles Triangle Theorem.

   $\overline{BC} \cong \overline{AC}$

   $\angle A$ and $\angle B$ are base angles in relation to $\overline{BC}$ and $\overline{AC}$.

   $\angle A \cong \angle B$ because of the Isosceles Triangle Theorem.

   By the Transitive Property, $\angle A \cong \angle B \cong \angle C$; therefore, $\triangle ABC$ is equiangular.

3. Write the information in a paragraph proof.

   Since $\triangle ABC$ is equilateral, $\overline{AB} \cong \overline{BC}$ and $\overline{BC} \cong \overline{AC}$. By the Isosceles Triangle Theorem, $\angle A \cong \angle C$ and $\angle A \cong \angle B$. By the Transitive Property, $\angle A \cong \angle B \cong \angle C$; therefore, $\triangle ABC$ is equiangular.

## Practice 5.6.2: Proving Theorems About Isosceles Triangles

Use what you know about isosceles triangles to find each angle measure.

1. $m\angle A$ and $m\angle C$

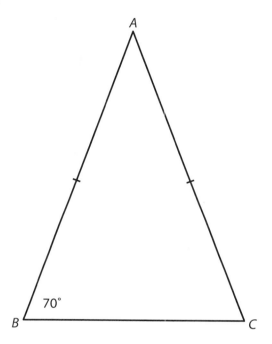

2. $m\angle ADB$, $m\angle DCB$, and $m\angle DBC$

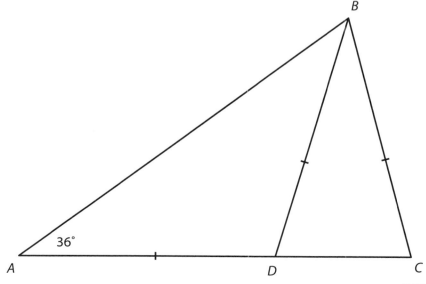

**continued**

3. $m\angle A$, $m\angle B$, and $m\angle C$

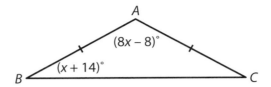

4. $m\angle A$, $m\angle B$, and $m\angle C$

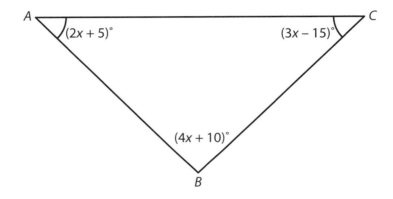

Find each value using the given information.

5. $x$

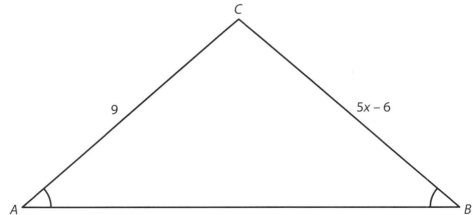

 *continued*

6. $m\angle x$ and $m\angle y$

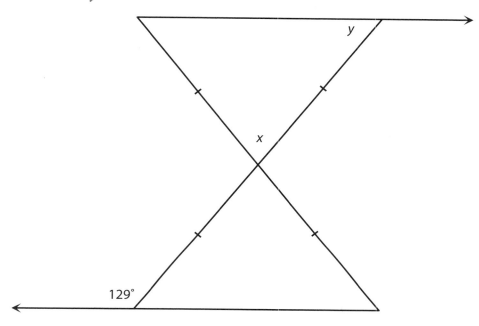

7. $x$

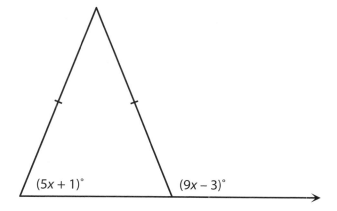

*continued*

For problems 8 and 9, use the given vertices to determine whether $\triangle ABC$ is an isosceles triangle. If it is isosceles, name a pair of congruent angles.

8.  $A\,(-3, -4)$, $B\,(-3, 2)$, $C\,(4, -4)$

9.  $A\,(5, 0)$, $B\,(-3, 0)$, $C\,(3, 0)$

Complete the following paragraph proof.

10.  Given that $\triangle ABC$ is equiangular, prove $\triangle ABC$ is equilateral.

# Lesson 5.6.3: Proving the Midsegment of a Triangle

## Introduction

Triangles are typically thought of as simplistic shapes constructed of three angles and three segments. As we continue to explore this shape, we discover there are many more properties and qualities than we may have first imagined. Each property and quality, such as the midsegment of a triangle, acts as a tool for solving problems.

## Key Concepts

- The midpoint is the point on a line segment that divides the segment into two equal parts.

- A **midsegment** of a triangle is a line segment that joins the midpoints of two sides of a triangle.

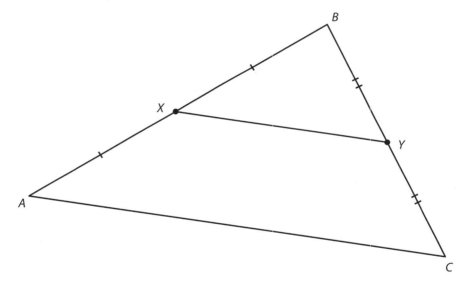

- In the diagram above, the midpoint of $\overline{AB}$ is $X$.

- The midpoint of $\overline{BC}$ is $Y$.

- A midsegment of $\triangle ABC$ is $\overline{XY}$.

- The midsegment of a triangle is parallel to the third side of the triangle and is half as long as the third side. This is known as the Triangle Midsegment Theorem.

## Triangle Midsegment Theorem

A midsegment of a triangle is parallel to the third side and is half as long.

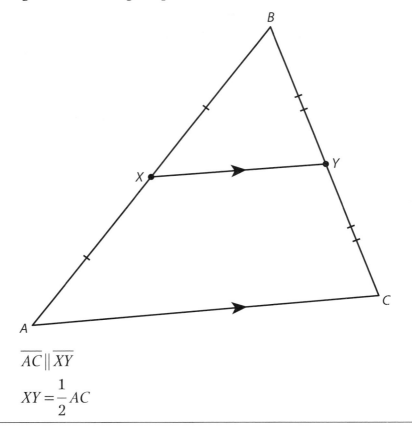

$$\overline{AC} \parallel \overline{XY}$$

$$XY = \frac{1}{2}AC$$

- Every triangle has three midsegments.

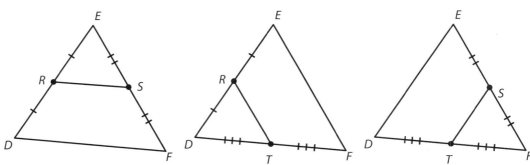

- When all three of the midsegments of a triangle are connected, a **midsegment triangle** is created.

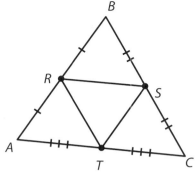

- In the diagram above, $\triangle ABC \sim \triangle TSR$.

- **Coordinate proofs**, proofs that involve calculations and make reference to the coordinate plane, are often used to prove many theorems.

# Guided Practice 5.6.3

## Example 1

Find the lengths of $BC$ and $YZ$ and the measure of $\angle AXZ$.

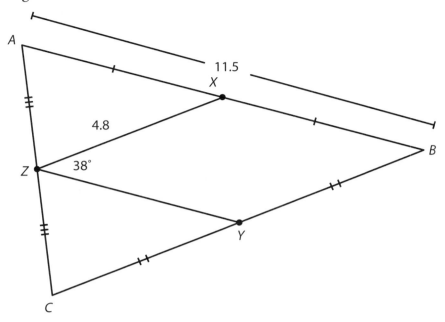

1.  Identify the known information.

    Tick marks indicate that $X$ is the midpoint of $\overline{AB}$, $Y$ is the midpoint of $\overline{BC}$, and $Z$ is the midpoint of $\overline{AC}$.

    $\overline{XZ}$ and $\overline{YZ}$ are midsegments of $\triangle ABC$.

2.  Calculate the length of $BC$.

    $\overline{XZ}$ is the midsegment that is parallel to $\overline{BC}$.

    The length of $\overline{XZ}$ is $\dfrac{1}{2}$ the length of $\overline{BC}$.

    | | |
    |---|---|
    | $XZ = \dfrac{1}{2}BC$ | Triangle Midsegment Theorem |
    | $4.8 = \dfrac{1}{2}BC$ | Substitute 4.8 for $XZ$. |
    | $BC = 9.6$ | Solve for $BC$. |

3. Calculate the measure of *YZ*.

   $\overline{YZ}$ is the midsegment parallel to $\overline{AB}$.

   The length of $\overline{YZ}$ is $\dfrac{1}{2}$ the length of $\overline{AB}$.

   $YZ = \dfrac{1}{2}AB$          Triangle Midsegment Theorem

   $YZ = \dfrac{1}{2}(11.5)$          Substitute 11.5 for *AB*.

   $YZ = 5.75$          Solve for *YZ*.

4. Calculate the measure of $\angle AXZ$.

   $\overline{YZ} \parallel \overline{AB}$          Triangle Midsegment Theorem

   $m\angle AXZ = m\angle XZY$          Alternate Interior Angles Theorem

   $m\angle AXZ = 38$

5. State the answers.

   *BC* is 9.6 units long. *YZ* is 5.75 units long. $m\angle AXZ$ is 38°.

## Example 2

If $AB = 2x + 7$ and $YZ = 3x - 6.5$, what is the length of $AB$?

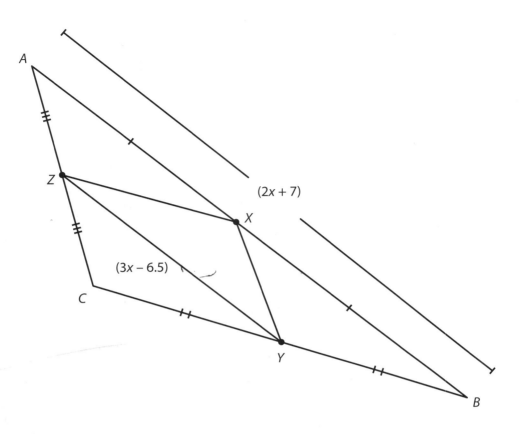

1.  Identify the known information.

    Tick marks indicate that $X$ is the midpoint of $\overline{AB}$, $Y$ is the midpoint of $\overline{BC}$, and $Z$ is the midpoint of $\overline{AC}$.

    $\overline{XY}$, $\overline{XZ}$, and $\overline{YZ}$ are the midsegments of $\triangle ABC$.

2. Calculate the length of $AB$.

The length of $\overline{YZ}$ is $\dfrac{1}{2}$ the length of $\overline{AB}$.

$YZ = \dfrac{1}{2}AB$                          Triangle Midsegment Theorem

$3x - 6.5 = \dfrac{1}{2}(2x+7)$            Substitute values for $YZ$ and $AB$.

$3x - 6.5 = x + 3.5$               Solve for $x$.

$2x - 6.5 = 3.5$

$2x = 10$

$x = 5$

Use the value of $x$ to find the length of $AB$.

$AB = 2x + 7$

$\phantom{AB} = 2(5) + 7$

$\phantom{AB} = 10 + 7$

$\phantom{AB} = 17$

3. State the answer.

$AB = 17$

## Example 3

The midpoints of a triangle are $X\,(-2, 5)$, $Y\,(3, 1)$, and $Z\,(4, 8)$. Find the coordinates of the vertices of the triangle.

1.  Plot the midpoints on a coordinate plane.

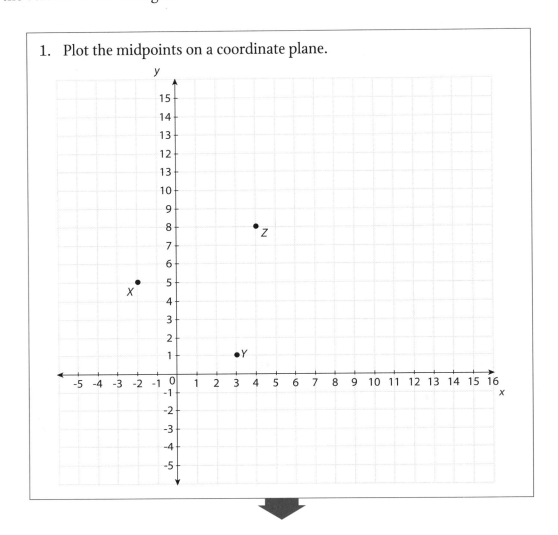

2. Connect the midpoints to form the midsegments $\overline{XY}$, $\overline{YZ}$, and $\overline{XZ}$.

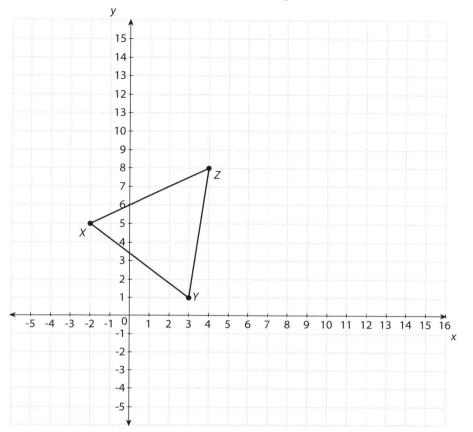

3. Calculate the slope of each midsegment.

Calculate the slope of $\overline{XY}$.

$$m = \frac{y_2 - y_1}{x_2 - x_1}$$ 　　　　Slope formula

$$m = \frac{(1)-(5)}{(3)-(-2)}$$ 　　　　Substitute (–2, 5) and (3, 1) for $(x_1, y_1)$ and $(x_2, y_2)$.

$$m = \frac{-4}{5}$$ 　　　　Simplify.

The slope of $\overline{XY}$ is $-\dfrac{4}{5}$.

Calculate the slope of $\overline{YZ}$.

$$m = \frac{y_2 - y_1}{x_2 - x_1}$$ 　　　　Slope formula

$$m = \frac{(8)-(1)}{(4)-(3)}$$ 　　　　Substitute (3, 1) and (4, 8) for $(x_1, y_1)$ and $(x_2, y_2)$.

$$m = \frac{7}{1} = 7$$ 　　　　Simplify.

The slope of $\overline{YZ}$ is 7.

Calculate the slope of $\overline{XZ}$.

$$m = \frac{y_2 - y_1}{x_2 - x_1}$$ 　　　　Slope formula

$$m = \frac{(8)-(5)}{(4)-(-2)}$$ 　　　　Substitute (–2, 5) and (4, 8) for $(x_1, y_1)$ and $(x_2, y_2)$.

$$m = \frac{3}{6} = \frac{1}{2}$$ 　　　　Simplify.

The slope of $\overline{XZ}$ is $\dfrac{1}{2}$.

4. Draw the lines that contain the midpoints.

The endpoints of each midsegment are the midpoints of the larger triangle.

Each midsegment is also parallel to the opposite side.

The slope of $\overline{XZ}$ is $\dfrac{1}{2}$.

From point $Y$, draw a line that has a slope of $\dfrac{1}{2}$.

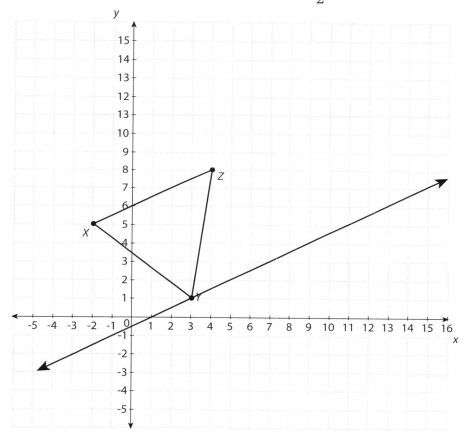

(*continued*)

The slope of $\overline{YZ}$ is 7.

From point $X$, draw a line that has a slope of 7.

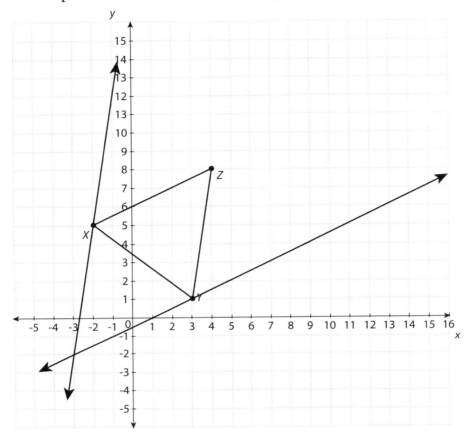

*(continued)*

The slope of $\overline{XY}$ is $-\dfrac{4}{5}$.

From point $Z$, draw a line that has a slope of $-\dfrac{4}{5}$.

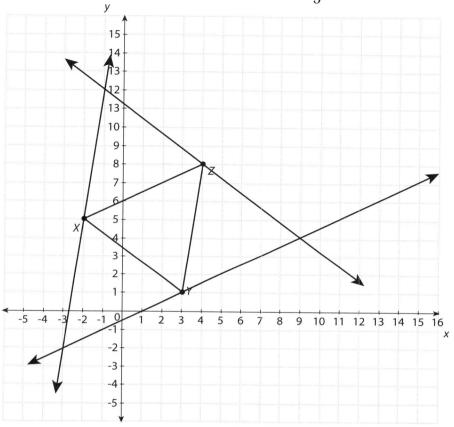

The intersections of the lines form the vertices of the triangle.

5. Determine the vertices of the triangle.

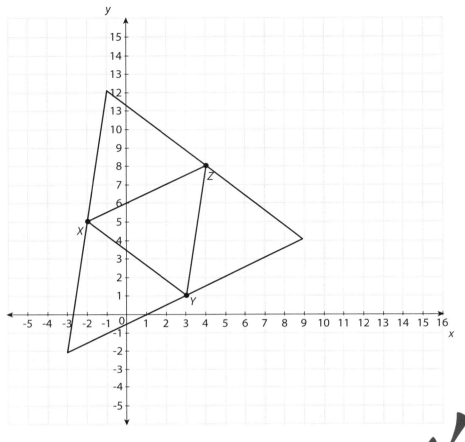

The vertices of the triangle are (−3, −2), (9, 4), and (−1, 12).

## Example 4

Write a coordinate proof of the Triangle Midsegment Theorem using the graph below.

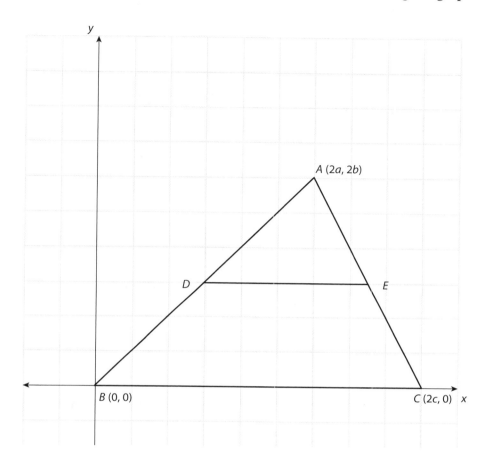

1. Identify the known information.

   According to the graph, $\triangle ABC$ has vertices located at $(2a, 2b)$, $(0, 0)$, and $(2c, 0)$.

2. Find the coordinates of $D$, which is the midpoint of $\overline{AB}$.

Use the midpoint formula to find the midpoint of $\overline{AB}$.

$$\left(\frac{x_1+x_2}{2}, \frac{y_1+y_2}{2}\right)$$   Midpoint formula

$$\left(\frac{2a+0}{2}, \frac{2b+0}{2}\right)$$   Substitute $(2a, 2b)$ and $(0, 0)$ for $(x_1, y_1)$ and $(x_2, y_2)$.

$$\left(\frac{2a}{2}, \frac{2b}{2}\right)$$   Simplify.

$(a, b)$

The midpoint of $\overline{AB}$ is $(a, b)$.

3. Find the coordinates of $E$, which is the midpoint of $\overline{AC}$.

Use the midpoint formula to find the midpoint of $\overline{AC}$.

$$\left(\frac{x_1+x_2}{2}, \frac{y_1+y_2}{2}\right)$$   Midpoint formula

$$\left(\frac{2a+2c}{2}, \frac{2b+0}{2}\right)$$   Substitute $(2a, 2b)$ and $(2c, 0)$ for $(x_1, y_1)$ and $(x_2, y_2)$.

$$\left(\frac{2a+2c}{2}, \frac{2b}{2}\right)$$   Simplify.

$(a + c, b)$

The midpoint of $\overline{AC}$ is $(a + c, b)$.

4. Calculate the slope of the midsegment.

   Use the slope formula to calculate the slope of $\overline{DE}$.

   $$m = \frac{y_2 - y_1}{x_2 - x_1}$$    Slope formula

   $$m = \frac{(b) - (b)}{(a+c) - (a)}$$    Substitute $(a, b)$ and $(a + c, b)$ for $(x_1, y_1)$ and $(x_2, y_2)$.

   $$m = \frac{0}{c} = 0$$    Simplify.

   The slope of $\overline{DE}$ is 0.

5. Calculate the slope of $\overline{BC}$.

   Use the slope formula to calculate the slope of $\overline{BC}$.

   $$m = \frac{y_2 - y_1}{x_2 - x_1}$$    Slope formula

   $$m = \frac{(0) - (0)}{(2c) - (0)}$$    Substitute $(0, 0)$ and $(2c, 0)$ for $(x_1, y_1)$ and $(x_2, y_2)$.

   $$m = \frac{0}{2c} = 0$$    Simplify.

   The slope of $\overline{BC}$ is 0.

6. Calculate the length of $\overline{DE}$.

Use the distance formula to calculate the length of the segment.

$$d = \sqrt{(x_2 - x_1)^2 + (y_2 - y_1)^2}$$   Distance formula

$$d = \sqrt{[(a+c)-(a)]^2 + [(b)-(b)]^2}$$   Substitute $(a, b)$ and $(a + c, b)$ for $(x_1, y_1)$ and $(x_2, y_2)$.

$$d = \sqrt{c^2 + 0}$$   Simplify.

$$d = \sqrt{c^2}$$

$$d = c$$

The distance of $\overline{DE}$ is $c$ units.

7. Calculate the length of $\overline{BC}$.

Use the distance formula to calculate the length of the segment.

$$d = \sqrt{(x_2 - x_1)^2 + (y_2 - y_1)^2}$$   Distance formula

$$d = \sqrt{[(2c)-(0)]^2 + [(0)-(0)]^2}$$   Substitute $(0, 0)$ and $(2c, 0)$ for $(x_1, y_1)$ and $(x_2, y_2)$.

$$d = \sqrt{(2c)^2 + 0}$$   Simplify.

$$d = \sqrt{4c^2}$$

$$d = 2c$$

The distance of $\overline{BC}$ is $2c$ units.

8. State your conclusion.

The slopes of $\overline{DE}$ and $\overline{BC}$ are both 0; therefore, the segments are parallel.

The length of $\overline{DE}$ is $c$ units and the length of $\overline{BC}$ is $2c$ units; therefore, $\overline{DE}$ is $\dfrac{1}{2}$ the length of $\overline{BC}$.

## Practice 5.6.3: Proving the Midsegment of a Triangle

Use your knowledge of midsegments to solve each problem.

1. Find the lengths of *BC* and *XZ* and the measure of ∠*BZX*.

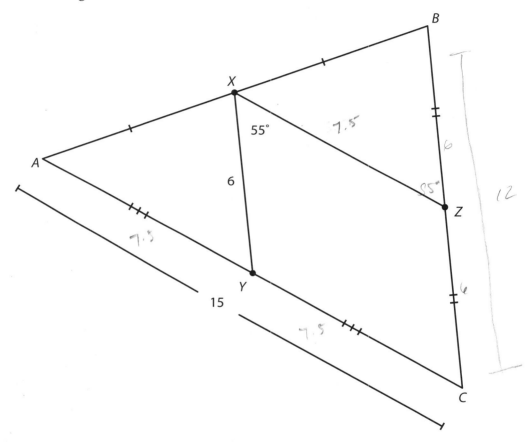

2. Find the lengths of $BC$ and $YZ$ and the measure of $\angle AXY$.

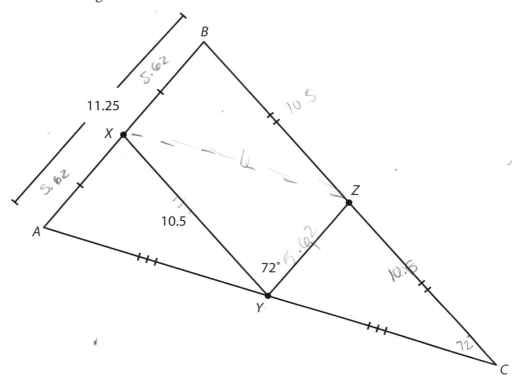

3. If $AB = 10x - 5$ and $XY = 3x + 0.5$, what is the length of $XY$?

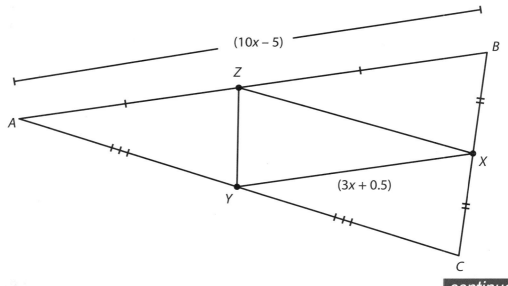

*continued*

4.  If $AB = 6x + 6$ and $XY = 5x - 9$, what is the length of $AB$?

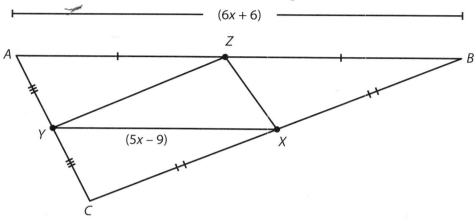

5.  The midpoints of a triangle are $X(-2, -2)$, $Y(-2, 3)$, and $Z(5, 3)$. Find the coordinates of the vertices of the triangle.

6.  The vertices of a triangle are $A(-2, 4)$, $B(10, 2)$, and $C(6, 8)$. Find the coordinates of the midpoints of the triangle.

7. Use a coordinate proof to show that $\overline{EF} \parallel \overline{BC}$ and $EF = \dfrac{1}{2}BC$.

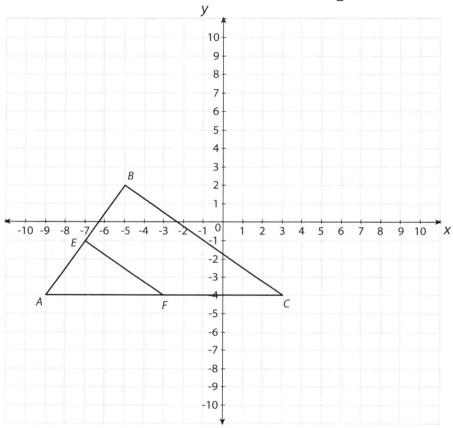

*continued*

8. Use a coordinate proof to show that $\overline{EF} \parallel \overline{BC}$ and $EF = \dfrac{1}{2}BC$.

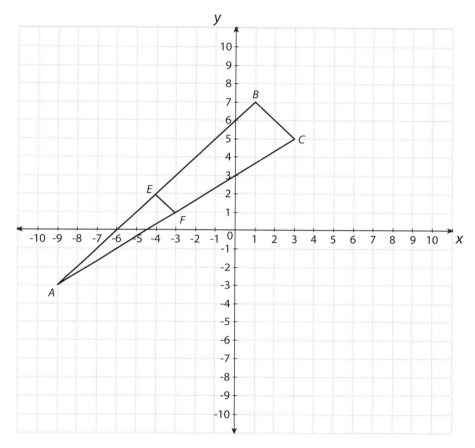

*continued*

9.  Determine the midpoints of $\overline{AC}$ and $\overline{BC}$. Label the points $E$ and $F$. Show that $\overline{EF} \parallel \overline{AB}$ and $EF = \frac{1}{2}AB$.

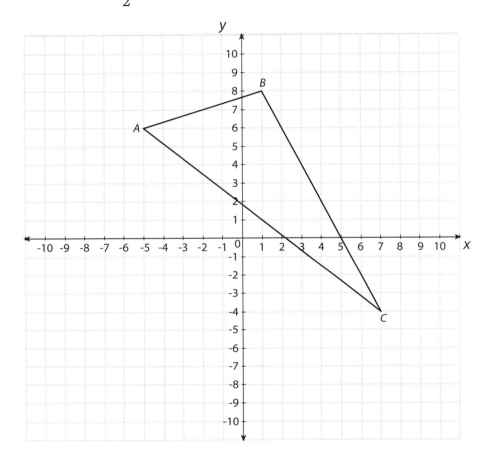

*continued*

10. Determine the midpoints of $\overline{AC}$ and $\overline{BC}$. Label the points $E$ and $F$. Show that $\overline{EF} \parallel \overline{AB}$ and $EF = \dfrac{1}{2} AB$.

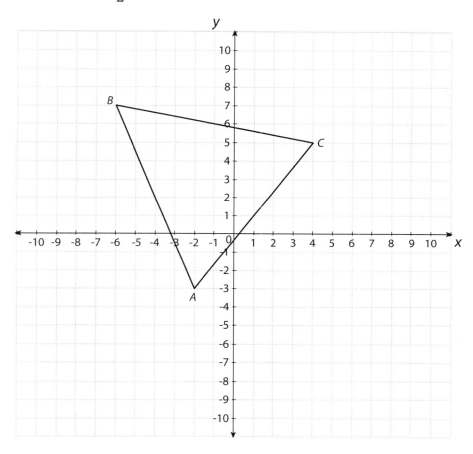

# Lesson 5.6.4: Proving Centers of Triangles

## Introduction

Think about all the properties of triangles we have learned so far and all the constructions we are able to perform. What properties exist when the perpendicular bisectors of triangles are constructed? Is there anything special about where the angle bisectors of a triangle intersect? We know triangles have three altitudes, but can determining each one serve any other purpose? How can the midpoints of each side of a triangle help find the center of gravity of a triangle? Each of these questions will be answered as we explore the centers of triangles.

## Key Concepts

- Every triangle has four centers.

- Each center is determined by a different **point of concurrency**—the point at which three or more lines intersect.

- These centers are the circumcenter, the incenter, the orthocenter, and the centroid.

### Circumcenters

- The perpendicular bisector is the line that is constructed through the midpoint of a segment. In the case of a triangle, the perpendicular bisectors are the midpoints of each of the sides.

- The three perpendicular bisectors of a triangle are **concurrent**, or intersect at one point.

- This point of concurrency is called the **circumcenter** of the triangle.

- The circumcenter of a triangle is equidistant, or the same distance, from the vertices of the triangle. This is known as the Circumcenter Theorem.

## Circumcenter Theorem

The circumcenter of a triangle is equidistant from the vertices of a triangle.

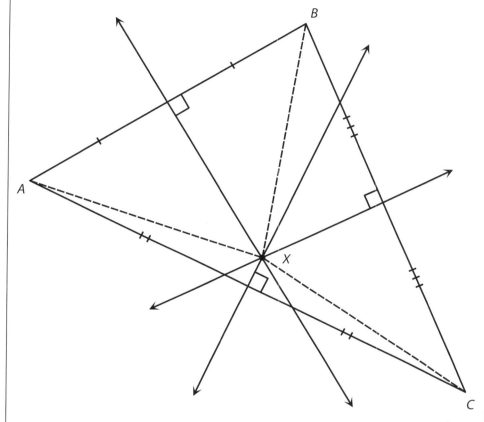

The circumcenter of this triangle is at $X$.

$$XA = XB = XC$$

- The circumcenter can be inside the triangle, outside the triangle, or even on the triangle depending on the type of triangle.

- The circumcenter is inside acute triangles, outside obtuse triangles, and on the midpoint of the hypotenuse of right triangles.

- Look at the placement of the circumcenter, point *X*, in the following examples.

| Acute triangle | Obtuse triangle | Right triangle |
|---|---|---|
| *X* is inside the triangle. | *X* is outside the triangle. | *X* is on the midpoint of the hypotenuse. |

- The circumcenter of a triangle is also the center of the circle that connects each of the vertices of a triangle. This is known as the circle that **circumscribes** the triangle.

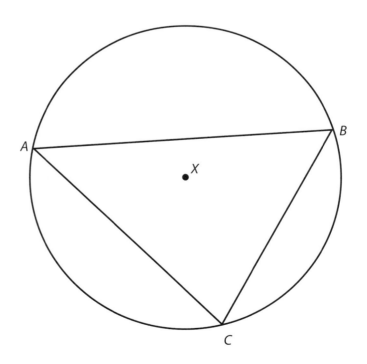

## Incenters

- The angle bisectors of a triangle are rays that cut the measure of each vertex in half.

- The three angle bisectors of a triangle are also concurrent.

- This point of concurrency is called the **incenter** of the triangle.

- The incenter of a triangle is equidistant from the sides of the triangle. This is known as the Incenter Theorem.

| Theorem |
|---|
| **Incenter Theorem** |

The incenter of a triangle is equidistant from the sides of a triangle.

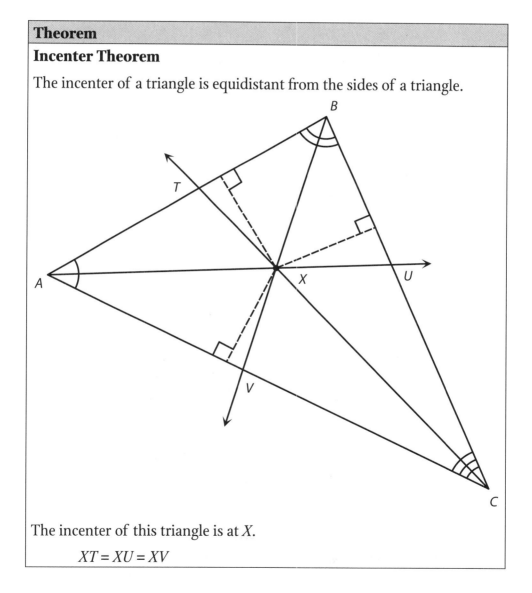

The incenter of this triangle is at $X$.

$$XT = XU = XV$$

- The incenter is always inside the triangle.

| Acute triangle | Obtuse triangle | Right triangle |
|---|---|---|
| 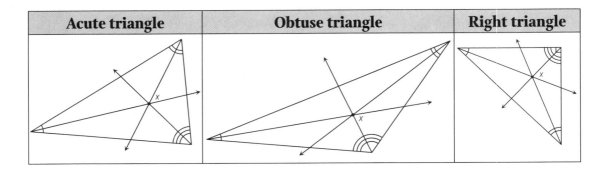 | | |

- The incenter of a triangle is the center of the circle that connects each of the sides of a triangle. This is known as the circle that **inscribes** the triangle.

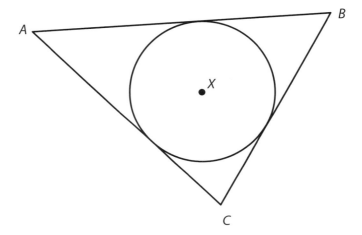

## Orthocenters

- The altitudes of a triangle are the perpendicular lines from each vertex of the triangle to its opposite side, also called the height of the triangle.

- The three altitudes of a triangle are also concurrent.

- This point of concurrency is called the **orthocenter** of the triangle.

- The orthocenter can be inside the triangle, outside the triangle, or even on the triangle depending on the type of triangle.

- The orthocenter is inside acute triangles, outside obtuse triangles, and at the vertex of the right angle of right triangles.

- Look at the placement of the orthocenter, point $X$, in the following examples.

| Acute triangle | Obtuse triangle | Right triangle |
|---|---|---|
| | | |
| $X$ is inside the triangle. | $X$ is outside the triangle. | $X$ is at the vertex of the right angle. |

## Centroids

- The **medians of a triangle** are segments that join the vertices of the triangle to the midpoint of the opposite sides.

- Every triangle has three medians.

- The three medians of a triangle are also concurrent.

- This point of concurrency is called the **centroid** of the triangle.

- The centroid is always located inside the triangle $\frac{2}{3}$ the distance from each vertex to the midpoint of the opposite side. This is known as the Centroid Theorem.

**Theorem**

**Centroid Theorem**

The centroid of a triangle is $\frac{2}{3}$ the distance from each vertex to the midpoint of the opposite side.

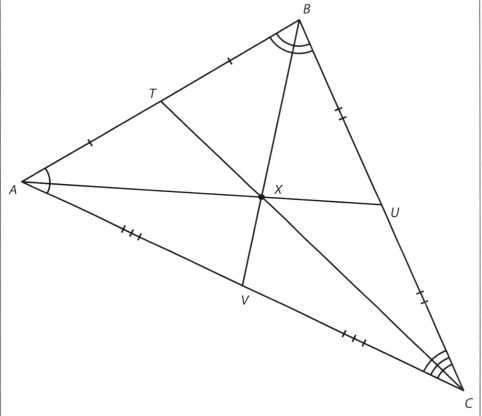

The centroid of this triangle is at point $X$.

$$AX = \frac{2}{3}AU \; ; \; BX = \frac{2}{3}BV \; ; \; CX = \frac{2}{3}CT$$

- The centroid is always located inside the triangle.

| Acute triangle | Obtuse triangle | Right triangle |
|---|---|---|
| | | |

- The centroid is also called the center of gravity of a triangle because the triangle will always balance at this point.

- Each point of concurrency discussed is considered a center of the triangle.

- Each center serves its own purpose in design, planning, and construction.

| Center of triangle | Intersection of... |
|---|---|
| Circumcenter | Perpendicular bisectors |
| Incenter | Angle bisectors |
| Orthocenter | Altitudes |
| Centroid | Medians |

# Guided Practice 5.6.4

## Example 1

$\triangle ABC$ has vertices $A$ (3, 3), $B$ (7, 3), and $C$ (3, −3). Justify that (5, 0) is the circumcenter of $\triangle ABC$.

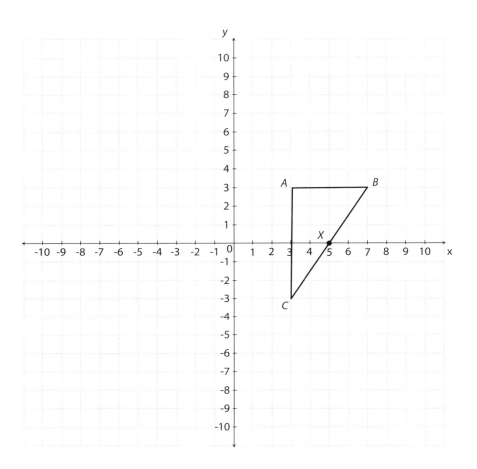

1. Identify the known information.

   $\triangle ABC$ has vertices $A$ (3, 3), $B$ (7, 3), and $C$ (3, −3).

   The circumcenter is $X$ (5, 0).

   The circumcenter of a triangle is equidistant from the vertices of the triangle.

2. Determine the distance from the circumcenter to each of the vertices.

Use the distance formula to calculate the distance from $X$ to $A$.

$d = \sqrt{(x_2 - x_1)^2 + (y_2 - y_1)^2}$    Distance formula

$d = \sqrt{[(3) - (5)]^2 + [(3) - (0)]^2}$    Substitute (5, 0) and (3, 3) for $(x_1, y_1)$ and $(x_2, y_2)$.

$d = \sqrt{(-2)^2 + (3)^2}$    Simplify.

$d = \sqrt{4 + 9}$

$d = \sqrt{13}$

The distance from $X$ to $A$ is $\sqrt{13}$ units.

Use the distance formula to calculate the distance from $X$ to $B$.

$d = \sqrt{(x_2 - x_1)^2 + (y_2 - y_1)^2}$    Distance formula

$d = \sqrt{[(7) - (5)]^2 + [(3) - (0)]^2}$    Substitute (5, 0) and (7, 3) for $(x_1, y_1)$ and $(x_2, y_2)$.

$d = \sqrt{(2)^2 + (3)^2}$    Simplify.

$d = \sqrt{4 + 9}$

$d = \sqrt{13}$

The distance from $X$ to $B$ is $\sqrt{13}$ units.

*(continued)*

Use the distance formula to calculate the distance from $X$ to $C$.

$$d = \sqrt{(x_2 - x_1)^2 + (y_2 - y_1)^2}$$     Distance formula

$$d = \sqrt{[(3) - (5)]^2 + [(-3) - (0)]^2}$$     Substitute (5, 0) and (3, –3) for $(x_1, y_1)$ and $(x_2, y_2)$.

$$d = \sqrt{(-2)^2 + (3)^2}$$     Simplify.

$$d = \sqrt{4 + 9}$$

$$d = \sqrt{13}$$

The distance from $X$ to $C$ is $\sqrt{13}$ units.

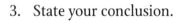

3.  State your conclusion.

$X(5, 0)$ is the circumcenter of $\triangle ABC$ with vertices $A(3, 3)$, $B(7, 3)$, and $C(3, -3)$ because the distance from $X$ to each of the vertices is $\sqrt{13}$ units.

## Example 2

$\triangle ABC$ has vertices $A\,(1, 6)$, $B\,(7, 6)$, and $C\,(3, 2)$. Find the equation of each altitude of $\triangle ABC$ to verify that $(3, 4)$ is the orthocenter of $\triangle ABC$.

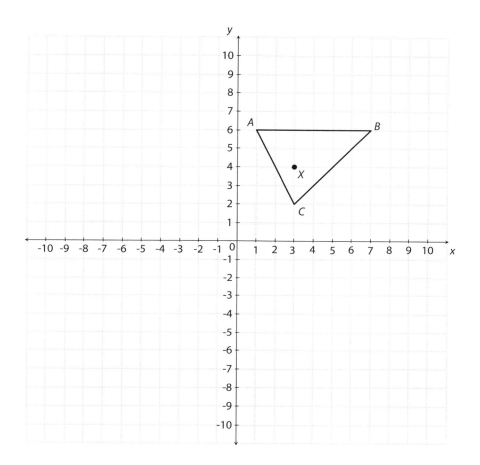

1. Identify known information.

   $\triangle ABC$ has vertices $A\,(1, 6)$, $B\,(7, 6)$, and $C\,(3, 2)$.

   The orthocenter is $X\,(3, 4)$.

   The orthocenter of a triangle is the intersection of the altitudes of the triangle.

2. Determine the altitudes of $\triangle ABC$.

Find an equation of the line that is perpendicular to $\overline{BC}$ and passes through $A$.

Use the slope formula to calculate the slope of $\overline{BC}$.

$$m = \frac{y_2 - y_1}{x_2 - x_1}$$      Slope formula

$$m = \frac{(2) - (6)}{(3) - (7)}$$      Substitute (7, 6) and (3, 2) for $(x_1, y_1)$ and $(x_2, y_2)$.

$$m = \frac{-4}{-4} = 1$$      Simplify.

The slope of $\overline{BC}$ is 1.

The slope of the line that is perpendicular to $\overline{BC}$ has the opposite reciprocal of the slope of $\overline{BC}$.

The slope of the perpendicular line is –1.

Find the $y$-intercept of the altitude from point $A$.

$$y - y_1 = m(x - x_1)$$      Point-slope form of a line

$$y - 6 = -1(x - 1)$$      Substitute (1, 6) for $(x_1, y_1)$ and –1 for $m$.

$$y - 6 = -1x + 1$$      Simplify.

$$y = -x + 7$$

The equation of the altitude from point $A$ to $\overline{BC}$ is $y = -x + 7$.

Find an equation of the line that is perpendicular to $\overline{AC}$ and passes through $B$.

Use the slope formula to calculate the slope of $\overline{AC}$.

$$m = \frac{y_2 - y_1}{x_2 - x_1}$$      Slope formula

$$m = \frac{(2) - (6)}{(3) - (1)}$$      Substitute (1, 6) and (3, 2) for $(x_1, y_1)$ and $(x_2, y_2)$.

$$m = \frac{-4}{2} = -2$$      Simplify.

The slope of $\overline{AC}$ is –2.

*(continued)*

The slope of the line that is perpendicular to $\overline{AC}$ has the opposite reciprocal of the slope of $\overline{AB}$.

The slope of the perpendicular line is $\dfrac{1}{2}$.

Find the $y$-intercept of the altitude from point $B$.

$$y - y_1 = m(x - x_1) \qquad \text{Point-slope form of a line}$$

$$y - 6 = \frac{1}{2}(x - 7) \qquad \text{Substitute (7, 6) for } (x_1, y_1) \text{ and } \frac{1}{2} \text{ for } m.$$

$$y - 6 = \frac{1}{2}x - \frac{7}{2} \qquad \text{Simplify.}$$

$$y = \frac{1}{2}x + \frac{5}{2}$$

The equation of the altitude from point $B$ to $\overline{AC}$ is $y = \dfrac{1}{2}x + \dfrac{5}{2}$.

Find an equation of the line that is perpendicular to $\overline{AB}$ and passes through $C$.

Use the slope formula to calculate the slope of $\overline{AB}$.

$$m = \frac{y_2 - y_1}{x_2 - x_1} \qquad \text{Slope formula}$$

$$m = \frac{(6) - (6)}{(7) - (1)} \qquad \begin{array}{l}\text{Substitute (1, 6) and (7, 6) for}\\ (x_1, y_1) \text{ and } (x_2, y_2).\end{array}$$

$$m = \frac{0}{6} = 0 \qquad \text{Simplify.}$$

The slope of $\overline{AB}$ is 0.

$\overline{AB}$ is a horizontal line; therefore, the altitude is vertical.

The vertical line that passes through point $C$ is $x = 3$.

The equation of the altitude from point $C$ to $\overline{AB}$ is $x = 3$.

3. Verify that $X(3, 4)$ is the intersection of the three altitudes.

For $(3, 4)$ to be the intersection of the three altitudes, the point must satisfy each of the equations: $y = -x + 7$, $y = \frac{1}{2}x + \frac{5}{2}$, and $x = 3$.

| | |
|---|---|
| $y = -x + 7$ | Equation of the altitude from $A$ through $\overline{BC}$ |
| $(4) = -(3) + 7$ | Substitute $X(3, 4)$ for $(x, y)$. |
| $4 = 4$ | Simplify. |

$(3, 4)$ satisfies the equation of the altitude from $A$ through $\overline{BC}$.

| | |
|---|---|
| $y = \frac{1}{2}x + \frac{5}{2}$ | Equation of the altitude from $B$ through $\overline{AC}$ |
| $(4) = \frac{1}{2}(3) + \frac{5}{2}$ | Substitute $X(3, 4)$ for $(x, y)$. |
| $4 = \frac{3}{2} + \frac{5}{2}$ | Simplify. |
| $4 = \frac{8}{2}$ | |
| $4 = 4$ | |

$(3, 4)$ satisfies the equation of the altitude from $B$ through $\overline{AC}$.

| | |
|---|---|
| $x = 3$ | Equation of altitude from $C$ through $\overline{AB}$. |
| $3 = 3$ | Substitute $X(3, 4)$ for $x$. |

$(3, 4)$ satisfies the equation of the altitude from $C$ through $\overline{AB}$.

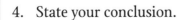

4. State your conclusion.

$X(3, 4)$ is the orthocenter of $\triangle ABC$ with vertices $A(1, 6)$, $B(7, 6)$, and $C(3, 2)$ because $X$ satisfies each of the equations of the altitudes of the triangle.

## Example 3

$\triangle ABC$ has vertices $A$ (−2, 4), $B$ (5, 4), and $C$ (3, −2). Find the equation of each median of $\triangle ABC$ to verify that (2, 2) is the centroid of $\triangle ABC$.

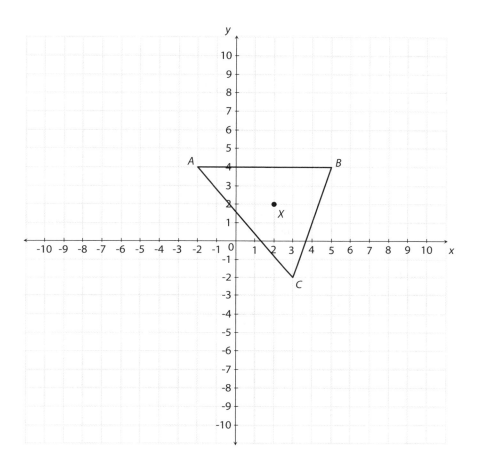

1. Identify known information.

   $\triangle ABC$ has vertices $A$ (−2, 4), $B$ (5, 4), and $C$ (3, −2).

   The centroid is $X$ (2, 2).

   The centroid of a triangle is the intersection of the medians of the triangle.

2. Determine the midpoint of each side of the triangle.

Use the midpoint formula to find the midpoint of $\overline{AB}$.

$\left( \dfrac{x_1 + x_2}{2}, \dfrac{y_1 + y_2}{2} \right)$     Midpoint formula

$\left( \dfrac{(-2)+(5)}{2}, \dfrac{(4)+(4)}{2} \right)$     Substitute $(-2, 4)$ and $(5, 4)$ for $(x_1, y_1)$ and $(x_2, y_2)$.

$\left( \dfrac{3}{2}, \dfrac{8}{2} \right)$     Simplify.

$\left( \dfrac{3}{2}, 4 \right)$

The midpoint of $\overline{AB}$ is $\left( \dfrac{3}{2}, 4 \right)$.

Use the midpoint formula to find the midpoint of $\overline{BC}$.

$\left( \dfrac{x_1 + x_2}{2}, \dfrac{y_1 + y_2}{2} \right)$     Midpoint formula

$\left( \dfrac{(5)+(3)}{2}, \dfrac{(4)+(-2)}{2} \right)$     Substitute $(5, 4)$ and $(3, -2)$ for $(x_1, y_1)$ and $(x_2, y_2)$.

$\left( \dfrac{8}{2}, \dfrac{2}{2} \right)$     Simplify.

$(4, 1)$

The midpoint of $\overline{BC}$ is $(4, 1)$.

(*continued*)

Use the midpoint formula to find the midpoint of $\overline{AC}$.

$$\left(\frac{x_1 + x_2}{2}, \frac{y_1 + y_2}{2}\right)$$   Midpoint formula

$$\left(\frac{(-2)+(3)}{2}, \frac{(4)+(-2)}{2}\right)$$   Substitute $(-2, 4)$ and $(3, -2)$ for $(x_1, y_1)$ and $(x_2, y_2)$.

$$\left(\frac{1}{2}, \frac{2}{2}\right)$$   Simplify.

$$\left(\frac{1}{2}, 1\right)$$

The midpoint of $\overline{AC}$ is $\left(\frac{1}{2}, 1\right)$.

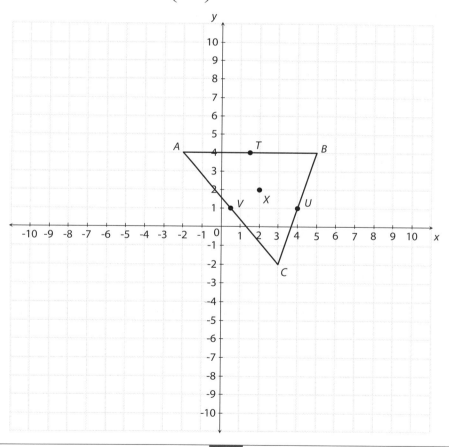

3. Determine the medians of the triangle.

Find the equation of $\overline{AU}$, which is the line that passes through $A$ and the midpoint of $\overline{BC}$.

Use the slope formula to calculate the slope of $\overline{AU}$.

$m = \dfrac{y_2 - y_1}{x_2 - x_1}$      Slope formula

$m = \dfrac{(1) - (4)}{(4) - (-2)}$      Substitute (–2, 4) and (4, 1) for $(x_1, y_1)$ and $(x_2, y_2)$.

$m = \dfrac{-3}{6}$      Simplify.

$m = -\dfrac{1}{2}$

The slope of $\overline{AU}$ is $-\dfrac{1}{2}$.

Find the $y$-intercept of $\overline{AU}$.

$y - y_1 = m(x - x_1)$      Point-slope form of a line

$y - 4 = -\dfrac{1}{2}[x - (-2)]$   Substitute (–2, 4) for $(x_1, y_1)$ and $-\dfrac{1}{2}$ for $m$.

$y - 4 = -\dfrac{1}{2}x - 1$      Simplify.

$y = -\dfrac{1}{2}x + 3$

The equation of $\overline{AU}$ that passes through $A$ and the midpoint of $\overline{BC}$ is $y = -\dfrac{1}{2}x + 3$.

(*continued*)

Find the equation of $\overline{BV}$, which is the line that passes through $B$ and the midpoint of $\overline{AC}$.

Use the slope formula to calculate the slope of $\overline{BV}$.

$$m = \frac{y_2 - y_1}{x_2 - x_1}$$   Slope formula

$$m = \frac{(1) - (4)}{\left(\frac{1}{2}\right) - (5)}$$   Substitute $(5, 4)$ and $\left(\frac{1}{2}, 1\right)$ for $(x_1, y_1)$ and $(x_2, y_2)$.

$$m = \frac{-3}{-\dfrac{9}{2}}$$   Simplify.

$$m = \frac{2}{3}$$

The slope of $\overline{BV}$ is $\dfrac{2}{3}$.

Find the $y$-intercept of $\overline{BV}$.

$$y - y_1 = m(x - x_1)$$   Point-slope form of a line

$$y - 4 = \frac{2}{3}(x - 5)$$   Substitute $(5, 4)$ for $(x_1, y_1)$ and $\dfrac{2}{3}$ for $m$.

$$y - 4 = \frac{2}{3}x - \frac{10}{3}$$   Simplify.

$$y = \frac{2}{3}x + \frac{2}{3}$$

The equation of $\overline{BV}$ that passes through $B$ and the midpoint of $\overline{AC}$ is $y = \dfrac{2}{3}x + \dfrac{2}{3}$.

*(continued)*

Find the equation of $\overline{CT}$, which is the line that passes through $C$ and the midpoint of $\overline{AB}$.

Use the slope formula to calculate the slope of $\overline{CT}$.

$$m = \frac{y_2 - y_1}{x_2 - x_1}$$  Slope formula

$$m = \frac{(4)-(-2)}{\left(\dfrac{3}{2}\right)-(3)}$$  Substitute $(3, -2)$ and $\left(\dfrac{3}{2}, 4\right)$ for $(x_1, y_1)$ and $(x_2, y_2)$.

$$m = \frac{6}{-\dfrac{3}{2}}$$  Simplify.

$$m = -4$$

The slope of $\overline{CT}$ is $-4$.

Find the $y$-intercept of $\overline{CT}$.

$y - y_1 = m(x - x_1)$  Point-slope form of a line

$y - (-2) = -4(x - 3)$  Substitute $(3, -2)$ for $(x_1, y_1)$ and $-4$ for $m$.

$y + 2 = -4(x - 3)$  Simplify.

$y + 2 = -4x + 12$

$y = -4x + 10$

The equation of $\overline{CT}$ that passes through $C$ and the midpoint of $\overline{AC}$ is $y = -4x + 10$.

4. Verify that $X(2, 2)$ is the intersection of the three medians.

For $(2, 2)$ to be the intersection of the three medians, the point must satisfy each of the equations: $y=-\dfrac{1}{2}x+3$, $y=\dfrac{2}{3}x+\dfrac{2}{3}$, and $y = -4x + 10$.

| | |
|---|---|
| $y=-\dfrac{1}{2}x+3$ | Equation of the median from $A$ to the midpoint of $\overline{BC}$ |
| $(2)=-\dfrac{1}{2}(2)+3$ | Substitute $X(2, 2)$ for $(x, y)$. |
| $2 = -1 + 3$ | Simplify. |
| $2 = 2$ | |

$(2, 2)$ satisfies the equation of the median from $A$ to the midpoint of $\overline{BC}$.

| | |
|---|---|
| $y=\dfrac{2}{3}x+\dfrac{2}{3}$ | Equation of the median from $B$ to the midpoint of $\overline{AC}$ |
| $(2)=\dfrac{2}{3}(2)+\dfrac{2}{3}$ | Substitute $X(2, 2)$ for $(x, y)$. |
| $2=\dfrac{4}{3}+\dfrac{2}{3}$ | Simplify. |
| $2=\dfrac{6}{3}$ | |
| $2 = 2$ | |

$(2, 2)$ satisfies the equation of the median from $B$ to the midpoint of $\overline{AC}$.

| | |
|---|---|
| $y = -4x +10$ | Equation of the median from $C$ to the midpoint of $\overline{AB}$ |
| $(2) = -4(2) + 10$ | Substitute $X(2, 2)$ for $(x, y)$. |
| $(2) = -8 + 10$ | Simplify. |
| $2 = 2$ | |

$(2, 2)$ satisfies the equation of the median from $C$ to the midpoint of $\overline{AB}$.

5.  State your conclusion.

    $X(2, 2)$ is the centroid of $\triangle ABC$ with vertices $A(-2, 4)$, $B(5, 4)$, and $C(3, -2)$ because $X$ satisfies each of the equations of the medians of the triangle.

## Example 4

Using $\triangle ABC$ from Example 3, which has vertices $A(-2, 4)$, $B(5, 4)$, and $C(3, -2)$, verify that the centroid, $X(2, 2)$, is $\dfrac{2}{3}$ the distance from each vertex.

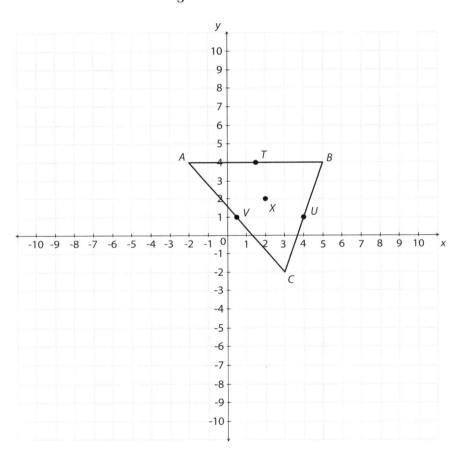

1. Identify the known information.

$\triangle ABC$ has vertices $A\,(-2, 4)$, $B\,(5, 4)$, and $C\,(3, -2)$.

The centroid is $X\,(2, 2)$.

The midpoints of $\triangle ABC$ are $T\left(\dfrac{3}{2}, 4\right)$, $U\,(4, 1)$, and $V\left(\dfrac{1}{2}, 1\right)$.

2. Use the distance formula to show that point $X\,(2, 2)$ is $\dfrac{2}{3}$ the distance from each vertex.

Use the distance formula to calculate the distance from $A$ to $U$.

$d = \sqrt{(x_2 - x_1)^2 + (y_2 - y_1)^2}$      Distance formula

$d = \sqrt{[(4) - (-2)]^2 + [(1) - (4)]^2}$      Substitute $(-2, 4)$ and $(4, 1)$ for $(x_1, y_1)$ and $(x_2, y_2)$.

$d = \sqrt{(6)^2 + (-3)^2}$      Simplify.

$d = \sqrt{36 + 9}$

$d = \sqrt{45} = \sqrt{9 \bullet 5} = 3\sqrt{5}$

The distance from $A$ to $U$ is $3\sqrt{5}$ units.

Calculate the distance from $X$ to $A$.

$d = \sqrt{(x_2 - x_1)^2 + (y_2 - y_1)^2}$      Distance formula

$d = \sqrt{[(-2) - (2)]^2 + [(4) - (2)]^2}$      Substitute $(2, 2)$ and $(-2, 4)$ for $(x_1, y_1)$ and $(x_2, y_2)$.

$d = \sqrt{(-4)^2 + (2)^2}$      Simplify.

$d = \sqrt{16 + 4}$

$d = \sqrt{20} = \sqrt{4 \bullet 5} = 2\sqrt{5}$

The distance from $X$ to $A$ is $2\sqrt{5}$ units.

*(continued)*

$$\frac{2}{3}AU = XA \qquad\qquad \text{Centroid Theorem}$$

$$\frac{2}{3}\left(3\sqrt{5}\right)=2\sqrt{5} \qquad\qquad \text{Substitute the distances found for } AU \text{ and } XA.$$

$$2\sqrt{5}=2\sqrt{5} \qquad\qquad \text{Simplify.}$$

$X$ is $\dfrac{2}{3}$ the distance from $A$.

Use the distance formula to calculate the distance from $B$ to $V$.

$$d=\sqrt{(x_2-x_1)^2+(y_2-y_1)^2} \qquad\qquad \text{Distance formula}$$

$$d=\sqrt{\left[\left(\frac{1}{2}\right)-(5)\right]^2+[(1)-(4)]^2} \qquad\qquad \text{Substitute } (5,4) \text{ and } \left(\frac{1}{2},1\right) \text{ for } (x_1,y_1) \text{ and } (x_2,y_2).$$

$$d=\sqrt{\left(-\frac{9}{2}\right)^2+(-3)^2} \qquad\qquad \text{Simplify.}$$

$$d=\sqrt{\frac{81}{4}+9}$$

$$d=\sqrt{\frac{117}{4}}=\frac{\sqrt{9\bullet 13}}{\sqrt{4}}=\frac{3\sqrt{13}}{2}$$

The distance from $B$ to $V$ is $\dfrac{3\sqrt{13}}{2}$ units.

Calculate the distance from $X$ to $B$.

$$d=\sqrt{(x_2-x_1)^2+(y_2-y_1)^2} \qquad\qquad \text{Distance formula}$$

$$d=\sqrt{[(5)-(2)]^2+[(4)-(2)]^2} \qquad\qquad \text{Substitute } (2,2) \text{ and } (5,4) \text{ for } (x_1,y_1) \text{ and } (x_2,y_2).$$

$$d=\sqrt{(3)^2+(2)^2} \qquad\qquad \text{Simplify.}$$

$$d=\sqrt{9+4}$$

$$d=\sqrt{13}$$

The distance from $X$ to $B$ is $\sqrt{13}$ units. (*continued*)

$$\frac{2}{3}BV = XB \qquad \text{Centroid Theorem}$$

$$\frac{2}{3}\left(\frac{3\sqrt{13}}{2}\right) = \sqrt{13} \qquad \text{Substitute the distances found for } BV \text{ and } XB.$$

$$\sqrt{13} = \sqrt{13} \qquad \text{Simplify.}$$

$X$ is $\dfrac{2}{3}$ the distance from $B$.

Use the distance formula to calculate the distance from $C$ to $T$.

$$d = \sqrt{(x_2 - x_1)^2 + (y_2 - y_1)^2} \qquad \text{Distance formula}$$

$$d = \sqrt{\left[\left(\frac{3}{2}\right) - (3)\right]^2 + [(4) - (-2)]^2} \qquad \text{Substitute } (3, -2) \text{ and } \left(\frac{3}{2}, 4\right) \text{ for } (x_1, y_1) \text{ and } (x_2, y_2).$$

$$d = \sqrt{\left(-\frac{3}{2}\right)^2 + (6)^2} \qquad \text{Simplify.}$$

$$d = \sqrt{\frac{9}{4} + 36}$$

$$d = \sqrt{\frac{153}{4}} = \frac{\sqrt{9 \bullet 17}}{\sqrt{4}} = \frac{3\sqrt{17}}{2}$$

The distance from $C$ to $T$ is $\dfrac{3\sqrt{17}}{2}$ units.

(*continued*)

Calculate the distance from $X$ to $C$.

$$d = \sqrt{(x_2 - x_1)^2 + (y_2 - y_1)^2}$$   Distance formula

$$d = \sqrt{[(3) - (2)]^2 + [(-2) - (2)]^2}$$   Substitute (2, 2) and (3, –2) for $(x_1, y_1)$ and $(x_2, y_2)$.

$$d = \sqrt{(1)^2 + (-4)^2}$$   Simplify.

$$d = \sqrt{1 + 16}$$

$$d = \sqrt{17}$$

The distance from $X$ to $C$ is $\sqrt{17}$ units.

$$\frac{2}{3}CT = XC$$   Centroid Theorem

$$\frac{2}{3}\left(\frac{3\sqrt{17}}{2}\right) = \sqrt{17}$$   Substitute the distances found for $CT$ and $XC$.

$$\sqrt{17} = \sqrt{17}$$   Simplify.

$X$ is $\dfrac{2}{3}$ the distance from $C$.

The centroid, $X$ (2, 2), is $\dfrac{2}{3}$ the distance from each vertex.

## Practice 5.6.4: Proving Centers of Triangles

Use what you know about centers of triangles to complete each problem.

1. $\triangle ABC$ has vertices $A$ (0, 0), $B$ (0, –6), and $C$ (–2, 0). Justify that (–1, –3) is the circumcenter of $\triangle ABC$.

2. $\triangle ABC$ has vertices $A$ (–2, 6), $B$ (–2, 1), and $C$ (4, 1). Justify that (–2, 1) is the orthocenter of $\triangle ABC$.

3. $\triangle ABC$ has vertices $A$ (7, 3), $B$ (8, –4), and $C$ (0, –2). Justify that (5, –1) is the centroid of $\triangle ABC$.

4. Verify that the centroid, (5, –1), of $\triangle ABC$ with vertices $A$ (7, 3), $B$ (8, –4), and $C$ (0, –2) is $\dfrac{2}{3}$ the distance from each vertex to the midpoint of the opposite side.

5. $\triangle ABC$ has vertices $A$ (2, 8), $B$ (0, 9), and $C$ (5, –1). Will the incenter be inside, outside, or on a side of $\triangle ABC$? Explain your answer.

6. $\triangle ABC$ has vertices $A$ (–3, 7), $B$ (2, 7), and $C$ (2, –4). Will the orthocenter be inside, outside, or on a side of $\triangle ABC$? Explain your answer.

7. The Circumcenter Theorem states the circumcenter of a triangle is equidistant from the vertices of the triangle. Prove this theorem using the information below.

   Given: $\triangle ABC$ has perpendicular bisectors $p$, $q$, and $r$ of $\overline{AB}$, $\overline{BC}$, and $\overline{AC}$.

   Prove: $AX = BX = CX$

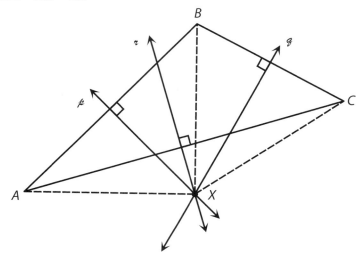

8. A trauma center is to be built to assist three towns. The relative location of the towns and the concurrent roads connecting the towns are shown below. If the trauma center cannot be built outside the area of the triangle, which point(s) of concurrency cannot be used to determine the location of the trauma center?

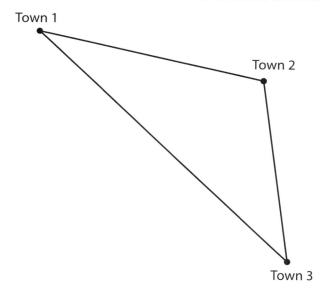

*continued*

9. A new first aid station at a local park is to be placed in a location that is equidistant from the information booth, the picnic area, and the water fountain. Which center of the triangle created between each location should be determined? Explain your answer.

10. A dog's leash is staked in a triangular backyard. Which center of the yard should be found to ensure the dog has the maximum amount of space without going into the neighbor's yard?

# Lesson 7: Proving Theorems About Parallelograms

## Common Core State Standard

**G–CO.11**  Prove theorems about parallelograms. *Theorems include: opposite sides are congruent, opposite angles are congruent, the diagonals of a parallelogram bisect each other, and conversely, rectangles are parallelograms with congruent diagonals.*

## Essential Questions

1. What makes a quadrilateral a parallelogram?

2. What is the hierarchy of quadrilaterals?

3. What theorems are used for parallelograms?

4. How are rectangles, rhombuses, squares, kites, and trapezoids alike and different?

## WORDS TO KNOW

| | |
|---|---|
| **concave polygon** | a polygon with at least one interior angle greater than 180° and at least one diagonal that does not lie entirely inside the polygon |
| **consecutive angles** | angles that lie on the same side of a figure |
| **convex polygon** | a polygon with no interior angle greater than 180°; all diagonals lie inside the polygon |
| **diagonal** | a line that connects nonconsecutive vertices |
| **isosceles trapezoid** | a trapezoid with one pair of opposite parallel lines and congruent legs |
| **kite** | a quadrilateral with two distinct pairs of congruent sides that are adjacent |
| **parallelogram** | a special type of quadrilateral with two pairs of opposite sides that are parallel; denoted by the symbol □ |
| **quadrilateral** | a polygon with four sides |

| | |
|---|---|
| **rectangle** | a special parallelogram with four right angles |
| **rhombus** | a special parallelogram with all four sides congruent |
| **square** | a special parallelogram with four congruent sides and four right angles |
| **trapezoid** | a quadrilateral with exactly one pair of opposite parallel lines |

## Recommended Resources

- MathIsFun.com. "Interactive Quadrilaterals."

  http://www.walch.com/rr/00037

  Review different quadrilaterals with this interactive site. Click the name of a quadrilateral to view its shape and definition, then select and drag the vertices to change or rotate the shape. Options to view the angle measures and/or diagonals of each given quadrilateral are also included.

- Math Warehouse. "Parallelograms."

  http://www.walch.com/rr/00038

  This website gives a brief overview of the properties of parallelograms. Users can examine the relationships among sides and angles with an interactive parallelogram. Each section offers three test questions, with answers provided when you click on the "Answer" button.

- Math Warehouse. "Rhombus: Properties and Shape."

  http://www.walch.com/rr/00039

  Rhombuses are defined and explained with examples at this site. Clickable practice questions are provided to test understanding.

- Oswego City School District Regents Exam Prep Center. "Theorems Dealing with Rectangles, Rhombuses, Squares."

  http://www.walch.com/rr/00040

  This site provides a simple lesson on the properties of rectangles, rhombuses, and squares, with concise descriptions and examples.

# Lesson 5.7.1: Proving Properties of Parallelograms

## Introduction

What does it mean to be opposite? What does it mean to be consecutive? Think about a rectangular room. If you put your back against one corner of that room and looked directly across the room, you would be looking at the opposite corner. If you looked to your right, that corner would be a consecutive corner. If you looked to your left, that corner would also be a consecutive corner. The walls of the room could also be described similarly. If you were to stand with your back at the center of one wall, the wall straight across from you would be the opposite wall. The walls next to you would be consecutive walls. There are two pairs of opposite walls in a rectangular room, and there are two pairs of opposite angles. Before looking at the properties of parallelograms, it is important to understand what the terms opposite and consecutive mean.

## Key Concepts

- A **quadrilateral** is a polygon with four sides.

- A **convex polygon** is a polygon with no interior angle greater than 180° and all diagonals lie inside the polygon.

- A **diagonal** of a polygon is a line that connects nonconsecutive vertices.

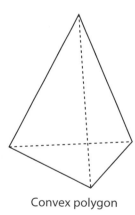

Convex polygon

- Convex polygons are contrasted with concave polygons.

- A **concave polygon** is a polygon with at least one interior angle greater than 180° and at least one diagonal that does not lie entirely inside the polygon.

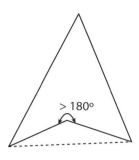

Concave polygon

- A **parallelogram** is a special type of quadrilateral with two pairs of opposite sides that are parallel.

- By definition, if a quadrilateral has two pairs of opposite sides that are parallel, then the quadrilateral is a parallelogram.

- Parallelograms are denoted by the symbol $\square$ .

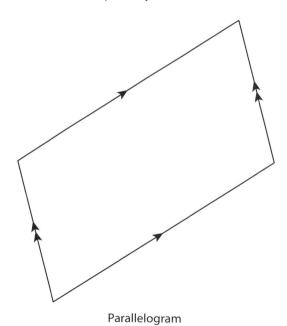

Parallelogram

- If a polygon is a parallelogram, there are five theorems associated with it.

- In a parallelogram, both pairs of opposite sides are congruent.

---

**Theorem**

If a quadrilateral is a parallelogram, opposite sides are congruent.

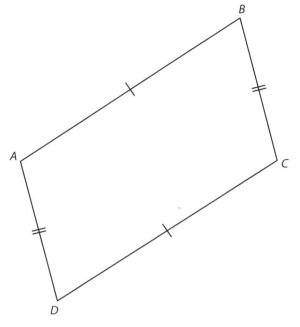

$$\overline{AB} \cong \overline{DC}$$

$$\overline{AD} \cong \overline{BC}$$

The converse is also true. If the opposite sides of a quadrilateral are congruent, then the quadrilateral is a parallelogram.

---

- Parallelograms also have two pairs of opposite angles that are congruent.

---

## Theorem

If a quadrilateral is a parallelogram, opposite angles are congruent.

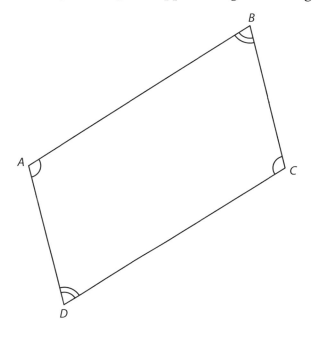

$\angle A \cong \angle C$

$\angle B \cong \angle D$

The converse is also true. If the opposite angles of a quadrilateral are congruent, then the quadrilateral is a parallelogram.

---

- **Consecutive angles** are angles that lie on the same side of a figure.

- In a parallelogram, consecutive angles are supplementary; that is, they sum to 180°.

---

**Theorem**

If a quadrilateral is a parallelogram, then consecutive angles are supplementary.

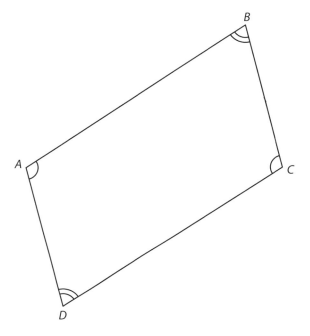

$$m\angle A + m\angle B = 180$$
$$m\angle B + m\angle C = 180$$
$$m\angle C + m\angle D = 180$$
$$m\angle D + m\angle A = 180$$

---

- The diagonals of a parallelogram have a relationship. They bisect each other.

---

**Theorem**

The diagonals of a parallelogram bisect each other.

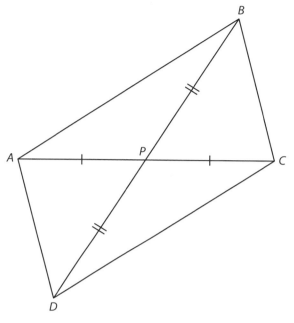

$$\overline{AP} \cong \overline{PC}$$

$$\overline{BP} \cong \overline{PD}$$

The converse is also true. If the diagonals of a quadrilateral bisect each other, then the quadrilateral is a parallelogram.

---

- Notice that each diagonal divides the parallelogram into two triangles. Those two triangles are congruent.

**Theorem**

The diagonal of a parallelogram forms two congruent triangles.

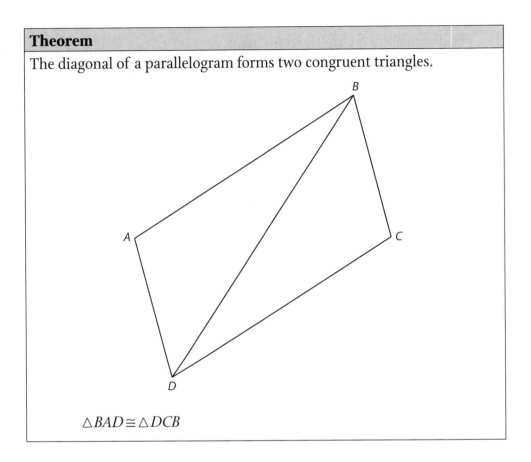

$$\triangle BAD \cong \triangle DCB$$

# Guided Practice 5.7.1

**Example 1**

Quadrilateral *ABCD* has the following vertices: *A* (–4, 4), *B* (2, 8), *C* (3, 4), and *D* (–3, 0). Determine whether the quadrilateral is a parallelogram. Verify your answer using slope and distance to prove or disprove that opposite sides are parallel and opposite sides are congruent.

1. Graph the figure.

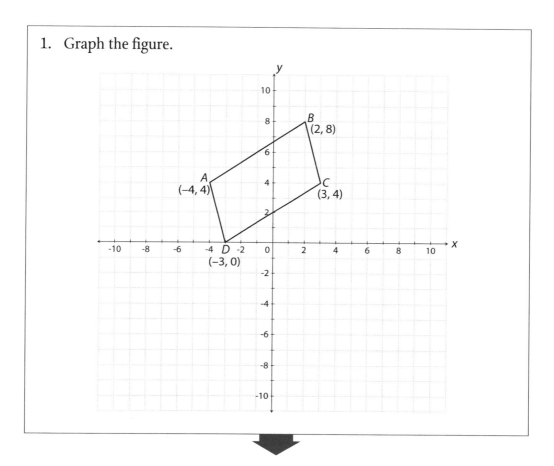

2. Determine whether opposite pairs of lines are parallel.

   Calculate the slope of each line segment.

   $\overline{AB}$ is opposite $\overline{DC}$; $\overline{BC}$ is opposite $\overline{AD}$.

   $$m_{\overline{AB}} = \frac{\Delta y}{\Delta x} = \frac{(8-4)}{[2-(-4)]} = \frac{4}{6} = \frac{2}{3} \qquad m_{\overline{BC}} = \frac{\Delta y}{\Delta x} = \frac{(4-8)}{(3-2)} = \frac{-4}{1} = -4$$

   $$m_{\overline{DC}} = \frac{\Delta y}{\Delta x} = \frac{(4-0)}{[3-(-3)]} = \frac{4}{6} = \frac{2}{3} \qquad m_{\overline{AD}} = \frac{\Delta y}{\Delta x} = \frac{(0-4)}{[-3-(-4)]} = \frac{-4}{1} = -4$$

   Calculating the slopes, we can see that the opposite sides are parallel because the slopes of the opposite sides are equal. By the definition of a parallelogram, quadrilateral $ABCD$ is a parallelogram.

3. Verify that the opposite sides are congruent.

   Calculate the distance of each segment using the distance formula.

   $$d = \sqrt{(x_2 - x_1)^2 + (y_2 - y_1)^2}$$

   $AB = \sqrt{[2-(-4)]^2 + (8-4)^2}$    $BC = \sqrt{(3-2)^2 + (4-8)^2}$

   $AB = \sqrt{(6)^2 + (4)^2}$          $BC = \sqrt{(1)^2 + (-4)^2}$

   $AB = \sqrt{36+16}$                  $BC = \sqrt{1+16}$

   $AB = \sqrt{52} = 2\sqrt{13}$        $BC = \sqrt{17}$

   $DC = \sqrt{[3-(-3)]^2 + (4-0)^2}$   $AD = \sqrt{[-3-(-4)]^2 + (0-4)^2}$

   $DC = \sqrt{(6)^2 + (4)^2}$          $AD = \sqrt{(1)^2 + (-4)^2}$

   $DC = \sqrt{36+16}$                  $AD = \sqrt{1+16}$

   $DC = \sqrt{52} = 2\sqrt{13}$        $AD = \sqrt{17}$

   From the distance formula, we can see that opposite sides are congruent. Because of the definition of congruence and since $AB = DC$ and $BC = AD$, then $\overline{AB} \cong \overline{DC}$ and $\overline{BC} \cong \overline{AD}$.

## Example 2

Use the parallelogram from Example 1 to verify that the opposite angles in a parallelogram are congruent and consecutive angles are supplementary given that $\overline{AD} \parallel \overline{BC}$ and $\overline{AB} \parallel \overline{DC}$.

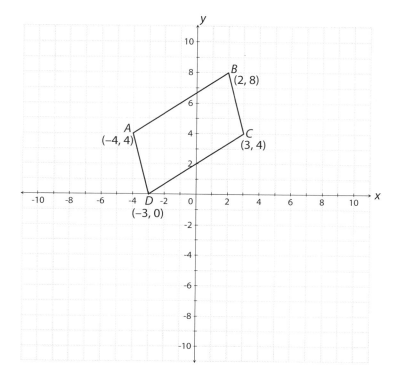

1. Extend the lines in the parallelogram to show two pairs of intersecting lines and label the angles with numbers.

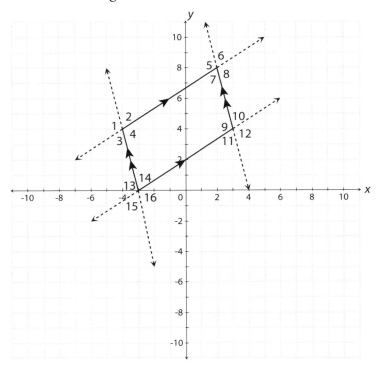

2. Prove $\angle 4 \cong \angle 9$.

| | |
|---|---|
| $\overline{AD} \parallel \overline{BC}$ and $\overline{AB} \parallel \overline{DC}$ | Given |
| $\angle 4 \cong \angle 13$ | Alternate Interior Angles Theorem |
| $\angle 13 \cong \angle 16$ | Vertical Angles Theorem |
| $\angle 16 \cong \angle 9$ | Alternate Interior Angles Theorem |
| $\angle 4 \cong \angle 9$ | Transitive Property |

We have proven that one pair of opposite angles in a parallelogram is congruent.

3.  Prove $\angle 7 \cong \angle 14$.

$\overline{AD} \| \overline{BC}$ and $\overline{AB} \| \overline{DC}$     Given

$\angle 7 \cong \angle 10$                     Alternate Interior Angles Theorem

$\angle 10 \cong \angle 11$                    Vertical Angles Theorem

$\angle 11 \cong \angle 14$                    Alternate Interior Angles Theorem

$\angle 7 \cong \angle 14$                     Transitive Property

We have proven that both pairs of opposite angles in a parallelogram are congruent.

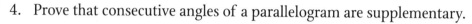

4.  Prove that consecutive angles of a parallelogram are supplementary.

$\overline{AD} \| \overline{BC}$ and $\overline{AB} \| \overline{DC}$          Given

$\angle 4$ and $\angle 14$ are supplementary.     Same-Side Interior Angles Theorem

$\angle 14$ and $\angle 9$ are supplementary.     Same-Side Interior Angles Theorem

$\angle 9$ and $\angle 7$ are supplementary.      Same-Side Interior Angles Theorem

$\angle 7$ and $\angle 4$ are supplementary.      Same-Side Interior Angles Theorem

We have proven consecutive angles in a parallelogram are supplementary using the Same-Side Interior Angles Theorem of a set of parallel lines intersected by a transversal.

# Example 3

Use the parallelogram from Example 1 to prove that diagonals of a parallelogram bisect each other.

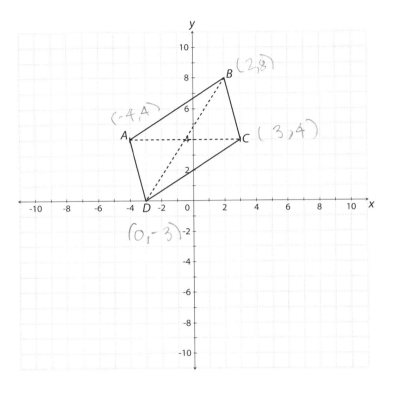

1. Find the midpoint of $\overline{AC}$, where $M$ stands for midpoint.

   By definition, the midpoint is the point on a segment that divides the segment into two congruent parts.

   $$M = \left( \frac{x_1 + x_2}{2}, \frac{y_1 + y_2}{2} \right) \qquad \text{Midpoint formula}$$

   $$M_{\overline{AC}} = \left( \frac{-4 + 3}{2}, \frac{4 + 4}{2} \right) = \left( \frac{-1}{2}, \frac{8}{2} \right) = \left( -\frac{1}{2}, 4 \right) \qquad \begin{array}{l} \text{Substitute values} \\ \text{for } x_1, x_2, y_1, \text{ and } y_2, \\ \text{then solve.} \end{array}$$

2. Find the midpoint of $\overline{DB}$.

$$M = \left( \frac{x_1 + x_2}{2}, \frac{y_1 + y_2}{2} \right)$$    Midpoint formula

$$M_{\overline{DB}} = \left( \frac{-3+2}{2}, \frac{0+8}{2} \right) = \left( \frac{-1}{2}, \frac{8}{2} \right) = \left( -\frac{1}{2}, 4 \right)$$    Substitute values for $x_1$, $x_2$, $y_1$, and $y_2$, then solve.

3. Mark the midpoint of each segment on the graph.

Notice that the midpoint of $\overline{AC}$ and the midpoint of $\overline{DB}$ are the same point.

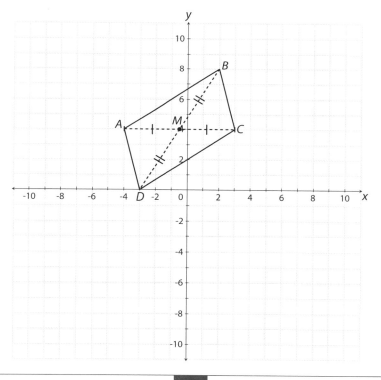

4. Write statements that prove the diagonals bisect each other.

Since $M$ is the midpoint of $\overline{AC}$, $\overline{AM} \cong \overline{MC}$. $M$ is also a point on $\overline{DB}$. Therefore, $\overline{DB}$ is the bisector of $\overline{AC}$. The midpoint of $\overline{DB}$ is $M$. This means that $\overline{DM} \cong \overline{DB}$. Since $M$ is a point on $\overline{AC}$, $\overline{AC}$ is the bisector of $\overline{DB}$. The diagonals bisect each other.

## Example 4

Use the parallelogram from Example 1 and the diagonal $\overline{DB}$ to prove that a diagonal of a parallelogram separates the parallelogram into two congruent triangles.

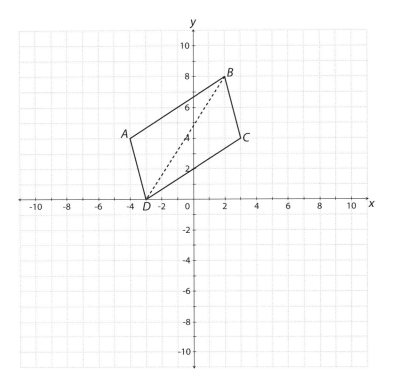

1. Use theorems about parallelograms to mark congruent sides.

   Opposite sides of a parallelogram are congruent, as proven in Example 1.

   $\overline{AB} \cong \overline{DC}$ and $\overline{BC} \cong \overline{AD}$      Opposite sides of a parallelogram are congruent.

   So far, we know that the triangles each have two sides that are congruent to the corresponding sides of the other triangle. To prove triangles congruent, we could use ASA, SAS, or SSS. From the information we have, we could either try to find the third side congruent or the included angles congruent.

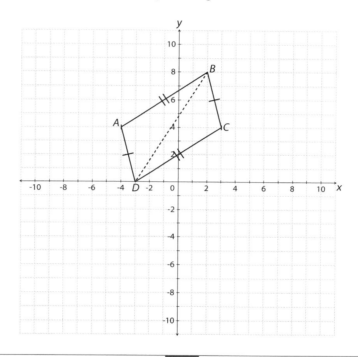

2.  Use the Reflexive Property to identify a third side of the triangle that is congruent.

$\overline{DB} \cong \overline{DB}$ by the Reflexive Property.

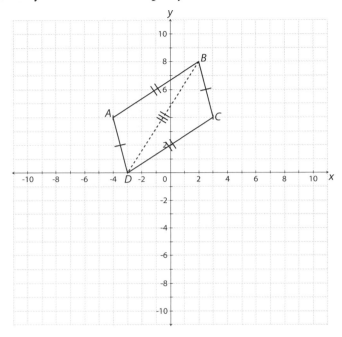

Now, all three sides of the triangles are congruent.

3.  State the congruent triangles.

Using SSS, we verified that $\triangle DAB \cong \triangle BCD$. Therefore, the diagonal splits the parallelogram into two congruent triangles.

# UNIT 5 • SIMILARITY, RIGHT TRIANGLE TRIGONOMETRY, AND PROOF
## Lesson 7: Proving Theorems About Parallelograms

## Practice 5.7.1: Proving Properties of Parallelograms

Use slope to determine whether the given vertices form a parallelogram.

1. $T(-1, 0)$, $U(0, 5)$, $V(3, 3)$, and $W(2, 1)$

2. $W(0, -2)$, $X(1, 3)$, $Y(6, 5)$, and $Z(5, 0)$

Use the distance formula to determine whether the given vertices form a parallelogram.

3. $G(1, 2)$, $H(2, 5)$, $I(7, 4)$, and $J(6, 1)$

4. $A(-2, 2)$, $B(0, 5)$, $C(2, 0)$, and $D(1, -1)$

Use the midpoint formula to determine whether the given vertices form a parallelogram.

5. $D(2, 0)$, $E(6, 0)$, $F(4, -3)$, and $G(0, -3)$

6. $M(-1, 0)$, $N(0, 2)$, $O(3, 2)$, and $P(3, 1)$

Determine the unknown angle measures and the values of $x$ and $y$ that make quadrilateral $ABCD$ a parallelogram.

7.

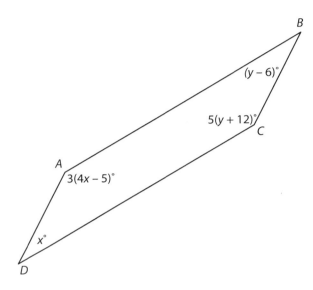

8.

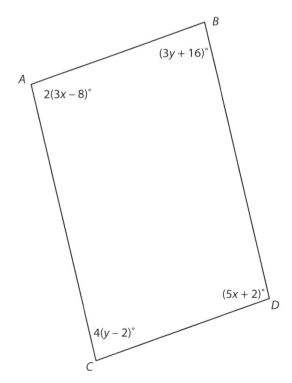

*continued*

# UNIT 5 • SIMILARITY, RIGHT TRIANGLE TRIGONOMETRY, AND PROOF
## Lesson 7: Proving Theorems About Parallelograms

Prove the following using the proof method of your choosing.

9.  Given $\square ABCD$, prove $\dfrac{AB}{ED} = \dfrac{BF}{DA}$.

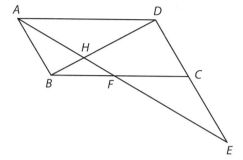

10. Let quadrilateral $ABCD$ have vertices $A\,(0, 0)$, $B\,(a, b)$, $C\,(a + c, b)$, and $D\,(c, 0)$. Use the vertices to show that the quadrilateral is a parallelogram and the diagonals bisect each other.

# Lesson 5.7.2: Proving Properties of Special Quadrilaterals

## Introduction

There are many kinds of quadrilaterals. Some quadrilaterals are parallelograms; some are not. For example, trapezoids and kites are special quadrilaterals, but they are not parallelograms.

Some parallelograms are known as special parallelograms. What makes a parallelogram a more specialized parallelogram? Rectangles, rhombuses, and squares are all special parallelograms with special properties. They have all the same characteristics that parallelograms have, plus more.

## Key Concepts

- A **rectangle** has four sides and four right angles.

- A rectangle is a parallelogram, so opposite sides are parallel, opposite angles are congruent, and consecutive angles are supplementary.

- The diagonals of a rectangle bisect each other and are also congruent.

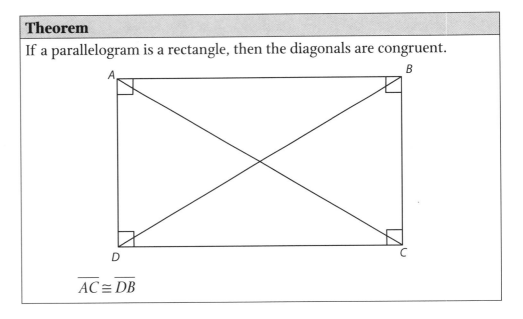

**Theorem**

If a parallelogram is a rectangle, then the diagonals are congruent.

$\overline{AC} \cong \overline{DB}$

- A **rhombus** is a special parallelogram with all four sides congruent.

- Since a rhombus is a parallelogram, opposite sides are parallel, opposite angles are congruent, and consecutive angles are supplementary.

- The diagonals bisect each other; additionally, they also bisect the opposite pairs of angles within the rhombus.

## Theorem

If a parallelogram is a rhombus, the diagonals of the rhombus bisect the opposite pairs of angles.

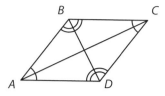

$$\angle BAC \cong \angle CAD \cong \angle BCA \cong \angle DCA$$
$$\angle CBD \cong \angle ABD \cong \angle ADB \cong \angle CDB$$

- The diagonals of a rhombus also form four right angles where they intersect.

## Theorem

If a parallelogram is a rhombus, the diagonals are perpendicular.

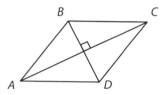

$$\overline{BD} \perp \overline{AC}$$

The converse is also true. If the diagonals of a parallelogram intersect at a right angle, then the parallelogram is a rhombus.

- A **square** has all the properties of a rectangle and a rhombus.

- Squares have four congruent sides and four right angles.

- The diagonals of a square bisect each other, are congruent, and bisect opposite pairs of angles.

- The diagonals are also perpendicular.

## Properties of Squares

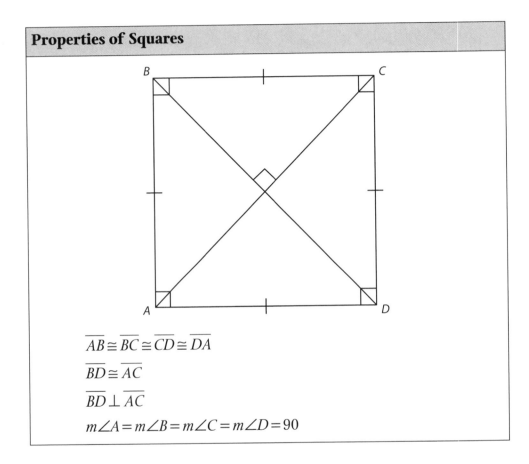

$$\overline{AB} \cong \overline{BC} \cong \overline{CD} \cong \overline{DA}$$

$$\overline{BD} \cong \overline{AC}$$

$$\overline{BD} \perp \overline{AC}$$

$$m\angle A = m\angle B = m\angle C = m\angle D = 90$$

- **Trapezoids** are quadrilaterals with exactly one pair of opposite parallel lines.

- Trapezoids are not parallelograms because they do not have two pairs of opposite lines that are parallel.

- The lines in a trapezoid that are parallel are called the bases, and the lines that are not parallel are called the legs.

## Properties of Trapezoids

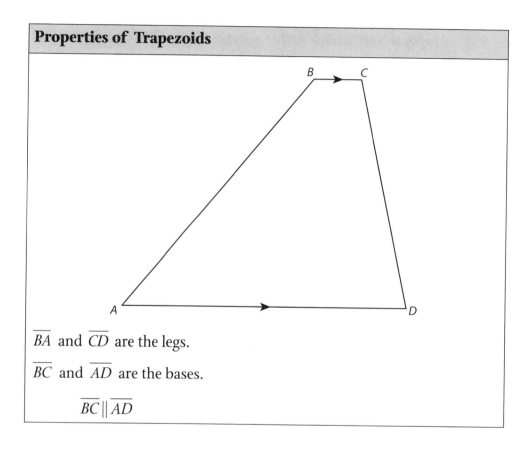

$\overline{BA}$ and $\overline{CD}$ are the legs.

$\overline{BC}$ and $\overline{AD}$ are the bases.

$$\overline{BC} \parallel \overline{AD}$$

- **Isosceles trapezoids** have one pair of opposite parallel lines. The legs are congruent.

- Since the legs are congruent, both pairs of base angles are also congruent, similar to the legs and base angles in an isosceles triangle.

- The diagonals of an isosceles trapezoid are congruent.

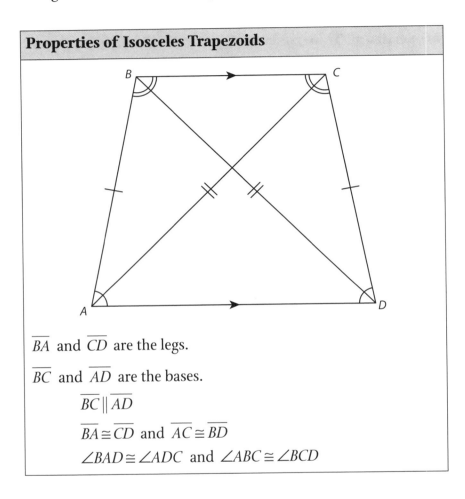

**Properties of Isosceles Trapezoids**

$\overline{BA}$ and $\overline{CD}$ are the legs.

$\overline{BC}$ and $\overline{AD}$ are the bases.

$\overline{BC} \parallel \overline{AD}$

$\overline{BA} \cong \overline{CD}$ and $\overline{AC} \cong \overline{BD}$

$\angle BAD \cong \angle ADC$ and $\angle ABC \cong \angle BCD$

- A **kite** is a quadrilateral with two distinct pairs of congruent sides that are adjacent.

- Kites are not parallelograms because opposite sides are not parallel.

- The diagonals of a kite are perpendicular.

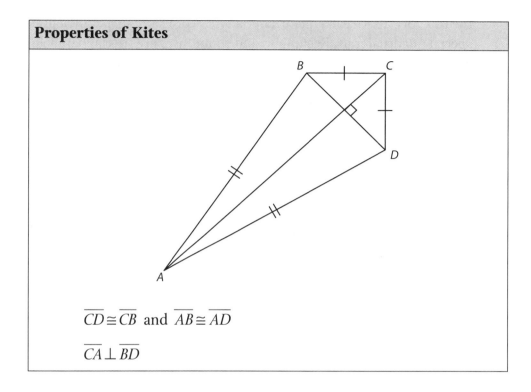

**Properties of Kites**

$\overline{CD} \cong \overline{CB}$ and $\overline{AB} \cong \overline{AD}$

$\overline{CA} \perp \overline{BD}$

- Quadrilaterals can be grouped according to their properties. This kind of grouping is called a hierarchy.

- In the following hierarchy of quadrilaterals, you can see that all quadrilaterals are polygons but that not all polygons are quadrilaterals.

- The arrows connecting the types of quadrilaterals indicate a special version of the category above each quadrilateral type. For example, parallelograms are special quadrilaterals. Rectangles and rhombuses are special parallelograms, and squares have all the properties of rectangles and rhombuses.

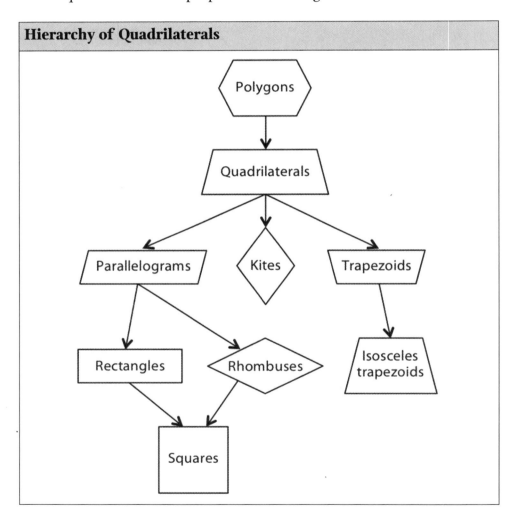

**Hierarchy of Quadrilaterals**

# Guided Practice 5.7.2

## Example 1

Quadrilateral *ABCD* has vertices *A* (–6, 8), *B* (2, 2), *C* (–1, –2), and *D* (–9, 4). Using slope, distance, and/or midpoints, classify $\square ABCD$ as a rectangle, rhombus, square, trapezoid, isosceles trapezoid, or kite.

1. Graph the quadrilateral.

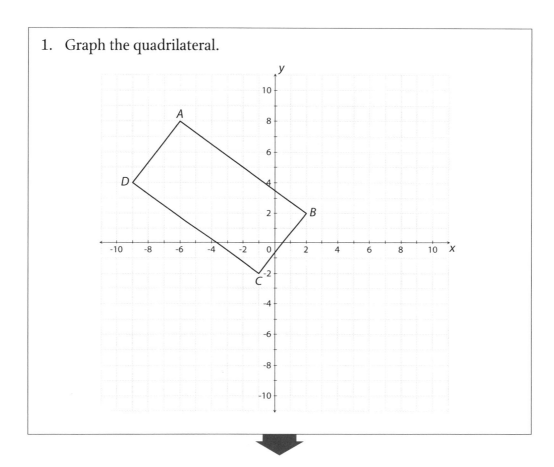

2. Calculate the slopes of the sides to determine if opposite sides are parallel.

   If opposite sides are parallel, the quadrilateral is a parallelogram.

   $$m_{\overline{AB}} = \frac{\Delta y}{\Delta x} = \frac{(2-8)}{[2-(-6)]} = \frac{-6}{8} = -\frac{3}{4}$$

   $$m_{\overline{DC}} = \frac{\Delta y}{\Delta x} = \frac{(-2-4)}{[-1-(-9)]} = \frac{-6}{8} = -\frac{3}{4}$$

   The first pair of opposite sides is parallel: $\overline{AB} \| \overline{DC}$.

   $$m_{\overline{AD}} = \frac{\Delta y}{\Delta x} = \frac{(4-8)}{[-9-(-6)]} = \frac{-4}{-3} = \frac{4}{3}$$

   $$m_{\overline{BC}} = \frac{\Delta y}{\Delta x} = \frac{(-2-2)}{(-1-2)} = \frac{-4}{-3} = \frac{4}{3}$$

   The second pair of opposite sides is parallel: $\overline{AD} \| \overline{BC}$. Therefore, the quadrilateral is a parallelogram.

3. Examine the slopes of the consecutive sides to determine if they intersect at right angles.

   If the slopes are opposite reciprocals, the lines are perpendicular and therefore form right angles. If there are four right angles, the quadrilateral is a rectangle or a square.

   $$m_{\overline{AB}} = m_{\overline{DC}} = -\frac{3}{4}$$

   $$m_{\overline{AD}} = m_{\overline{BC}} = \frac{4}{3}$$

   $-\frac{3}{4}$ is the opposite reciprocal of $\frac{4}{3}$.

   The slopes of the consecutive sides are perpendicular: $\overline{AB} \perp \overline{AD}$ and $\overline{DC} \perp \overline{BC}$. There are four right angles at the vertices. The parallelogram is a rectangle or a square.

   You could also determine if the diagonals are congruent by calculating the length of each diagonal using the distance formula, $d = \sqrt{(x_2 - x_1)^2 + (y_2 - y_1)^2}$. If the diagonals are congruent, then the parallelogram is a rectangle or square.

   $$AC = \sqrt{[-1-(-6)]^2 + (-2-8)^2} \qquad DB = \sqrt{[2-(-9)]^2 + (2-4)^2}$$
   $$AC = \sqrt{(5)^2 + (-10)^2} \qquad DB = \sqrt{(11)^2 + (-2)^2}$$
   $$AC = \sqrt{25+100} \qquad DB = \sqrt{121+4}$$
   $$AC = \sqrt{125} \qquad DB = \sqrt{125}$$
   $$AC = 5\sqrt{5} \qquad DB = 5\sqrt{5}$$

   The diagonals are congruent: $\overline{AC} \cong \overline{DB}$. The parallelogram is a rectangle.

4. Calculate the lengths of the sides.

   If all sides are congruent, the parallelogram is a rhombus or a square. Since we established that the angles are right angles, the rectangle can be more precisely classified as a square if the sides are congruent. If the sides are not congruent, the parallelogram is a rectangle.

   Use the distance formula to calculate the lengths of the sides.

   $$d = \sqrt{(x_2 - x_1)^2 + (y_2 - y_1)^2}$$

   $AB = \sqrt{[2-(-6)]^2 + (2-8)^2}$  $\qquad$  $AD = \sqrt{[-9-(-6)]^2 + (4-8)^2}$

   $AB = \sqrt{(8)^2 + (-6)^2}$  $\qquad$  $AD = \sqrt{(-3)^2 + (-4)^2}$

   $AB = \sqrt{64 + 36}$  $\qquad$  $AD = \sqrt{9 + 16}$

   $AB = \sqrt{100}$  $\qquad$  $AD = \sqrt{25}$

   $AB = 10$  $\qquad$  $AD = 5$

   $DC = \sqrt{[-1-(-9)]^2 + (-2-4)^2}$  $\qquad$  $BC = \sqrt{(-1-2)^2 + (-2-2)^2}$

   $DC = \sqrt{(8)^2 + (-6)^2}$  $\qquad$  $BC = \sqrt{(-3)^2 + (-4)^2}$

   $DC = \sqrt{64 + 36}$  $\qquad$  $BC = \sqrt{9 + 16}$

   $DC = \sqrt{100}$  $\qquad$  $BC = \sqrt{25}$

   $DC = 10$  $\qquad$  $BC = 5$

   Opposite sides are congruent, which is consistent with a parallelogram, but all sides are not congruent.

5. Summarize your findings.

   The quadrilateral has opposite sides that are parallel and four right angles, but not four congruent sides. This makes the quadrilateral a parallelogram and a rectangle.

## Example 2

Quadrilateral $ABCD$ has vertices $A$ $(0, 8)$, $B$ $(11, 1)$, $C$ $(0, -6)$, and $D$ $(-11, 1)$. Using slope, distance, and/or midpoints, classify $\square ABCD$ as a rectangle, rhombus, square, trapezoid, isosceles trapezoid, or kite.

1. Graph the quadrilateral.

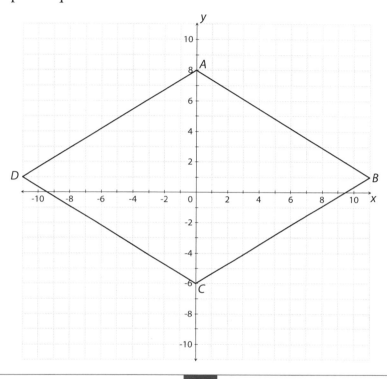

2. Calculate the slopes of the sides to determine if the quadrilateral is a parallelogram.

   If opposite sides are parallel, the quadrilateral is a parallelogram.

   $\overline{AB}$ is opposite $\overline{DC}$. $\overline{BC}$ is opposite $\overline{AD}$.

   $$m_{\overline{AB}} = \frac{\Delta y}{\Delta x} = \frac{(1-8)}{(11-0)} = -\frac{7}{11} \qquad m_{\overline{BC}} = \frac{\Delta y}{\Delta x} = \frac{(-6-1)}{(0-11)} = \frac{-7}{-11} = \frac{7}{11}$$

   $$m_{\overline{DC}} = \frac{\Delta y}{\Delta x} = \frac{(-6-1)}{[0-(-11)]} = -\frac{7}{11} \qquad m_{\overline{AD}} = \frac{\Delta y}{\Delta x} = \frac{(1-8)}{(-11-0)} = \frac{-7}{-11} = \frac{7}{11}$$

   The opposite sides are parallel: $\overline{AB} \parallel \overline{DC}$ and $\overline{BC} \parallel \overline{AD}$. Therefore, the quadrilateral is a parallelogram.

3.  Examine the slopes of consecutive sides to determine if the sides are perpendicular.

    If the slopes of consecutive sides are opposite reciprocals of each other, then the sides intersect at right angles.

    If the sides intersect at right angles, then the parallelogram is a rhombus or square.

    Let's use consecutive sides $\overline{AB}$ and $\overline{BC}$.

    $$m_{\overline{AB}} = -\frac{7}{11} \qquad m_{\overline{BC}} = \frac{7}{11}$$

    The slopes are not opposite reciprocals, so the parallelogram is not a rectangle or a square.

4.  Calculate the lengths of the sides.

    In a rhombus, the sides are congruent.

    Use the distance formula to calculate the lengths of the sides.

    $$d = \sqrt{(x_2 - x_1)^2 + (y_2 - y_1)^2}$$

    $$AB = \sqrt{(11-0)^2 + (1-8)^2} \qquad\qquad BC = \sqrt{(0-11)^2 + (-6-1)^2}$$
    $$AB = \sqrt{(11)^2 + (-7)^2} \qquad\qquad BC = \sqrt{(-11)^2 + (-7)^2}$$
    $$AB = \sqrt{121 + 49} \qquad\qquad BC = \sqrt{121 + 49}$$
    $$AB = \sqrt{170} \qquad\qquad BC = \sqrt{170}$$

    $$DC = \sqrt{[0-(-11)]^2 + (-6-1)^2} \qquad AD = \sqrt{(-11-0)^2 + (1-8)^2}$$
    $$DC = \sqrt{(11)^2 + (-7)^2} \qquad\qquad AD = \sqrt{(-11)^2 + (-7)^2}$$
    $$DC = \sqrt{121 + 49} \qquad\qquad AD = \sqrt{121 + 49}$$
    $$DC = \sqrt{170} \qquad\qquad AD = \sqrt{170}$$

    The sides are all congruent.

5. Summarize your findings.

    The quadrilateral has opposite sides that are parallel and all four sides are congruent, but the sides are not perpendicular. Therefore, the quadrilateral is a parallelogram and a rhombus, but not a square. ✓

## Example 3

Quadrilateral $ABCD$ has vertices $A$ (−1, 2), $B$ (1, 5), $C$ (4, 3), and $D$ (2, 0). Using slope, distance, and/or midpoints, classify $\square ABCD$ as a rectangle, rhombus, square, trapezoid, or kite.

1. Graph the quadrilateral.

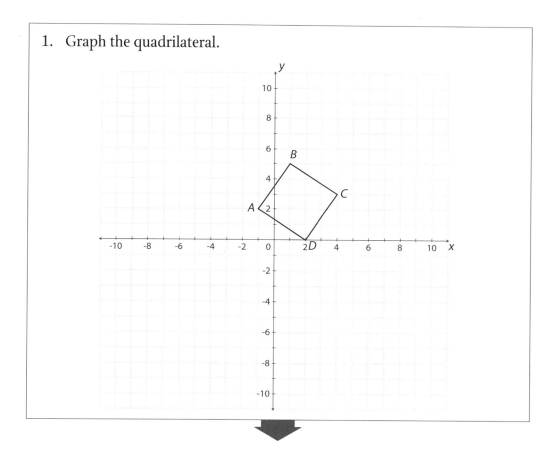

2. Calculate the slopes of the sides to determine if the quadrilateral is a parallelogram.

   If opposites sides are parallel, the quadrilateral is a parallelogram.

   $\overline{AB}$ is opposite $\overline{DC}$. $\overline{BC}$ is opposite $\overline{AD}$.

   $$m_{\overline{AB}} = \frac{\Delta y}{\Delta x} = \frac{(5-2)}{[1-(-1)]} = \frac{3}{2} \qquad m_{\overline{BC}} = \frac{\Delta y}{\Delta x} = \frac{(3-5)}{(4-1)} = -\frac{2}{3}$$

   $$m_{\overline{DC}} = \frac{\Delta y}{\Delta x} = \frac{(3-0)}{(4-2)} = \frac{3}{2} \qquad m_{\overline{AD}} = \frac{\Delta y}{\Delta x} = \frac{(0-2)}{[2-(-1)]} = -\frac{2}{3}$$

   The opposite sides are parallel: $\overline{AB} \| \overline{DC}$ and $\overline{BC} \| \overline{AD}$. The quadrilateral is a parallelogram.

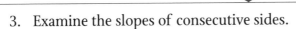

3. Examine the slopes of consecutive sides.

   If consecutive sides are perpendicular, the angles at the vertices are right angles and the parallelogram is a rectangle or a square.

   The slopes are opposite reciprocals; therefore, $\overline{AB} \perp \overline{BC}$ and $\overline{DC} \perp \overline{AD}$, and the angles at the vertices are right angles, indicating a rectangle or square.

4. Calculate the lengths of the sides.

If the sides are congruent, the parallelogram with four right angles is a square.

Use the distance formula to calculate the lengths of the sides.

$$d=\sqrt{(x_2-x_1)^2+(y_2-y_1)^2}$$

$AB=\sqrt{[1-(-1)]^2+(5-2)^2}$ $\qquad$ $BC=\sqrt{(4-1)^2+(3-5)^2}$

$AB=\sqrt{(2)^2+(3)^2}$ $\qquad$ $BC=\sqrt{(3)^2+(-2)^2}$

$AB=\sqrt{4+9}$ $\qquad$ $BC=\sqrt{9+4}$

$AB=\sqrt{13}$ $\qquad$ $BC=\sqrt{13}$

$DC=\sqrt{(4-2)^2+(3-0)^2}$ $\qquad$ $AD=\sqrt{[2-(-1)]^2+(0-2)^2}$

$DC=\sqrt{(2)^2+(3)^2}$ $\qquad$ $AD=\sqrt{(3)^2+(-2)^2}$

$DC=\sqrt{4+9}$ $\qquad$ $AD=\sqrt{9+4}$

$DC=\sqrt{13}$ $\qquad$ $AD=\sqrt{13}$

The sides are all congruent.

5. Summarize your findings.

The quadrilateral has opposite sides that are parallel, four right angles, and four congruent sides, making the quadrilateral a parallelogram, a rectangle, a rhombus, and most specifically, a square.

## Example 4

Use what you know about the diagonals of rectangles, rhombuses, squares, kites, and trapezoids to classify the quadrilateral given the vertices $M\,(0, 3)$, $A\,(5, 2)$, $T\,(6, -3)$, and $H\,(-1, -4)$.

1. Graph the quadrilateral.

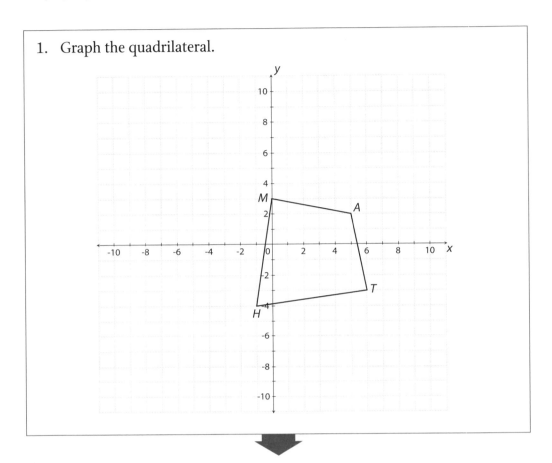

2. Determine if the diagonals bisect each other.

   If the diagonals bisect each other, then the quadrilateral is a parallelogram.

   Find the midpoints of the diagonals using the midpoint formula.

   Let's start with the midpoint of the diagonal $\overline{MT}$.

$$M = \left( \frac{x_1 + x_2}{2}, \frac{y_1 + y_2}{2} \right) \qquad \text{Midpoint formula}$$

$$M_{\overline{MT}} = \left( \frac{0+6}{2}, \frac{3+(-3)}{2} \right) = \left( \frac{6}{2}, \frac{0}{2} \right) = (3, 0) \qquad \text{Substitute values for } x_1, x_2, y_1, \text{ and } y_2, \text{ then solve.}$$

   Now find the midpoint of the diagonal $\overline{AH}$.

$$M_{\overline{AH}} = \left( \frac{5+(-1)}{2}, \frac{2+(-4)}{2} \right) = \left( \frac{4}{2}, \frac{-2}{2} \right) = (2, -1) \qquad \text{Substitute values for } x_1, x_2, y_1, \text{ and } y_2, \text{ then solve.}$$

   The midpoints are not the same, so the diagonals do not bisect each other. This rules out the quadrilateral being any type of parallelogram, including a rectangle, rhombus, or square.

3. Calculate the slopes of the diagonals.

   If the diagonals are perpendicular, then the quadrilateral could be a rhombus or a kite.

$$m_{\overline{MT}} = \frac{\Delta y}{\Delta x} = \frac{(-3-3)}{(6-0)} = \frac{-6}{6} = -1 \qquad m_{\overline{AH}} = \frac{\Delta y}{\Delta x} = \frac{(-4-2)}{(-1-5)} = \frac{-6}{-6} = 1$$

   The slopes are opposite reciprocals, so the diagonals are perpendicular: $\overline{MT} \perp \overline{AH}$. Therefore, the quadrilateral could be a rhombus or a kite.

   However, since we established earlier that the diagonals do not bisect each other, the quadrilateral cannot be a rhombus.

4. Calculate the lengths of the sides of the quadrilateral.

Use the distance formula: $d = \sqrt{(x_2 - x_1)^2 + (y_2 - y_1)^2}$

$$MA = \sqrt{(5-0)^2 + (2-3)^2}$$
$$MA = \sqrt{(5)^2 + (-1)^2}$$
$$MA = \sqrt{25+1}$$
$$MA = \sqrt{26}$$

$$AT = \sqrt{(6-5)^2 + (-3-2)^2}$$
$$AT = \sqrt{(1)^2 + (-5)^2}$$
$$AT = \sqrt{1+25}$$
$$AT = \sqrt{26}$$

$$MH = \sqrt{(-1-0)^2 + (-4-3)^2}$$
$$MH = \sqrt{(-1)^2 + (-7)^2}$$
$$MH = \sqrt{1+49}$$
$$MH = \sqrt{50} = 5\sqrt{2}$$

$$TH = \sqrt{(-1-6)^2 + [-4-(-3)]^2}$$
$$TH = \sqrt{(-7)^2 + (-1)^2}$$
$$TH = \sqrt{49+1}$$
$$TH = \sqrt{50} = 5\sqrt{2}$$

The adjacent pairs of sides are congruent.

5. Summarize your findings.

The diagonals do not bisect each other but are perpendicular. Since the diagonals do not bisect each other, the quadrilateral is not a rectangle, rhombus, or square. Since the diagonals are perpendicular and two distinct pairs of adjacent sides are congruent, the quadrilateral is a kite.

## Example 5

Use what you know about the diagonals of rectangles, rhombuses, squares, kites, and trapezoids to classify the quadrilateral given vertices $P(1, 5)$, $Q(5, 2)$, $R(4, -3)$, and $S(-4, 3)$.

1. Graph the quadrilateral.

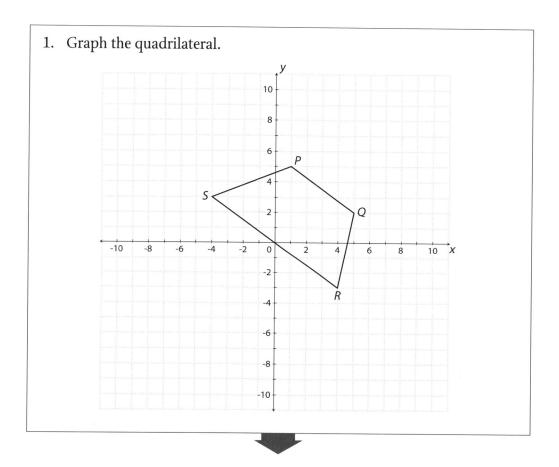

2. Determine if the diagonals bisect each other.

If the diagonals bisect each other, then the quadrilateral is a parallelogram.

Find the midpoints of the diagonals using the midpoint formula.

Let's start with the midpoint of the diagonal $\overline{PR}$.

$$M = \left( \frac{x_1 + x_2}{2}, \frac{y_1 + y_2}{2} \right) \qquad \text{Midpoint formula}$$

$$M_{\overline{PR}} = \left( \frac{1+4}{2}, \frac{5+(-3)}{2} \right) = \left( \frac{5}{2}, \frac{2}{2} \right) = \left( \frac{5}{2}, 1 \right) \qquad \begin{array}{l} \text{Substitute values for } x_1, \\ x_2, y_1, \text{ and } y_2, \text{ then solve.} \end{array}$$

Now find the midpoint of the diagonal $\overline{QS}$.

$$M_{\overline{QS}} = \left( \frac{5+(-4)}{2}, \frac{2+3}{2} \right) = \left( \frac{1}{2}, \frac{5}{2} \right) \qquad \begin{array}{l} \text{Substitute values for } x_1, \\ x_2, y_1, \text{ and } y_2, \text{ then solve.} \end{array}$$

The midpoints are not the same, so the diagonals do not bisect each other. This rules out the quadrilateral being any type of parallelogram, including a rectangle, rhombus, or square.

3. Determine the slopes of the diagonals.

If the slopes are opposite reciprocals, then the diagonals are perpendicular and the quadrilateral could be a kite.

$$m_{\overline{PR}} = \frac{\Delta y}{\Delta x} = \frac{(-3-5)}{(4-1)} = -\frac{8}{3} \qquad\qquad m_{\overline{QS}} = \frac{\Delta y}{\Delta x} = \frac{(3-2)}{(-4-5)} = -\frac{1}{9}$$

The slopes are not opposite reciprocals. Therefore, the diagonals are not perpendicular. The quadrilateral is neither a parallelogram nor a kite.

4. Determine the lengths of the diagonals.

If the diagonals are congruent, the quadrilateral could be an isosceles trapezoid.

Use the distance formula, $d = \sqrt{(x_2 - x_1)^2 + (y_2 - y_1)^2}$, to determine if the diagonals are congruent.

$$PR = \sqrt{(4-1)^2 + (-3-5)^2} \qquad QS = \sqrt{(-4-5)^2 + (3-2)^2}$$
$$PR = \sqrt{(3)^2 + (-8)^2} \qquad QS = \sqrt{(-9)^2 + (1)^2}$$
$$PR = \sqrt{9+64} \qquad QS = \sqrt{81+1}$$
$$PR = \sqrt{73} \qquad QS = \sqrt{82}$$

The diagonals are not congruent. Therefore, the quadrilateral is not an isosceles trapezoid.

5. Calculate the slopes of opposite pairs of sides.

If one pair of opposite sides is parallel, then the quadrilateral is a trapezoid.

$$m_{\overline{PS}} = \frac{\Delta y}{\Delta x} = \frac{(3-5)}{(-4-1)} = \frac{-2}{-5} = \frac{2}{5} \qquad m_{\overline{PQ}} = \frac{\Delta y}{\Delta x} = \frac{(2-5)}{(5-1)} = -\frac{3}{4}$$

$$m_{\overline{QR}} = \frac{\Delta y}{\Delta x} = \frac{(-3-2)}{(4-5)} = \frac{-5}{-1} = 5 \qquad m_{\overline{SR}} = \frac{\Delta y}{\Delta x} = \frac{(-3-3)}{[4-(-4)]} = -\frac{6}{8} = -\frac{3}{4}$$

One pair of opposite sides, $\overline{PQ}$ and $\overline{SR}$, is parallel since the slopes are equal: $\overline{PQ} \parallel \overline{SR}$. Therefore, the quadrilateral is a trapezoid.

6. Summarize your findings.

The diagonals do not bisect each other, ruling out the quadrilateral being a parallelogram; therefore, it cannot be a rectangle, rhombus, or square. The diagonals are not perpendicular, ruling out a kite. However, one pair of opposite sides is parallel, indicating that the quadrilateral is a trapezoid. The diagonals are not congruent. Therefore, the quadrilateral is not an isosceles trapezoid.

## Practice 5.7.2: Proving Properties of Special Quadrilaterals

For problems 1–8, use the given coordinates as well as slope, distance, midpoints, and/or diagonals to classify each quadrilateral in as many ways as possible (parallelogram, rectangle, rhombus, square, kite, trapezoid, and/or isosceles trapezoid). Justify your answers.

1. $A$ (2, –6), $B$ (5, –3), $C$ (8, –6), $D$ (5 –9)

2. $E$ (6, –2), $F$ (9, –5), $G$ (3, –11), $H$ (0, –8)

3. $J$ (–4, 1), $K$ (2, 7), $L$ (4, 3), $M$ (0, –1)

4. $N$ (–4, 1), $O$ (2, 7), $P$ (6, 6), $Q$ (0, 0)

5. $S$ (6, 10), $T$ (8, 2), $U$ (0, 0), $V$ (–2, 8)

6. $W$ (0, 5), $X$ (5, 2), $Y$ (2, –3), $Z$ (–3, 0)

7. $A$ (3, 0), $B$ (–2, –2), $C$ (–5, 0), $D$ (–2, 2)

8. $F$ (3, 6), $G$ (7, 6), $H$ (7, –3), $J$ (3, –3)

# UNIT 5 • SIMILARITY, RIGHT TRIANGLE TRIGONOMETRY, AND PROOF
## Lesson 7: Proving Theorems About Parallelograms

Use the information given in each problem that follows to write proofs.

9. Given that quadrilateral *ABCD* is a square, prove that the diagonals form four congruent triangles.

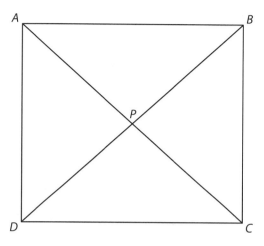

10. Given $\triangle APD \cong \triangle APB \cong \triangle CPB \cong \triangle CPD$, prove that quadrilateral *ABCD* below is a rhombus.

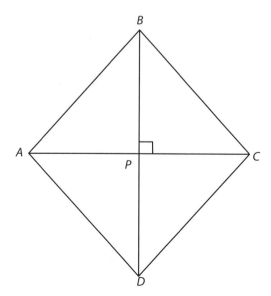

# Lesson 8: Exploring Trigonometric Ratios

## Common Core State Standards

**G–SRT.6**  Understand that by similarity, side ratios in right triangles are properties of the angles in the triangle, leading to definitions of trigonometric ratios for acute angles.

**G–SRT.7**  Explain and use the relationship between the sine and cosine of complementary angles.

## Essential Questions

1. How are the properties of similar triangles used to create trigonometric ratios?

2. What are the relationships between the sides and angles of right triangles?

3. On what variable inputs are the ratios in trigonometry dependent?

4. What is the relationship between the sine and cosine ratios for the two acute angles in a right triangle?

## WORDS TO KNOW

| | |
|---|---|
| **adjacent side** | the leg next to an acute angle in a right triangle that is not the hypotenuse |
| **cofunction** | a trigonometric function whose ratios have the same values when applied to the two acute angles in the same right triangle. The sine of one acute angle is the cofunction of the cosine of the other acute angle. |
| **complementary angles** | two angles whose sum is 90° |
| **cosecant** | the reciprocal of the sine ratio; the cosecant of $\theta = \csc \theta = \dfrac{\text{length of hypotenuse}}{\text{length of opposite side}}$ or $\csc \theta = \dfrac{1}{\sin \theta}$ |
| **cosine** | a trigonometric function of an acute angle in a right triangle that is the ratio of the length of the side adjacent to the length of the hypotenuse; the cosine of $\theta = \cos \theta = \dfrac{\text{length of adjacent side}}{\text{length of hypotenuse}}$ |

| | |
|---|---|
| **cotangent** | the reciprocal of tangent; the cotangent of $\theta = \cot \theta =$ $\dfrac{\text{length of adjacent side}}{\text{length of opposite side}}$ or $\cot \theta = \dfrac{1}{\tan \theta}$ |
| **hypotenuse** | the side opposite the vertex of the 90° angle in a right triangle |
| **identity** | an equation that is true regardless of what values are chosen for the variables |
| **opposite side** | the side across from an angle |
| *phi* ($\phi$) | a Greek letter sometimes used to refer to an unknown angle measure |
| **ratio** | the relation between two quantities; can be expressed in words, fractions, decimals, or as a percentage |
| **reciprocal** | a number that, when multiplied by the original number, has a product of 1 |
| **right triangle** | a triangle with one angle that measures 90° |
| **scale factor** | a multiple of the lengths of the sides from one figure to the transformed figure. If the scale factor is larger than 1, then the figure is enlarged. If the scale factor is between 0 and 1, then the figure is reduced. |
| **secant** | the reciprocal of cosine; the secant of $\theta = \sec \theta =$ $\dfrac{\text{length of hypotenuse}}{\text{length of adjacent side}}$ |
| **similar** | two figures that are the same shape but not necessarily the same size. Corresponding angles must be congruent and sides must have the same ratio. The symbol for representing similarity is $\sim$ . |
| **sine** | a trigonometric function of an acute angle in a right triangle that is the ratio of the length of the opposite side to the length of the hypotenuse; the sine of $\theta =$ $\sin \theta = \dfrac{\text{length of opposite side}}{\text{length of hypotenuse}}$ |

| tangent | a trigonometric function of an acute angle in a right triangle that is the ratio of the length of the opposite side to the length of the adjacent side; the tangent of $\theta$ $= \tan\theta = \dfrac{\text{length of opposite side}}{\text{length of adjacent side}}$ |
|---|---|
| *theta* ($\theta$) | a Greek letter commonly used to refer to unknown angle measures |
| **trigonometry** | the study of triangles and the relationships between their sides and the angles between these sides |

## Recommended Resources

- AJ Design Software. "Triangle Equations Formulas Calculator."

  http://www.walch.com/rr/00041

  This excellent website provides links to interactive calculators that help users solve for the various attributes of different types of triangles. For the Pythagorean Theorem, users can plug in known values for the legs of a right triangle, and the site will calculate the length of the hypotenuse.

- Keisan: High Accuracy Calculation. "Solar elevation angle (for a day)."

  http://www.walch.com/rr/00042

  This website features a solar calculator that will return the angle of elevation of the sun for any time of day at any latitude. The results are shown in a table and a graph.

- MathIsFun.com. "Sine, Cosine and Tangent."

  http://www.walch.com/rr/00043

  Scroll down to the bottom of this site to find a tool for changing an angle and seeing the three main ratios of trigonometry change.

- Teach Engineering. "Hands-on Activity: Stay in Shape."

  http://www.walch.com/rr/00044

  This site provides a real-life example of how the equations in basic geometry and trigonometry are used in navigation.

# Lesson 5.8.1: Defining Trigonometric Ratios

## Introduction

Navigators and surveyors use the properties of similar right triangles. Designers and builders use right triangles in constructing structures and objects. Cell phones and Global Positioning Systems (GPS) use the mathematical principles of algebra, geometry, and trigonometry. **Trigonometry** is the study of triangles and the relationships between their sides and the angles between these sides. In this lesson, we will learn about the ratios between angles and side lengths in right triangles. A **ratio** is the relation between two quantities; it can be expressed in words, fractions, decimals, or as a percentage.

## Key Concepts

- Two triangles are similar if they have congruent angles.

- Remember that two figures are similar when they are the same shape but not necessarily the same size; the symbol for representing similarity is $\sim$.

- Recall that the **hypotenuse** is the side opposite the vertex of the 90° angle in a right triangle. Every right triangle has one 90° angle.

- If two right triangles each have a second angle that is congruent with the other, the two triangles are similar.

- Similar triangles have proportional side lengths. The side lengths are related to each other by a scale factor.

- Examine the proportional relationships between similar triangles $\triangle ABC$ and $\triangle DEF$ in the diagram that follows. The scale factor is $k = 2$. Notice how the ratios of corresponding side lengths are the same as the scale factor.

## Proportional Relationships in Similar Triangles

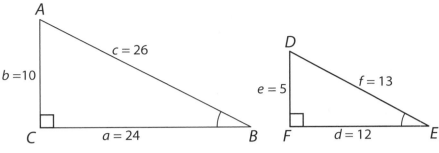

**Corresponding sides**

$$\frac{a}{d}=\frac{b}{e}=\frac{c}{f}$$

**Side lengths**

$$\frac{24}{12}=\frac{10}{5}=\frac{26}{13}$$

Examine the three ratios of side lengths in $\triangle ABC$. Notice how these ratios are equal to the same ratios in $\triangle DEF$.

**Corresponding sides**

$$\frac{a}{c}=\frac{d}{f}$$

$$\frac{b}{c}=\frac{e}{f}$$

$$\frac{a}{b}=\frac{d}{e}$$

**Side lengths**

$$\frac{24}{26}=\frac{12}{13}$$

$$\frac{10}{26}=\frac{5}{13}$$

$$\frac{24}{10}=\frac{12}{5}$$

- The ratio of the lengths of two sides of a triangle is the same as the ratio of the corresponding sides of any similar triangle.

- The three main ratios in a right triangle are the sine, the cosine, and the tangent. These ratios are based on the side lengths relative to one of the acute angles.

- The **sine** of an acute angle in a right triangle is the ratio of the length of the opposite side to the length of the hypotenuse; the sine of $\theta = \sin\theta = \dfrac{\text{length of opposite side}}{\text{length of hypotenuse}}$.

- The **cosine** of an acute angle in a right triangle is the ratio of the length of the side adjacent to the length of the hypotenuse; the cosine of $\theta = \cos\theta = \dfrac{\text{length of adjacent side}}{\text{length of hypotenuse}}$.

- The **tangent** of an acute angle in a right triangle is the ratio of the length of the opposite side to the length of the adjacent side; the tangent of $\theta = \tan\theta = \dfrac{\text{length of opposite side}}{\text{length of adjacent side}}$.

- The acute angle that is being used for the ratio can be called the angle of interest. It is commonly marked with the symbol $\theta$ (*theta*).

- **Theta ($\theta$)** is a Greek letter commonly used as an unknown angle measure.

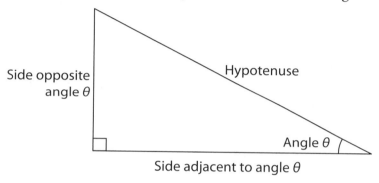

- See the following examples of the ratios for sine, cosine, and tangent.

$$\text{sine of } \theta = \sin\theta = \frac{\text{length of opposite side}}{\text{length of hypotenuse}} \qquad \text{Abbreviation: } \frac{\text{opposite}}{\text{hypotenuse}}$$

$$\text{cosine of } \theta = \cos\theta = \frac{\text{length of adjacent side}}{\text{length of hypotenuse}} \qquad \text{Abbreviation: } \frac{\text{adjacent}}{\text{hypotenuse}}$$

$$\text{tangent of } \theta = \tan\theta = \frac{\text{length of opposite side}}{\text{length of adjacent side}} \qquad \text{Abbreviation: } \frac{\text{opposite}}{\text{adjacent}}$$

- Unknown angle measures can also be written using the Greek letter **phi ($\phi$)**.

- The three main ratios can also be shown as reciprocals.

- The **reciprocal** is a number that when multiplied by the original number the product is 1.

- The reciprocal of sine is **cosecant**. The reciprocal of cosine is **secant**, and the reciprocal of tangent is **cotangent**.

$$\text{cosecant of } \theta = \csc \theta = \frac{\text{length of hypotenuse}}{\text{length of opposite side}}$$

$$\text{secant of } \theta = \sec \theta = \frac{\text{length of hypotenuse}}{\text{length of adjacent side}}$$

$$\text{cotangent of } \theta = \cot \theta = \frac{\text{length of adjacent side}}{\text{length of opposite side}}$$

- Each acute angle in a right triangle has different ratios of sine, cosine, and tangent.

- The length of the hypotenuse remains the same, but the sides that are opposite or adjacent for each acute angle will be different for different angles of interest.

- The two rays of each acute angle in a right triangle are made up of a leg and the hypotenuse. The leg is called the **adjacent side** to the angle. Adjacent means "next to."

- In a right triangle, the side of the triangle opposite the angle of interest is called the **opposite side**.

- Calculations in trigonometry will vary due to the variations that come from measuring angles and distances.

- A final calculation in trigonometry is frequently expressed as a decimal.

- A calculation can be made more accurate by including more decimal places.

- The context of the problem will determine the number of decimals places to which to round. Examples:

  - A surveyor usually measures tracts of land to the nearest tenth of a foot.

  - A computer manufacturer needs to measure a microchip component to a size smaller than an atom.

  - A carpenter often measures angles in whole degrees.

  - An astronomer measures angles to $\frac{1}{3600}$ of a degree or smaller.

# Guided Practice 5.8.1

## Example 1

Find the sine, cosine, and tangent ratios for $\angle A$ and $\angle B$ in $\triangle ABC$. Convert the ratios to decimal equivalents.

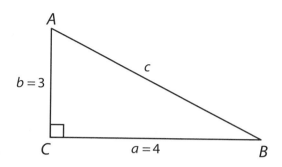

1.  Find the length of the hypotenuse using the Pythagorean Theorem.

    $a^2 + b^2 = c^2$          Pythagorean Theorem

    $4^2 + 3^2 = c^2$          Substitute values for $a$ and $b$.

    $16 + 9 = c^2$          Simplify.

    $25 = c^2$

    $\pm\sqrt{25} = \sqrt{c^2}$

    $c = \pm 5$

    Since $c$ is a length, use the positive value, $c = 5$.

2. Find the sine, cosine, and tangent of $\angle A$.

Set up the ratios using the lengths of the sides and hypotenuse, then convert to decimal form.

$$\sin A = \frac{\text{opposite}}{\text{hypotenuse}} = \frac{4}{5} = 0.8$$

$$\cos A = \frac{\text{adjacent}}{\text{hypotenuse}} = \frac{3}{5} = 0.6$$

$$\tan A = \frac{\text{opposite}}{\text{adjacent}} = \frac{4}{3} = 1.33\overline{3}$$

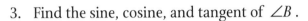

3. Find the sine, cosine, and tangent of $\angle B$.

Set up the ratios using the lengths of the sides and the hypotenuse, and then convert to decimal form.

$$\sin B = \frac{\text{opposite}}{\text{hypotenuse}} = \frac{3}{5} = 0.6$$

$$\cos B = \frac{\text{adjacent}}{\text{hypotenuse}} = \frac{4}{5} = 0.8$$

$$\tan B = \frac{\text{opposite}}{\text{adjacent}} = \frac{3}{4} = 0.75$$

## Example 2

Given the triangle below, set up the three trigonometric ratios of sine, cosine, and tangent for the angle given. Compare these ratios to the trigonometric functions using your calculator.

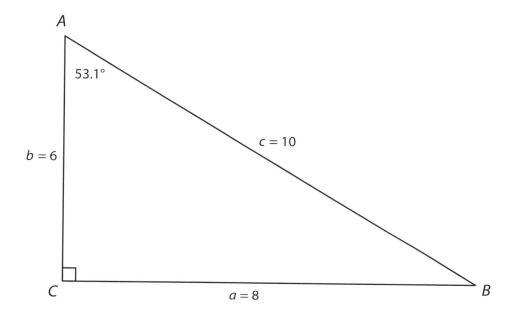

1.  Set up the ratios for sin $A$, cos $A$, and tan $A$ and calculate the decimal equivalents.

$$\sin 53.1° = \frac{8}{10} = 0.8$$

$$\cos 53.1° = \frac{6}{10} = 0.6$$

$$\tan 53.1° = \frac{8}{6} = 1.33\overline{3}$$

2. Use your graphing calculator to find sin 53.1°.

**On a TI-83/84:**

First, make sure your calculator is in Degree mode.

    Step 1: Press [MODE].

    Step 2: Arrow down to RADIAN.

    Step 3: Arrow over to DEGREE.

    Step 4: Press [ENTER]. The word DEGREE should be highlighted inside a black rectangle.

    Step 5: Press [2ND].

    Step 6: Press [MODE] to QUIT.

Important: You will not have to change to Degree mode again unless you have changed your calculator to Radian mode.

Now you can find the value of sin 53.1°:

    Step 1: Press [SIN].

    Step 2: Enter the angle measurement: 53.1.

    Step 3: Press [ ) ].

    Step 4: Press [ENTER].

**On a TI-Nspire:**

First, make sure the calculator is in Degree mode.

    Step 1: From the home screen, select 5: Settings & Status, then 2: Settings, then 2: Graphs & Geometry.

    Step 2: Press [tab] twice to move to the Geometry Angle field, and then select Degree from the drop-down menu.

    Step 3: Press [tab] to move to the "OK" option and select it using the center button on the navigation pad.

Next, calculate the sine of 53.1°.

    Step 1: From the home screen, select a new Calculate window.

    Step 2: Press [trig] to bring up the menu of trigonometric functions. Use the keypad to select "sin," then type 53.1 and press [enter].

    $\sin 53.1° \approx 0.7996846585$

3. Use your graphing calculator to find cos 53.1°.

**On a TI-83/84:**

Step 1: Press [COS].

Step 2: Enter the angle measurement: 53.1.

Step 3: Press [ ) ].

Step 4: Press [ENTER].

**On a TI-Nspire:**

Step 1: From the home screen, select a new Calculate window.

Step 2: Press [trig] to bring up the menu of trigonometric functions. Use the keypad to select "cos," then type 53.1 and press [enter].

cos 53.1° ≈ 0.6004202253

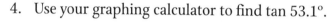

4. Use your graphing calculator to find tan 53.1°.

**On a TI-83/84:**

Step 1: Press [TAN].

Step 2: Enter the angle measurement: 53.1.

Step 3: Press [ ) ].

Step 4: Press [ENTER].

**On a TI-Nspire:**

Step 1: From the home screen, select a new Calculate window.

Step 2: Press [trig] to bring up the menu of trigonometric functions. Use the keypad to select "tan$^{-1}$," then type 53.1 and press [enter].

tan 53.1° ≈ 1.331874952

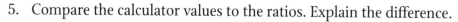

5. Compare the calculator values to the ratios. Explain the difference.

The values are very close to the ratios of the side lengths. The differences are due to the angle measurement of 53.1° being an approximation.

## Example 3

A right triangle has a hypotenuse of 5 and a side length of 2. Find the angle measurements and the unknown side length. Find the sine, cosine, and tangent for both angles. Without drawing another triangle, compare the trigonometric ratios of $\triangle ABC$ with those of a triangle that has been dilated by a factor of $k = 3$.

1. First, draw the triangle with a ruler, and label the side lengths and angles.

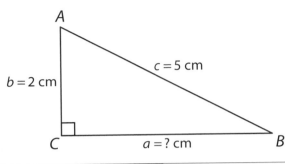

2. Find $a$ by using the Pythagorean Theorem.

$a^2 + b^2 = c^2$     Pythagorean Theorem

$a^2 + 2^2 = 5^2$     Substitute values for $b$ and $c$.

$a^2 + 4 = 25$     Simplify.

$a^2 = 21$

$a \approx 4.5826$ centimeters

3. Use a protractor to measure one of the acute angles, and then use that measurement to find the other acute angle.

$m\angle A \approx 66.5$

We know that $m\angle C = 90$ by the definition of right angles.

The measures of the angles of a triangle sum to 180.

Subtract $m\angle A$ and $m\angle C$ from 180 to find $m\angle B$.

$m\angle B = 180 - m\angle A - m\angle C$

$m\angle B = 180 - (66.5) - (90)$

$m\angle B = 180 - 156.5$

$m\angle B \approx 23.5$

4. Find the sine, cosine, and tangent ratios for both acute angles. Express your answer in decimal form to the nearest thousandth.

| $\angle A$ | $\angle B$ |
|---|---|
| $\sin 66.5° \approx \dfrac{4.5826}{5} \approx 0.916$ | $\sin 23.5° \approx \dfrac{2}{5} \approx 0.4$ |
| $\cos 66.5° \approx \dfrac{2}{5} \approx 0.4$ | $\cos 23.5° \approx \dfrac{4.5826}{5} \approx 0.916$ |
| $\tan 66.5° \approx \dfrac{4.5826}{2} \approx 2.291$ | $\tan 23.5° \approx \dfrac{2}{4.5826} \approx 0.436$ |

5. Without drawing a triangle, find the sine, cosine, and tangent for a triangle that has a scale factor of 3 to $\triangle ABC$. Compare the trigonometric ratios for the two triangles.

Multiply each side length ($a$, $b$, and $c$) by 3 to find $a'$, $b'$, and $c'$.

$a' = 3 \bullet a = 3 \bullet (4.5826) = 13.7478$

$b' = 3 \bullet b = 3 \bullet (2) = 6$

$c' = 3 \bullet c = 3 \bullet (5) = 15$

Set up the ratios using the side lengths of the dilated triangle.

$$\sin 66.5° \approx \frac{13.7478}{15} \approx 0.916 \qquad \sin 23.5° \approx \frac{6}{15} \approx 0.4$$

$$\cos 66.5° \approx \frac{6}{15} \approx 0.4 \qquad \cos 23.5° \approx \frac{13.7478}{15} \approx 0.916$$

$$\tan 66.5° \approx \frac{13.7478}{6} \approx 2.291 \qquad \tan 23.5° \approx \frac{6}{13.7478} \approx 0.436$$

The sine, cosine, and tangent do not change in the larger triangle. Similar triangles have identical side length ratios and, therefore, identical trigonometric ratios.

## Example 4

What are the secant (sec), cosecant (csc), and cotangent (cot) ratios for an isosceles right triangle?

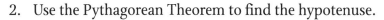

1. An isosceles right triangle has two angles that measure 45°. The two side lengths have equal lengths of 1 unit.

2. Use the Pythagorean Theorem to find the hypotenuse.

$$1^2 + 1^2 = c^2$$

$$1 + 1 = c^2$$

$$2 = c^2$$

$$\sqrt{2} = c$$

3. Substitute the side lengths into the ratios.

$$\csc 45° = \frac{\text{hypotenuse}}{\text{opposite}} = \frac{\sqrt{2}}{1} \approx 1.414$$

$$\sec 45° = \frac{\text{hypotenuse}}{\text{adjacent}} = \frac{\sqrt{2}}{1} \approx 1.414$$

$$\cot 45° = \frac{\text{adjacent}}{\text{opposite}} = \frac{1}{1} = 1$$

## Example 5

Triangle $ABC$ is a right triangle where $m\angle A = 40°$ and side $a = 10$ centimeters. What is the sine of $\angle A$? Check your work with the sin function on your graphing calculator.

1. Draw $\triangle ABC$ with a ruler and protractor.

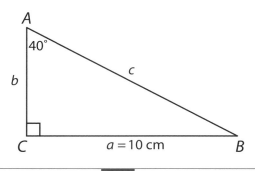

2. Measure the length of hypotenuse $c$.

   $c \approx 15.6$ centimeters

   Substitute the side lengths into the ratios to determine the sine of $\angle A$.

   $$\sin 40° \approx \frac{10}{15.6} \approx 0.641$$

3. Use your calculator to check the answer.

   Follow the steps outlined in Example 2.

   $\sin 40° \approx 0.6427876097$

   The two answers are fairly close. The difference is due to the imprecise nature of manually drawing and measuring a triangle.

## Practice 5.8.1: Defining Trigonometric Ratios

Use $\triangle ABC$ to complete problems 1–4. Round your answers to the nearest thousandths.

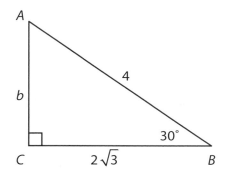

1. Set up and calculate the trigonometric ratios for the sine, cosine, and tangent of $\angle A$.

2. Set up and calculate the trigonometric ratios for the cosecant, secant, and cotangent of $\angle A$.

3. Set up and calculate the trigonometric ratios for the sine, cosine, and tangent of $\angle B$.

4. Set up and calculate the trigonometric ratios for cosecant, secant, and cotangent of $\angle B$.

Draw triangles using the given information to complete problems 5 and 6.

5. A right triangle has side lengths of $a = 3$ and $b = 4$. Find the angle measurements and the length of the hypotenuse. Then, find the sine, cosine, and tangent for both angles.

6. A right triangle has a side length of $a = 5$ and a hypotenuse of 6. Find the angle measurements and the other side length. Then, find the sine, cosine, and tangent for both acute angles.

*continued*

Use the given information to complete problems 7–10.

7. A ship's sonar radio tracking system detected a mysterious object on the ocean floor. The object is straight ahead of the ship and at a 30° angle beneath the ocean's surface. The distance from the ship to the object is 0.577 mile. The ship moves 0.5 mile toward the object. The object is now directly beneath the ship. How deep is the water? Use your graphing calculator to find the tangent of 30°.

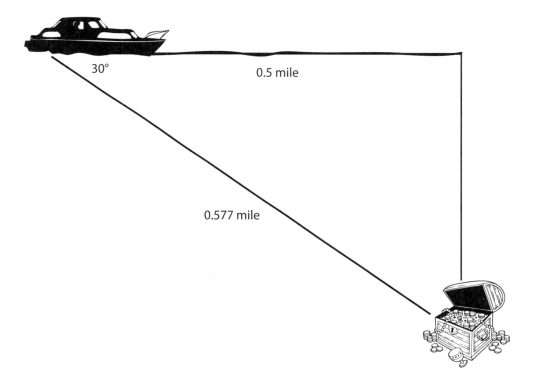

8. Students are planning a flower garden around the perimeter of the triangular base of a statue. They know the following information: The statue's base is a right triangle; the lengths of the two sides are each 5.657 meters; and both of the acute angles are 45°. Find the hypotenuse of the triangular base. What is the perimeter of the base of the statue? Use your graphing calculator to find the cosine of 45°.

9. A surveyor is mapping a large marsh in a state park. He walks and measures a straight line south from a cliff for 0.75 mile to a large tree. He walks east, but he has to make a detour around the marsh. He gets around the marsh to a spot where he is perpendicular to the large tree and the trail he originally walked south on. He looks northwest and measures a 40° angle northwest to the cliff from his line of sight to the large tree. He measures the distance back to the cliff as 1.17 miles. What is the straight-line distance from the large tree east to $\angle A$? What is the tangent of $\angle B$?

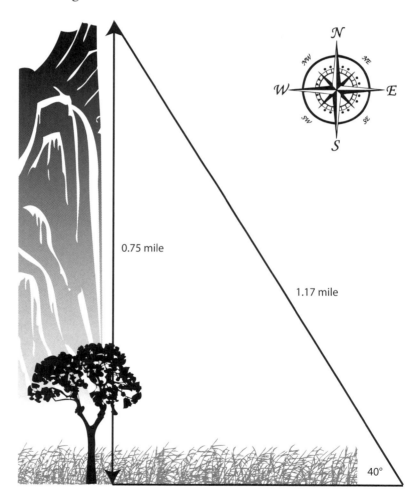

*continued*

# UNIT 5 • SIMILARITY, RIGHT TRIANGLE TRIGONOMETRY, AND PROOF
## Lesson 8: Exploring Trigonometric Ratios

10. A ramp needs to be built to the front door of an office building. The ramp will start 40 feet from the door and rise 5 feet. The ramp will rise at angle of 7.2°. How long will the ramp be? Use your calculator to find the sine of 7.2°.

# Lesson 5.8.2: Exploring Sine and Cosine As Complements

## Introduction

In the previous lesson, we applied the properties of similar triangles to find unknown side lengths. We discovered that the side ratios of similar triangles are always the same. As a preparation to using trigonometry to solve problems, we will look more deeply into the relationship between sine and cosine in this lesson.

### Key Concepts

- Sine and cosine are side length ratios in right triangles.

- The ratio for the sine of an angle is as follows: $\sin \theta = \dfrac{\text{opposite}}{\text{hypotenuse}}$.

- The ratio for the cosine of an angle is as follows: $\cos \theta = \dfrac{\text{adjacent}}{\text{hypotenuse}}$.

- Examine $\triangle ABC$.

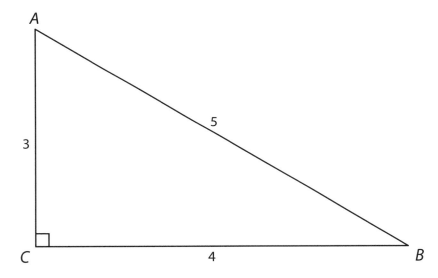

- Determine the sine of $\angle A$.

$$\sin A = \frac{4}{5}$$

- Determine the cosine of $\angle B$.

$$\cos B = \frac{4}{5}$$

- This shows $\sin A = \cos B$.

- You can also see from the diagram that $\sin B = \dfrac{3}{5} = \cos A$.

- Show that this relationship will work for any right triangle.

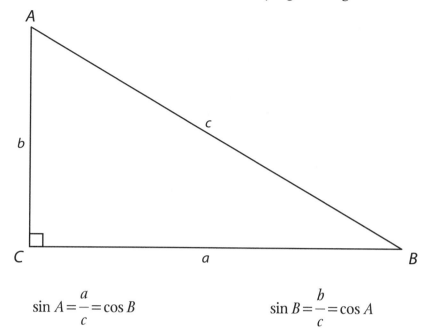

$$\sin A = \frac{a}{c} = \cos B \qquad\qquad \sin B = \frac{b}{c} = \cos A$$

- In $\triangle ABC$, $\sin A = \cos B$, and $\sin B = \cos A$.

- This relationship between sine and cosine is known as an identity. An equation is an **identity** if it is true for every value that is used in the equation.

- Sine and cosine are called **cofunctions** because the value of one ratio for one angle is the same as the value of the other ratio for the other angle.

- The two acute angles in a right triangle have a sum of 90°. They are complementary angles. If one acute angle has a measure of $x$, the other angle has a measure of $90° - x$.

- For example, if one acute angle $x$ has a measure of 70°, the other acute angle must measure $90 - x$.

    $90 - x = 20$ or $20°$

- The sine-cosine cofunction can be written as:

    $\sin \theta = \cos (90° - \theta)$

    $\cos \theta = \sin (90° - \theta)$

- In other words, you can use the sine of one acute angle to find the cosine of its complementary angle.

- Also, you can use the cosine of one acute angle to find the sine of its complementary angle.

- This identity relationship makes sense because the same side lengths are being used in the ratios for the different angles.

- Cofunctions such as sine-cosine give you flexibility in solving problems, particularly if several ratios of trigonometry are used in the same problem.

| Postulate |
|---|
| Sine and cosine are cofunction identities. |
| $\sin \theta = \cos (90° - \theta)$ |
| $\cos \theta = \sin (90° - \theta)$ |

# Guided Practice 5.8.2

**Example 1**

Find sin 28° if cos 62° ≈ 0.469.

---

1. Set up the identity.

   $\sin \theta = \cos (90° - \theta)$

---

2. Substitute the values of the angles into the identity and simplify.

   $\sin 28° = \cos (90° - 28°)$

   $\sin 28° = \cos 62°$

---

3. Verify the identity by calculating the sine of 28° and the cosine of 62° using a scientific calculator.

   $\sin 28° \approx 0.469$

   $\cos 62° \approx 0.469$

---

**Example 2**

Complete the table below using the sine and cosine identities.

| Angle | Sine | Cosine |
|---|---|---|
| 10° | 0.174 | 0.985 |
| 80° | | |

---

1. Determine the relationship between the two given angles.

   10° and 80° are complementary angles.

   $10° + 80° = 90°$

2. Apply the sine identity.

$$\sin \theta = \cos (90° - \theta)$$

$$\sin 10° = \cos 80°$$

3. Use the given value of sin 10° from the table to find sin 80°.

The sine of 10° = 0.174; therefore, the cosine of 80° = 0.174.

4. Apply the cosine identity.

$$\cos \theta = \sin (90° - \theta)$$

$$\cos 10° = \sin 80°$$

5. Use the given value of cos 10° from the table to find sin 80°.

The cosine of 10° = 0.985; therefore, the sine of 80° = 0.985.

6. Fill in the table.

| Angle | Sine | Cosine |
|---|---|---|
| 10° | 0.174 | 0.985 |
| 80° | 0.985 | 0.174 |

## Example 3

Find a value of $\theta$ for which $\sin \theta = \cos 15°$ is true.

1. Determine which identity to use.

   The cosine was given, so use the cosine identity.

   Since $\theta$ is used as the variable in the problem, use the variable *phi* ($\phi$) for the identity.

   $\cos \phi = \sin (90° - \phi)$

   $\phi = 15°$

   $\cos 15° = \sin (90° - 15°)$

   The cosine of $15°$ is equal to the sine of its complement.

2. Find the complement of $15°$.

   $90° - 15° = 75°$

   The complement of $15°$ is $75°$.

3. Substitute the complement of $15°$ into the identity.

   $\cos 15° = \sin 75°$ or $\sin 75° = \cos 15°$

4. Write the value of $\theta$.

   $\theta = 75°$

## Example 4

Complete the table below using the sine and cosine identities.

| Angle | Sine | Cosine |
|-------|------|--------|
| 28° | 0.470 | |
| | 0.883 | 0.470 |

1. Use a graphing calculator to find the cosine of 28°.

   $\cos 28° = 0.883$

2. Analyze the two sets of values for the sine and cosine.

   The values are switched, suggesting that the second angle of interest is the complement of the first angle of interest, 28°.

   Find the complement of the first angle of interest.

   $90° - 28° = 62°$

   The complement of 28° is 62°.

   The second angle must be 62°. Therefore, $\sin 62° = \cos 28°$.

3. Verify that the second angle of interest is correct using a scientific calculator.

   $\sin 62° = 0.883$

   $\cos 28° = 0.883$

   The second angle of interest is correct.

4. Use your findings to fill in the table.

| Angle | Sine | Cosine |
|-------|------|--------|
| 28° | 0.470 | 0.883 |
| 62° | 0.883 | 0.470 |

## Practice 5.8.2: Exploring Sine and Cosine As Complements

Use what you have learned about the sine-cosine identity relationship to complete the following problems.

1. $\cos 45° \approx 0.707$. What is $\sin 45°$?

2. $\sin 85° \approx 0.996$. Find the cosine of the complementary angle.

3. Find a value of $\theta$ for which $\cos \theta = \sin 52°$ is true.

4. Find a value of $\theta$ for which $\sin \theta = \cos 2°$ is true.

5. $\cos 21° \approx 0.934$. Use this information to write an equation for the sine.

6. $\sin 74° \approx 0.961$. Use this information to write an equation for the cosine.

7. $\cos 30° - \cos 50° \approx 0.223$. Find $\theta$ if $\sin \theta - \sin 40° \approx 0.223$.

8. Use the diagrams of $\triangle ABC$ and $\triangle DEF$ to fill in the empty boxes for the following equations.

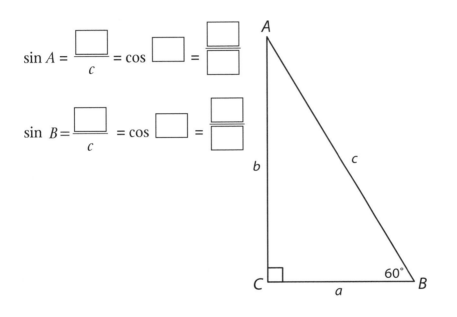

$$\sin A = \frac{\boxed{\phantom{x}}}{c} = \cos \boxed{\phantom{x}} = \frac{\boxed{\phantom{x}}}{\boxed{\phantom{x}}}$$

$$\sin B = \frac{\boxed{\phantom{x}}}{c} = \cos \boxed{\phantom{x}} = \frac{\boxed{\phantom{x}}}{\boxed{\phantom{x}}}$$

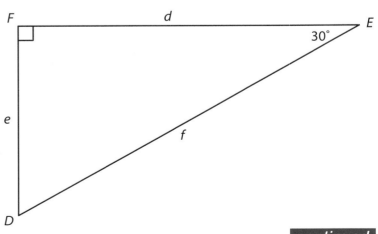

*continued*

9. Students in a biology class measured the length of a beaver pond to see if it is large enough to support other types of water-dependent mammals and birds. Most of the pond is surrounded by swampland, making it impractical to measure the pond directly. The following diagram shows the measurements the students were able to make. First, they put a two-meter-tall stake in the ground at $\angle A$. Next, they measured north on the walking path 30 meters, and west 40 meters to a spot that is in line with the stake and the Big Rock landmark on the west side of the pond. Going north on the path to the east end of the pond, they walked 450 meters to $\angle C$ using a rolling measuring wheel. Approximately how long is the pond?

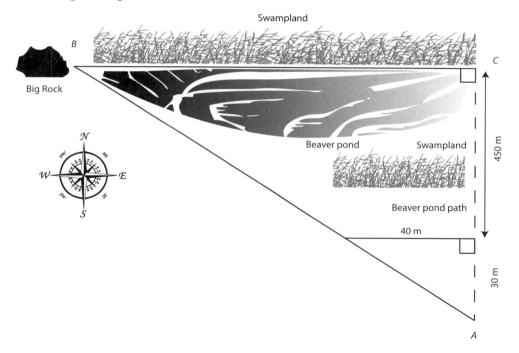

10. Use the information you found in problem 9 to calculate the sine and cosine values for angles $A$ and $B$.

# Lesson 9: Applying Trigonometric Ratios

## Common Core State Standards

**G–SRT.8**  Use trigonometric ratios and the Pythagorean Theorem to solve right triangles in applied problems.★

**F–TF.8**  Prove the Pythagorean identity $\sin^2(\theta) + \cos^2(\theta) = 1$ and use it to find $\sin(\theta)$, $\cos(\theta)$, or $\tan(\theta)$ given $\sin(\theta)$, $\cos(\theta)$, or $\tan(\theta)$ and the quadrant of the angle.

## Essential Questions

1. How could you use sine, cosine, tangent, and the Pythagorean Theorem to find missing angles and side lengths of a right triangle?

2. How could you use cosecant, secant, cotangent, and the Pythagorean Theorem to find missing angles and side lengths of a right triangle?

3. How are the angle of depression and angle of elevation used to solve real-world right triangle problems?

4. How do you determine which trigonometric function to use when solving real-world triangle problems?

5. How can the Pythagorean Theorem be used to find a relationship between sine and cosine?

## WORDS TO KNOW

| | |
|---|---|
| **altitude** | the perpendicular line from a vertex of a figure to its opposite side; height |
| **angle of depression** | the angle created by a horizontal line and a downward line of sight to an object that is below the observer |
| **angle of elevation** | the angle created by a horizontal line and an upward line of sight to an object that is above the observer |
| **arccosine** | the inverse of the cosine function, written $\cos^{-1}\theta$ or $\arccos\theta$ |
| **arcsine** | the inverse of the sine function, written $\sin^{-1}\theta$ or $\arcsin\theta$ |

| | |
|---|---|
| **arctangent** | the inverse of the tangent function, written $\tan^{-1}\theta$ or $\arctan\theta$ |
| **cosecant** | the reciprocal of the sine ratio; $\csc\theta = \dfrac{1}{\sin\theta}$ |
| **cotangent** | the reciprocal of the tangent ratio; $\cot\theta = \dfrac{1}{\tan\theta}$ |
| **identity** | an equation that is true regardless of what values are chosen for the variables |
| **Pythagorean identities** | trigonometric identities that are derived from the Pythagorean Theorem: $\sin^2\theta + \cos^2\theta = 1$, $1 + \tan^2\theta = \sec^2\theta$, and $1 + \cot^2\theta = \csc^2\theta$ |
| **Pythagorean Theorem** | a theorem that relates the length of the hypotenuse of a right triangle ($c$) to the lengths of its legs ($a$ and $b$). The theorem states that $a^2 + b^2 = c^2$. |
| **ratio identities** | identities that define tangent and cotangent in terms of sine and cosine; the following two identities are ratio identities: $\tan\theta = \dfrac{\sin\theta}{\cos\theta}$ and $\cot\theta = \dfrac{\cos\theta}{\sin\theta}$ |
| **reciprocal identities** | trigonometric identities that define cosecant, secant, and cotangent in terms of sine, cosine, and tangent: $\csc\theta = \dfrac{1}{\sin\theta}$, $\sec\theta = \dfrac{1}{\cos\theta}$, $\cot\theta = \dfrac{1}{\tan\theta}$, $\sin\theta = \dfrac{1}{\csc\theta}$, $\cos\theta = \dfrac{1}{\sec\theta}$, and $\tan\theta = \dfrac{1}{\cot\theta}$ |
| **secant** | the reciprocal of the cosine ratio; $\sec\theta = \dfrac{1}{\cos\theta}$ |

## Recommended Resources

- Coolmath.com. "The Pythagorean Identities."

  http://www.walch.com/rr/00130

  This site illustrates the derivation of the Pythagorean identities through the use of a unit circle, and can serve as an informal introduction to the unit circle.

- MathIsFun.com. "Sine, Cosine, and Tangent."

  http://www.walch.com/rr/00064

  This website gives a brief overview of three trigonometric functions and shows some applications of the uses of the ratios. Toward the bottom of the page, a manipulative allows the user to drag the vertex of a triangle to change the acute angle and observe the relationships between the legs of the triangle and the trigonometric ratios when the hypotenuse is one unit.

- Oswego City School District Regents Exam Prep Center. "Practice with Pythagorean Identities."

  http://www.walch.com/rr/00131

  This site offers practice problems to check users' understanding of the application of trigonometric identities.

- ProProfs Flashcards. "Reciprocal, Quotient, and Pythagorean Identities."

  http://www.walch.com/rr/00132

  This site provides interactive flash cards for various identities. The first screen previews all the cards; click on "view flashcards" to flip through the cards from front to back. Users who create an account or log in with a Facebook or Twitter account can make their own flash cards and add missed terms to an online review list. Users can create up to 10 flash cards per set for free.

- Purplemath. "Angles of Elevation / Inclination and Angles of Depression / Declination."

  http://www.walch.com/rr/00045

  This website boasts a variety of resources regarding basic trigonometry. Specifically, the angles of depression and elevation links offer common misconceptions and additional tricks to mastering proper trigonometric equation setups.

- Wolfram MathWorld. "Trigonometry."

  http://www.walch.com/rr/00046

  This online math encyclopedia contains definitions for terms as well as visuals to support continued terminology mastery.

# Lesson 5.9.1: Calculating Sine, Cosine, and Tangent

## Introduction

In the real world, if you needed to verify the size of a television, you could get some measuring tools and hold them up to the television to determine that the TV was advertised at the correct size. Imagine, however, that you are a fact checker for *The Guinness Book of World Records*. It is your job to verify that the tallest building in the world is in fact Burj Khalifa, located in Dubai. Could you use measuring tools to determine the size of a building so large? It would be extremely difficult and impractical to do so. You can use measuring tools for direct measurements of distance, but you can use trigonometry to find indirect measurements. First, though, you must be able to calculate the three basic trigonometric functions that will be applied to finding those larger distances. Specifically, we are going study and practice calculating the sine, cosine, and tangent functions of right triangles as preparation for measuring indirect distances.

## Key Concepts

- The three basic trigonometric ratios are ratios of the side lengths of a right triangle with respect to one of its acute angles.

- As you learned previously:

  - Given the angle $\theta$, $\sin\theta = \dfrac{\text{opposite}}{\text{hypotenuse}}$.

  - Given the angle $\theta$, $\cos\theta = \dfrac{\text{adjacent}}{\text{hypotenuse}}$.

  - Given the angle $\theta$, $\tan\theta = \dfrac{\text{opposite}}{\text{adjacent}}$.

- Notice that the trigonometric ratios contain three unknowns: the angle measure and two side lengths.

- Given an acute angle of a right triangle and the measure of one of its side lengths, use sine, cosine, or tangent to find another side.

- If you know the value of a trigonometric function, you can use the inverse trigonometric function to find the measure of the angle.

- The inverse trigonometric functions are arcsine, arccosine, and arctangent.

- **Arcsine** is the inverse of the sine function, written $\sin^{-1}\theta$ or $\arcsin\theta$.

- **Arccosine** is the inverse of the cosine function, written $\cos^{-1}\theta$ or $\arccos\theta$.

- **Arctangent** is the inverse of the tangent function, written $\tan^{-1}\theta$ or $\arctan\theta$.

- There are two different types of notation for these functions:

  - $\sin^{-1}\theta = \arcsin\theta$; if $\sin\theta = \dfrac{2}{3}$, then $\arcsin\left(\dfrac{2}{3}\right) = \theta$.

  - $\cos^{-1}\theta = \arccos\theta$; if $\cos\theta = \dfrac{2}{3}$, then $\arccos\left(\dfrac{2}{3}\right) = \theta$.

  - $\tan^{-1}\theta = \arctan\theta$; if $\tan\theta = \dfrac{2}{3}$, then $\arctan\left(\dfrac{2}{3}\right) = \theta$.

- Note that "−1" is not an exponent; it is simply the notation for an inverse trigonometric function. Because this notation can lead to confusion, the "arc-" notation is frequently used instead.

  $\sin^{-1}\theta = \arcsin\theta$ but $(\sin\theta)^{-1} = \left(\sin\theta\right)^{-1} = \dfrac{1}{\sin\theta}$

- To calculate inverse trigonometric functions on your graphing calculator:

  | **On a TI-83/84:** |
  | --- |
  | Step 1: Press [2ND][SIN]. |
  | Step 2: Type in the ratio. |
  | Step 3: Press [ENTER]. |

  | **On a TI-Nspire:** |
  | --- |
  | Step 1: In the calculate window from the home screen, press [trig] to bring up the menu of trigonometric functions. Use the keypad to select "sin⁻¹." |
  | Step 2: Type in the ratio. |
  | Step 3: Press [enter]. |

- Use the inverses of the trigonometric functions to find the acute angle measures given two sides of a right triangle.

# Guided Practice 5.9.1

**Example 1**

Leo is building a concrete pathway 150 feet long across a rectangular courtyard, as shown below. What is the length of the courtyard, $x$, to the nearest thousandth?

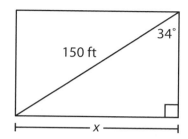

1. Determine which trigonometric function to use by identifying the given information.

   Given an angle of 34°, the length of the courtyard, $x$, is opposite the angle.

   The pathway is the hypotenuse since it is opposite the right angle of the triangle.

   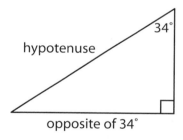

   Sine is the trigonometric function that uses opposite and hypotenuse, $\sin\theta = \dfrac{\text{opposite}}{\text{hypotenuse}}$, so we will use it to calculate the length of the courtyard.

2. Set up an equation using the sine function and the given measurements.

$\theta = 34°$

opposite side = $x$

hypotenuse = 150 ft

Therefore, $\sin 34° = \dfrac{x}{150}$ .

3. Solve for $x$ by multiplying both sides of the equation by 150.

$150 \cdot \sin 34° = x$

4. Use a calculator to determine the value of $x$.

**On a TI-83/84:**

First, make sure your calculator is in Degree mode.

Step 1: Press [MODE].
Step 2: Arrow down twice to RADIAN.
Step 3: Arrow right to DEGREE.
Step 4: Press [ENTER]. The word "DEGREE" should be highlighted inside a black rectangle.
Step 5: Press [2ND].
Step 6: Press [MODE] to QUIT.
*Note*: You will not have to change to Degree mode again unless you have changed your calculator to Radian mode.

Next, perform the calculation.

Step 1: Enter [150][×][SIN][34][)].
Step 2: Press [ENTER].
$x = 83.879$

(*continued*)

**On a TI-Nspire:**

First, make sure the calculator is in Degree mode.

> Step 1: Choose 5: Settings & Status, then 2: Settings, and 2: Graphs and Geometry.
> Step 2: Move to the Geometry Angle field and choose "Degree".
> Step 3: Press [tab] to "ok" and press [enter].

Then, if necessary, set the Scratchpad in Degree mode.

> Step 1: In the calculate window from the home screen, press [doc].
>
> Step 2: Select 7: Settings and Status, then 2: Settings, and 1: General.
>
> Step 3: Move to the Angle field and choose "Degree".
>
> Step 4: Press [tab] to "Make Default" and press [enter] twice to apply this as the new default setting.

Next, perform the calculation.

> Step 1: In the calculate window from the home screen, enter (150), then press [×][trig]. Use the keypad to select "sin," then type 34.
> Step 2: Press [enter].
> $x = 83.879$

The length of Leo's courtyard is about 84 feet.

## Example 2

A trucker drives 1,027 feet up a hill that has a constant slope. When the trucker reaches the top of the hill, he has traveled a horizontal distance of 990 feet. At what angle did the trucker drive to reach the top? Round your answer to the nearest degree.

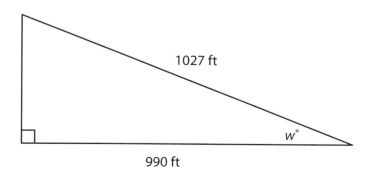

1027 ft

$w°$

990 ft

1. Determine which trigonometric function to use by identifying the given information.

   Given an angle of $w°$, the horizontal distance, 990 feet, is adjacent to the angle.

   The distance traveled by the trucker is the hypotenuse since it is opposite the right angle of the triangle.

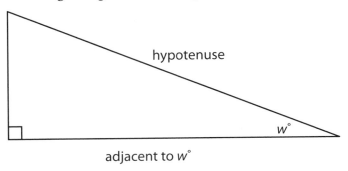

   adjacent to $w°$

   Cosine is the trigonometric function that uses adjacent and hypotenuse, $\cos\theta = \dfrac{\text{adjacent}}{\text{hypotenuse}}$, so we will use it to calculate the angle the truck drove to reach the bottom of the road.

   Set up an equation using the cosine function and the given measurements.

   $\theta = w°$

   adjacent leg = 990 ft

   hypotenuse = 1027 ft

   Therefore, $\cos w = \dfrac{990}{1027}$.

   Solve for $w$.

   Solve for $w$ by using the inverse cosine since we are finding an angle instead of a side length.

   $$\cos^{-1}\left(\dfrac{990}{1027}\right) = w$$

2. Use a calculator to calculate the value of *w*.

**On a TI-83/84:**

Check to make sure your calculator is in Degree mode first. Refer to the directions in Example 1.

Step 1: Press [2ND][COS][990][ ÷ ][1027][)].
Step 2: Press [ENTER].
*w* = 15.426, or 15°.

**On a TI-Nspire:**

Check to make sure your calculator is in Degree mode first. Refer to the directions in Example 1.

Step 1: In the calculate window from the home screen, press [trig] to bring up the menu of trigonometric functions. Use the keypad to select "cos⁻¹." Enter 990, then press [ ÷ ] and enter 1027.
Step 2: Press [enter].
*w* = 15.426, or 15°.

The trucker drove at an angle of 15° to the top of the hill.

## Example 3

In $\triangle TRY$, $\angle Y$ is a right angle and $\tan T = \dfrac{8}{15}$. What is $\sin R$? Express the answer as a fraction and as a decimal.

1. Draw a diagram.

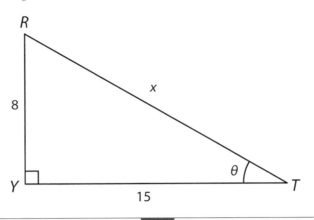

2. Use the Pythagorean Theorem to find the hypotenuse.

   $8^2 + 15^2 = x^2$

   $64 + 225 = x^2$

   $\sqrt{289} = x$

   $x = 17$

3. Calculate $\sin R$.

   $$\sin R = \frac{\text{opposite}}{\text{hypotenuse}} = \frac{15}{x} = \frac{15}{17} \approx 0.882$$

**Example 4**

Solve the right triangle below. Round sides to the nearest thousandth.

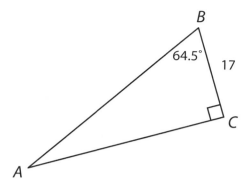

1. Find the measures of $\overline{AC}$ and $\overline{AB}$.

   Solving the right triangle means to find all the missing angle measures and all the missing side lengths. The given angle is 64.5° and 17 is the length of the adjacent side. With this information, we could either use cosine or tangent since both functions' ratios include the adjacent side of a right triangle. Start by using the tangent function to find $\overline{AC}$. Recall that $\tan \theta = \dfrac{\text{opposite}}{\text{adjacent}}$.

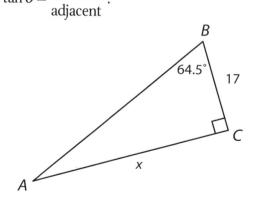

   $$\tan 64.5° = \frac{x}{17}$$

   $$17 \cdot \tan 64.5° = x$$

   *(continued)*

## On a TI-83/84:

Step 1: Press [17][TAN][64.5][)].
Step 2: Press [ENTER].
$x = 35.641$

## On a TI-Nspire:

Step 1: In the calculate window from the home screen, enter 17, then press [trig] to bring up the menu of trigonometric functions. Use the keypad to select "tan⁻¹," then enter 64.5.
Step 2: Press [enter].
$x = 35.641$

The measure of $AC = 35.641$.

To find the measure of $\overline{AB}$, either acute angle may be used as an angle of interest. Since two side lengths are known, the Pythagorean Theorem may be used as well.

*Note*: It is more precise to use the given values instead of approximated values.

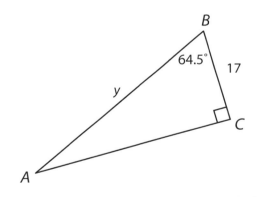

2. Use the cosine function based on the given information.

Recall that $\cos\theta = \dfrac{\text{adjacent}}{\text{hypotenuse}}$.

$\theta = 64.5°$

adjacent leg = 17

hypotenuse = $y$

$\cos 64.5° = \dfrac{17}{y}$

$y \bullet \cos 64.5° = 17$

$y = \dfrac{17}{\cos 64.5°}$

**On a TI-83/84:**

Check to make sure your calculator is in Degree mode first. Refer to the directions in Example 1.

Step 1: Press [17][ ÷ ][COS][64.5][)].
Step 2: Press [ENTER].
$y = 39.488$

**On a TI-Nspire:**

Check to make sure your calculator is in Degree mode first. Refer to the directions in Example 1.

Step 1: In the calculate window from the home screen, enter 17, then press [ ÷ ][trig]. Use the keypad to select "cos," and then enter 64.5.
Step 2: Press [enter].
$y = 39.488$

The measure of $AB = 39.488$.

3. Use the Pythagorean Theorem to check your trigonometry calculations.

$$17^2 + 35.641^2 = y^2$$

$$289 + 1267.36 = y^2$$

$$1559.281 = y^2$$

$$\sqrt{1559.281} = y$$

$$y = 39.488 \qquad \text{The answer checks out.}$$

$$AC = 35.641 \text{ and } AB = 39.488.$$

4. Find the value of $\angle A$.

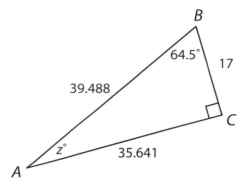

Using trigonometry, you could choose any of the three functions since you have solved for all three side lengths. In an attempt to be as precise as possible, let's choose the given side length and one of the approximate side lengths.

$$\sin z = \frac{17}{39.488}$$

5. Use the inverse trigonometric function since you are solving for an angle measure.

$$z = \arcsin\left(\frac{17}{39.488}\right)$$

**On a TI-83/84:**

Step 1: Press [2ND][SIN][17][ ÷ ][39.488][)].
Step 2: Press [ENTER].
$z = 25.500°$

**On a TI-Nspire:**

Step 1: In the calculate window from the home screen, press [trig] to bring up the menu of trigonometric functions. Use the keypad to select "$\sin^{-1}$," and then enter 17, press [ ÷ ], and enter 39.488.
Step 2: Press [enter].
$z = 25.500°$

Check your angle measure by using the Triangle Sum Theorem.

$m\angle A + 64.5 + 90 = 180$

$m\angle A + 154.5 = 180$

$m\angle A = 25.5$         The answer checks out.

$\angle A$ is 25.5°.

## Practice 5.9.1: Calculating Sine, Cosine, and Tangent

Draw a sketch of the triangle relationship for all problems that do not have a diagram. Unless otherwise stated, round all side lengths to the nearest thousandth and round angle measures to the nearest degree.

1. In $\triangle MAD$, $\angle D$ is a right angle and $\sin M = \dfrac{20}{29}$. What are the cosine and tangent of $\angle A$? Write your answers as fractions and as decimals.

2. In $\triangle TID$, $\angle D$ is a right angle and $\cos T = \dfrac{4}{5}$. What are the sine and tangent of $\angle I$? Write your answers as fractions and as decimals.

3. The sides of a rectangle are 30 cm and 10 cm. What is the measure of the angle formed by the short side and the diagonal of the rectangle?

4. A ladder rests against the side of a building. The ladder is 13 feet long and forms an angle of 70.5° with the ground. How far is the base of the ladder from the base of the building?

5.  A family is covering the windows in their home in anticipation of a coming storm. Each window in the house has the same size and shape, rectangular with a height of 4.5 feet. What is the length of each window?

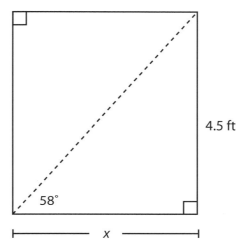

6.  What is the value of $y$?

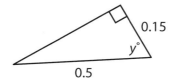

7.  You are standing on a riverbank. An observation tower on the other side of the river is known to be 150 feet tall. An imaginary line from the top of the observation tower to your feet makes an angle of 13° with the ground. How far are you from the base of the tower?

8. Solve the triangle $ABC$, given that $\angle C$ is a right angle, $m\angle A = 50°$, and $BC = 54$ centimeters.

9. Solve the triangle $XYZ$, given that $\angle Y$ is a right angle, $XZ = 9$ inches, and $XY = 6$ inches.

10. Keiko is flying a kite. The kite string makes a 69° angle with the horizontal, and she has let out 250 feet of string. She holds the string 5 feet off the ground. How high is the kite?

# Lesson 5.9.2: Calculating Cosecant, Secant, and Cotangent

## Introduction

In previous lessons, you defined and calculated using the three basic trigonometric functions, sine, cosine, and tangent. In this lesson, you will extend your working definitions of their reciprocal functions and use them to determine the unknown sides and angles of triangles.

## Key Concepts

- Remember:

  - Cosecant is the reciprocal of sine. Given the angle $\theta$, $\csc\theta = \dfrac{\text{hypotenuse}}{\text{opposite}}$.

  - Secant is the reciprocal of cosine. Given the angle $\theta$, $\sec\theta = \dfrac{\text{hypotenuse}}{\text{adjacent}}$.

  - Cotangent is the reciprocal of tangent. Given the angle $\theta$, $\cot\theta = \dfrac{\text{adjacent}}{\text{opposite}}$.

# Guided Practice 5.9.2

## Example 1

Determine the correct reciprocal trigonometric function to solve for $x$ in the triangle below. Write the value of $x$ to the nearest thousandth.

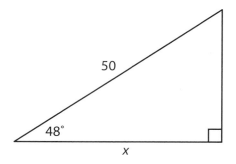

1. Identify the given information.

   $\theta = 48°$, the hypotenuse is 50, and we are trying to calculate the adjacent side, $x$.

2. Set up the correct reciprocal function.

   Recall that:

   $$\csc\theta = \frac{\text{hypotenuse}}{\text{opposite}} \qquad \sec\theta = \frac{\text{hypotenuse}}{\text{adjacent}} \qquad \cot\theta = \frac{\text{adjacent}}{\text{opposite}}$$

   Based on the given information, we must use the secant function, the reciprocal of cosine.

   $$\sec 48° = \frac{50}{x}$$

   $$x \cdot \sec 48° = 50$$

   $$x = \frac{50}{\sec 48°}$$

3. Use the calculator to determine the value of $x$.

Secant is the reciprocal of cosine. This means that $\sec 48° = \dfrac{1}{\cos 48°}$. Since most calculators do not have buttons for the reciprocal functions, you will have to substitute this value in the expression in order to correctly calculate the value of $x$.

$$x = \frac{50}{\sec 48°}$$

$$x = \frac{50}{\dfrac{1}{\cos 48°}}$$

**On a TI-83/84:**

Be sure that your calculator is in Degree mode.

Step 1: Press [50][÷][(][1][÷][COS][48][)][)].
Step 2: Press [ENTER].
$x \approx 33.457$

**On a TI-Nspire:**

Be sure that your calculator is in Degree mode.

Step 1: In the calculate window from the home screen, enter 50, then press [÷][(][trig]. Use the keypad to select "sec," then enter 48 and press [)].
Step 2: Press [enter].
$x \approx 33.457$

4. Check your solution by using the reciprocal function to the function you chose earlier.

We solved for $x$ by using the secant function, which is the reciprocal of cosine. To check the answer, use cosine to see if you get the same solution.

$$\cos 48° = \frac{x}{50}$$

$$50 \cdot \cos 48° = x$$

**On a TI-83/84:**

Step 1: Press [50][COS][48][)].
Step 2: Press [ENTER].
$x \approx 33.457$     The answer checks out.

**On a TI-Nspire:**

Step 1: In the calculate window from the home screen, enter 50, then press [×][trig]. Use the keypad to select "cos," and then enter 48.
Step 2: Press [enter].
$x \approx 33.457$     The answer checks out.

*Note*: You can check your solutions when using reciprocal functions by following the steps in this example.

## Example 2

Use cosecant, secant, or cotangent to find $m\angle C$.

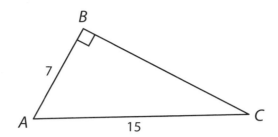

1. Identify the given information.

   The opposite side is given, $AB = 7$, as well as the hypotenuse, $AC = 15$. We are solving for $m\angle C$.

2. Set up the correct reciprocal function.

   Based on the given information, use the cosecant function, the reciprocal of sine.

   $$\csc\theta = \frac{\text{hypotenuse}}{\text{opposite}}$$

   $$\csc C = \frac{15}{7}$$

   Use the inverse of this function to find the desired angle measure.

   $$C = \csc^{-1}\left(\frac{15}{7}\right)$$

3.  Use the calculator to calculate the measure of $\angle C$.

Cosecant is the reciprocal of sine. This means that $\csc^{-1}\left(\dfrac{15}{7}\right) = \sin^{-1}\left(\dfrac{7}{15}\right)$. Because of calculator errors with domain, there is no other way to enter the reciprocal's inverse.

**On a TI-83/84:**

Step 1: Press [2ND][SIN][7][÷][15][)].
Step 2: Press [ENTER].
$m\angle C \approx 28°$

**On a TI-Nspire:**

Step 1: In the calculate window from the home screen, press [trig] to bring up the menu of trigonometric functions. Use the keypad to select "sin⁻¹," and then enter 7, press [÷], and enter 15.
Step 2: Press [enter].
$m\angle C \approx 28°$

## Example 3

The light from a 19-inch-tall egg incubator casts a 13-inch shadow across a shelf. Use reciprocal functions and the Pythagorean Theorem as necessary to determine the distance from the top of the incubator light to the farthest part of the shadow. What is the angle at which the incubator light casts its shadow?

1. Create a drawing of the scenario. Label the distance $d$ and the angle $A$.

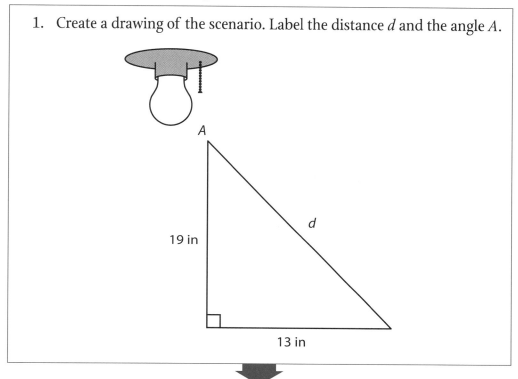

2. Identify the given information.

   Two side lengths are given: 19 inches and 13 inches.

3. Determine which trigonometric functions are necessary to find the unknown values.

Since the given information includes two side lengths, use the Pythagorean Theorem.

$19^2 + 13^2 = d^2$

$361 + 169 = d^2$

$530 = d^2$

$\sqrt{530} = d$

$d \approx 23.022$

The distance from the top of the incubator to the farthest tip of the shadow is about 23.022 inches.

Find the measure of $\angle A$.

To find the measure of $\angle A$, use the two side lengths that were given to produce the most precise answer possible. Since those sides are adjacent to the angle and opposite from the angle, use the cotangent function, which is the reciprocal of tangent.

$$\cot \theta = \frac{\text{adjacent}}{\text{opposite}}$$

$$\cot A = \frac{19}{13}$$

$$A = \cot^{-1}\left(\frac{19}{13}\right)$$

(*continued*)

To enter this into the calculator, first write it in its reciprocal format, $A = \tan^{-1}\left(\dfrac{13}{19}\right)$.

**On a TI-83/84:**

Step 1: Press [2ND][TAN][13][÷][19][)].
Step 2: Press [ENTER].
$m\angle A \approx 34°$

**On a TI-Nspire:**

Step 1: In the calculate window from the home screen, press [trig]. Use the keypad to select "tan⁻¹," then enter 13, press [÷], and enter 19.
Step 2: Press [enter].
$m\angle A \approx 34°$

The incubator casts a shadow at an angle of 34°.

## Practice 5.9.2: Calculating Cosecant, Secant, and Cotangent

Use what you've learned about cosecant, secant, and cotangent to solve the following problems. Unless otherwise stated, round your answers to the nearest thousandth.

1. Use cosecant, secant, or cotangent to find the value of $x$.

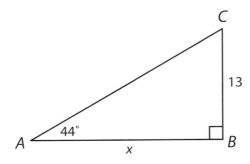

2. Use cosecant, secant, or cotangent to find the value of $x$.

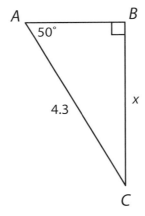

3. Use cosecant, secant, or cotangent to find the value of $x$.

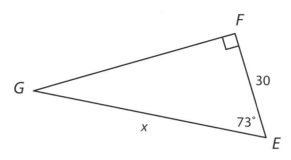

4. Use cosecant, secant, or cotangent to find $m\angle J$.

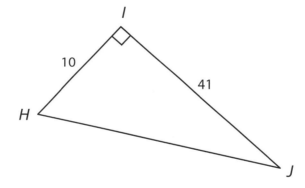

*continued*

In $\triangle EFG$, $\angle F$ is a right angle. Given the following trigonometric ratios for problems 5 and 6, find the cosecant, secant, and cotangent of $\angle E$. Write your answers as fractions and as decimals.

5.  $\sin E = \dfrac{3}{5}$

6.  $\cos E = \dfrac{8}{10}$

Use your knowledge of trigonometric ratios to complete the problems that follow.

7.  A tourist in Washington, D.C., is sitting in the grass gazing up at the Washington Monument. The angle of her line of sight from the ground to the top of the monument is 25°. Given that the Washington Monument is 555 feet tall, find her approximate distance from the base of the monument.

8.  An accessible ramp must be constructed so that the slope rises no more than 1 inch for every 1 foot of run. What is the maximum angle that the ramp can make with the ground?

*continued*

9. The triangle below is isosceles. Calculate the cosecant, secant, and tangent of the measure of ∠B.

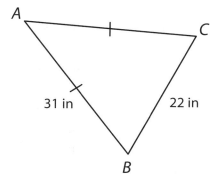

10. The triangle below is equilateral. Calculate the cosecant, secant, and tangent of the measure of ∠B.

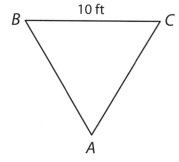

# Lesson 5.9.3: Problem Solving with the Pythagorean Theorem and Trigonometry

## Introduction

Imagine it is a beautiful afternoon in Utah. Your class has raised enough money to take a ride in a hot air balloon that overlooks Antelope Island, Great Salt Lake, the Rocky Mountains, and the Salt Lake City skyline, among other sights. As you fly high in the sky, you observe the geography below, and onlookers below marvel at the beauty of the hot air balloon. The angles of observation from both parties, downward toward the sights and upward toward the balloon, have specific names.

As you look down toward the onlookers, you view the landscape at an **angle of depression**, which is the angle created by a horizontal line and a downward line of sight. The onlookers view the hot air balloon at an **angle of elevation**, which is the angle created by a horizontal line and an upward line of sight. In the following diagram, notice the labeled angles given the horizontals.

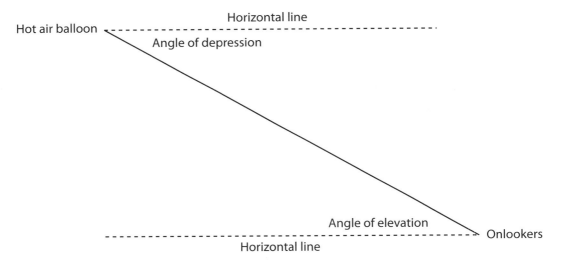

These two angles are very important to understand and will be the basis for our study and practice during this lesson. Specifically, you will study and practice calculating angles of depression and elevation and use these angles to calculate distances that are not easily measured by common devices.

It is important to note that, in this example, the horizontal lines are parallel to each other, and therefore the line of sight behaves as a transversal to the parallel lines. As such, the angle of elevation and angle of depression are alternate interior angles and, therefore, their angle measures are congruent.

## Key Concepts

- The angle of depression is the angle created by a horizontal line and a downward line of sight to an object below the observer.

- The angle of elevation is the angle created by a horizontal line and an upward line of sight to an object above the observer.

- Remember:

  - Given the angle $\theta$, $\sin\theta = \dfrac{\text{opposite}}{\text{hypotenuse}}$.

  - Given the angle $\theta$, $\cos\theta = \dfrac{\text{adjacent}}{\text{hypotenuse}}$.

  - Given the angle $\theta$, $\tan\theta = \dfrac{\text{opposite}}{\text{adjacent}}$.

  - Given right triangle $ABC$, $a^2 + b^2 = c^2$, where $a$ and $b$ are the legs and $c$ is the hypotenuse.

# Guided Practice 5.9.3

## Example 1

The height of a tree is 15 meters. To the nearest whole degree, what is the angle of elevation of the sun when the tree casts a shadow that is 9.3 meters long on level ground?

1. Make a drawing of the scenario.

   Make sure to correctly identify the angle of elevation as the measure from the ground, above the horizontal.

   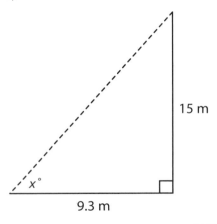

   15 m

   $x°$

   9.3 m

2. Identify the trigonometric function that you must use in order to find the angle of elevation.

   In this case, the height of the tree represents the side that is opposite the angle of elevation, $x$. The length of the shadow represents the adjacent side to $x$. Therefore, use the tangent ratio.

   Use the inverse since you are finding an angle and not a side length.

   $$\tan x = \frac{\text{opposite}}{\text{adjacent}} \text{; opposite leg} = 15\text{; adjacent leg} = 9.3$$

   $$\tan x = \frac{15}{9.3}$$

   $$x = \tan^{-1}\left(\frac{15}{9.3}\right)$$

   *(continued)*

### On a TI-83/84:

Step 1: Press [2ND][TAN][15][ ÷ ][9.3].
Step 2: Press [ENTER].
$x \approx 58.2°$

### On a TI-Nspire:

Step 1: In the calculate window from the home screen, press [trig].
Use the keypad to select "tan⁻¹," then enter 15, press [÷], and enter 9.3.
Step 2: Press [enter].
$x \approx 58.2°$

The angle of elevation of the sun is about 58°.

## Example 2

A meteorologist reads radio signals to get information from a weather balloon. The last alert indicated that the angle of depression of the weather balloon to the meteorologist was 41° and the balloon was 1,810 meters away from his location on the diagonal. To the nearest meter, how high above the ground was the balloon?

1.  Make a drawing of the scenario.

    Remember, the angle of depression is above the diagonal line of sight and below the horizontal.

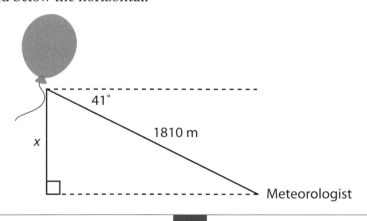

2. Identify the correct trigonometric function to use given the angle of depression.

   Recall that the angles of depression and elevation are congruent, so we can use this to determine the trigonometric function.

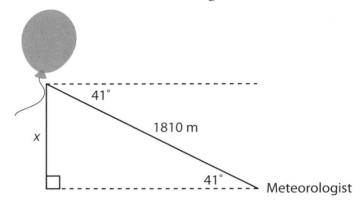

   Since x is opposite the angle of elevation (which yields the same information as the angle of depression), and the distance from the weather balloon to the meteorologist is represented by the hypotenuse of the right triangle, use sine to find the vertical height.

3. Set up the function and solve for the height.

$$\sin 41° = \frac{x}{1810}$$

$$1810 \sin 41° = x$$

**On a TI-83/84:**

   Step 1: Press [1810][SIN][41].
   Step 2: Press [ENTER].
   $x \approx 1187.467$ m

**On a TI-Nspire:**

   Step 1: In the calculate window from the home screen, enter 1810 and then press [trig]. Use the keypad to select "sin," then enter 41.
   Step 2: Press [enter].
   $x \approx 1187.467$ m

   The weather balloon was, vertically, about 1,188 meters from the meteorologist's location.

## Example 3

A sonar operator on an anchored cruiser detects a pod of dolphins feeding at a depth of about 255 meters directly below. If the cruiser travels 450 meters west and the dolphins remain at the same depth to feed, what is the angle of depression, $x$, from the cruiser to the pod? What is the distance, $y$, between the cruiser and the pod? Round your answers to the nearest whole number.

1. Make a drawing of the scenario.

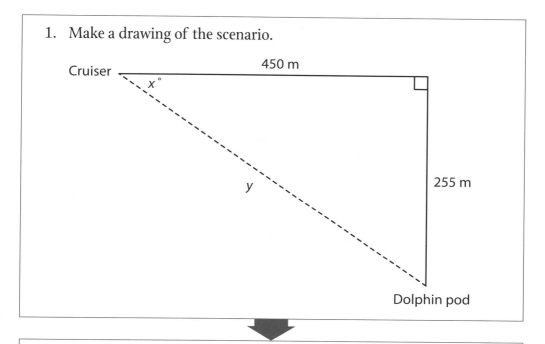

2. Find the angle of depression. Identify the given information to determine which trigonometric function to use.

   Since you are calculating an angle, use the inverse of the trigonometric function. Notice that because of the orientation of the triangle and the horizontal side, the angle of depression lies above the diagonal.

   We are given the distances opposite and adjacent to the angle of depression. Therefore, use the tangent function.

   $$\tan x = \frac{255}{450}$$

   $$x = \tan^{-1}\left(\frac{255}{450}\right)$$

   *(continued)*

**On a TI-83/84:**

Step 1: Press [2ND][TAN][255][ ÷ ][450].
Step 2: Press [ENTER].
$x \approx 29.539$

**On a TI-Nspire:**

Step 1: In the calculate window from the home screen, press [trig].
Use the keypad to select "$\tan^{-1}$," then enter 255, press [÷],
and enter 450.
Step 2: Press [enter].
$x \approx 29.539$

The angle of depression from the cruiser is about 30°.

3. Determine the distance, $y$.

Since two side lengths were given, to determine the distance
between the cruiser and the pod, there is the option of using either
a trigonometric ratio or the Pythagorean Theorem. However, since
the value of the angle of depression was not given and had to be
approximated, using the Pythagorean Theorem given the two
distances will yield a more precise answer.

$$450^2 + 255^2 = y^2$$

$$202{,}500 + 65{,}025 = y^2$$

$$267{,}525 = y^2$$

$$\pm\sqrt{267{,}525} = y$$

$$y \approx 517$$

The distance from the cruiser to the dolphin pod after
travelling 450 meters west of the vertical is about 517 meters.

# Example 4

You are on a steep hillside directly across from the axis of a wind turbine. The information post on the hill indicates that the wind turbines are 160 meters to their axis (or center of rotation) and that the rotor tips reach a height of 205 meters when they are in line, or at 180°, with the wind turbine pole. The information post also says that for an observer who is 6 feet tall, the angle of elevation to the rotor tip is 28° and the observer's eyes are level with the axis of the wind turbine. Use this information to answer the following questions.

- If an observer is 6 feet tall, to the nearest meter, what is the distance from the observer's eye level to the wind turbine's axis?

- What is the distance, to the nearest thousandth of a meter, from the observer's eye level to the base of the wind turbine?

- What is the distance, to the nearest meter, from the observer's eye level to the tip of a rotor when it reaches its highest point?

1. Make a drawing of the scenario.

   Label the given information accordingly.

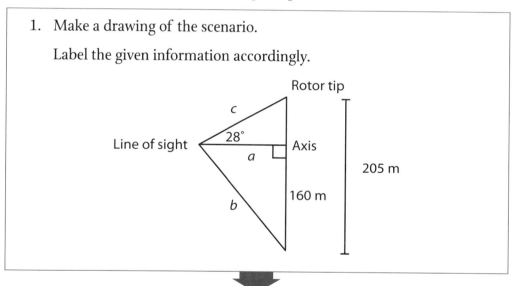

2. Use the given information to solve for the base in the top triangle to determine the distance from the observer's eye level to the wind turbine's axis.

   Given an angle of elevation in the top triangle, subtract 160 meters from 205 meters to get the height from the axis to the rotor tip, which is also a leg of the triangle. Calculate the distance from the axis to the tip of a rotor at its highest point. Knowing this side will help you to find the distance, $a$, from the observer's eye level to the wind turbine's axis.

   $$205 - 160 = 45$$

   The vertical distance from the axis to the rotor tip is 45 meters.

   Now use the angle of elevation and the distance from the axis to the rotor tip at its highest point to find $a$.

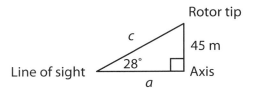

   Given that the opposite leg is 45 meters and the adjacent leg is the distance $a$ from the given angle 28°, use the tangent function.

   $$\tan 28° = \frac{45}{a}$$

   $$a \tan 28° = 45$$

   $$a = \frac{45}{\tan 28°}$$

   (*continued*)

**On a TI-83/84:**

Step 1: Press [45][÷][TAN][28][)].
Step 2: Press [ENTER].
$a \approx 84.633$

**On a TI-Nspire:**

Step 1: In the calculate window from the home screen, enter 45, then press [÷][trig]. Use the keypad to select "tan⁻¹," then enter 28.
Step 2: Press [enter].
$a \approx 84.633$

The distance from the observer's eye level to the axis of the wind turbine is about 85 meters.

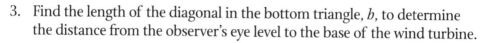

3. Find the length of the diagonal in the bottom triangle, $b$, to determine the distance from the observer's eye level to the base of the wind turbine.

Now that we know $a$, and since $a$ represents the length of the same segment for both triangles, we can use $a$ and the distance from the ground to the axis to find the distance from the observer's line of sight to the base of the wind turbine.

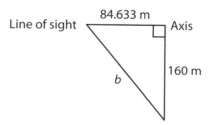

$84.633^2 + 160^2 = b^2$

$7162.692 + 25{,}600 = b^2$

$32{,}762.692 = b^2$

$\pm\sqrt{32762.692} = b$

$b \approx 181.004$

The distance from the observer's eye level to the base of the wind turbine is about 181 meters.

4. Solve for the diagonal of the top triangle, $c$, to determine the distance from the observer's eye level to the tallest tip of a rotor.

Use the top triangle to find $c$.

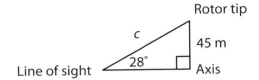

Use sine to find $c$.

$$\sin 28° = \frac{45}{c}$$

$$c \sin 28° = 45$$

$$c = \frac{45}{\sin 28°}$$

$$c \approx 95.852$$

The distance from the observer's line of sight to the tallest tip of a rotor is about 96 meters.

## Practice 5.9.3: Problem Solving with the Pythagorean Theorem and Trigonometry

Unless otherwise specified, round all final answers to the nearest whole number.

1. Brianna is hiking on a mountain trail. She hikes 345 feet uphill but a horizontal distance of 295 feet. To the nearest degree, what is the angle of elevation of the trail?

2. A building is 100 meters tall and, at a certain time of day, casts a shadow from the sun that is 56 meters long. What is the angle of elevation of the sun at that time?

3. A blimp provides aerial footage of a football game at an altitude, or vertical height, of 400 meters. The television crew estimates the distance of their line of sight to the stadium to be 3,282.2 meters. What is the television crew's angle of depression from inside the blimp?

4. It is estimated that 20,000 to 25,000 homes get their water through a pipeline from the Lake Lanier reservoir. One section of the pipeline slopes down with a 21° angle of depression for a horizontal distance of 4,000 feet. To the nearest foot, how long is that section of the pipeline?

5. A parasailing company uses a 50-foot cable to connect the parasail to the back of a boat. About how far is the parasail from the water when the cable has a 35° angle of elevation? What is the horizontal distance from the boat to the parasail at the same angle of elevation?

*continued*

6. Two office buildings are 36 meters apart. The height of the taller building is 196 meters. The angle of depression from the top of the taller building to the top of the shorter building is 19°. What is the height of the shorter building? Refer to the diagram below.

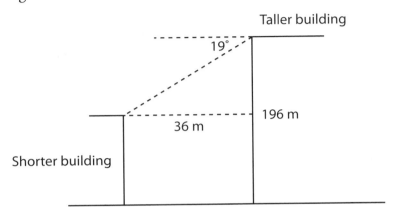

7. Kalani is standing at the bottom of a hill. Mark is standing on the hill so that when Kalani's line of sight is perpendicular to her body, she is looking at Mark's shoes. If Kalani's eyes are 5 feet above the ground and 14.5 feet from Mark's shoes, what is the angle of elevation of the hill to the nearest degree? How far are Kalani's shoes from Mark's shoes, to the nearest foot? Refer to the diagram below.

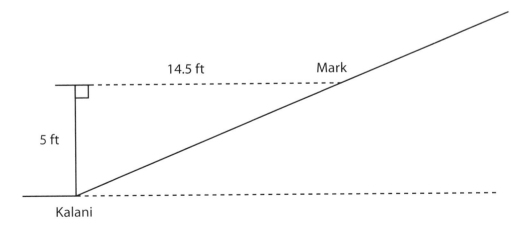

*continued*

# UNIT 5 • SIMILARITY, RIGHT TRIANGLE TRIGONOMETRY, AND PROOF
## Lesson 9: Applying Trigonometric Ratios

Use the following scenario to complete problems 8 and 9.

> A salvage ship's sonar locates wreckage at a 12° angle of depression east of the ship. A diver attached to a thick cord is lowered 45 meters to the ocean floor.

8. How far east does the diver have to swim to reach the wreckage? What is the length of the rope once the diver reaches the wreckage?

9. A sudden wind moves the boat 10 meters west of its starting location. What is the angle of elevation from the wreckage and how long is the rope extended now?

Read the scenario that follows and use the information to answer the questions.

10. You and your friend are standing on a steep hill directly across from the axis of a wind turbine. You know that this wind turbine is 160 meters to its axis (or center of rotation) and that the rotor tips reach a height of 205 meters when they are in line, or at 180°, with the wind turbine pole. Your friend is 6 feet tall, and says that the angle of elevation to the rotor tip is 32° and that his eyes are level with the axis of the wind turbine.

   a. What is the distance from your friend's line of sight to the axis?

   b. What is the distance from your friend's line of sight to the base of the wind turbine?

   c. What is the distance from your friend's line of sight to the tip of a rotor at its tallest point?

## Lesson 5.9.4: Proving the Pythagorean Identity

### Introduction

Previously in this unit, you learned how to calculate the values of trigonometric functions of an angle $\theta$ by using ratios involving the adjacent side, the opposite side, and the hypotenuse of a right triangle. In this lesson, you will discover another way to calculate these values by using what is known as a Pythagorean identity. Such identities are most often used to simplify expressions that contain trigonometric functions.

### Key Concepts

- An identity is an equation that is true regardless of what values are chosen for the variables.

- The **Pythagorean Theorem** is a theorem that relates the length of the hypotenuse of a right triangle ($c$) to the lengths of its legs ($a$ and $b$). The theorem states that $a^2 + b^2 = c^2$.

- There are three trigonometric identities, known as the **Pythagorean identities,** which are derived from the Pythagorean Theorem. In this lesson, we will take a look at the primary Pythagorean identity, $\sin^2\theta + \cos^2\theta = 1$. This identity describes the relationship between sine and cosine, which is true for any angle value for which the function is defined.

- In this lesson, we will only consider $\theta$ values between $0°$ and $90°$.

- Note that $\sin^2\theta$ is the same as $(\sin\theta)^2$. It is customary to write the exponent after the name of the trigonometric function to avoid confusing it with $\sin\theta^2$. To enter this into your calculator, enter $(\sin(\theta))^2$, as shown:

> **On a TI-83/84:**
>
> Step 1: Open a set of parentheses by typing [(].
>
> Step 2: Press the [SIN] button followed by [X, T, $\theta$, n].
>
> Step 3: Close both sets of parentheses by pressing [)] twice.
>
> Step 4: Press the [$x^2$] button to square the expression.

> **On a TI-Nspire:**
>
> Step 1: In the calculate window, open a set of parentheses by pressing [(].
>
> Step 2: Press [trig] to bring up the menu of trigonometric functions.
>
> Step 3: Use the keypad to select "sin." Press [X].
>
> Step 4: Close both sets of parentheses by pressing [)] twice.
>
> Step 5: Press [$x^2$] to square the expression.

- Algebraic manipulations of the terms in this identity produce equivalent identities. For example, the identity could be written $\sin^2\theta = 1 - \cos^2\theta$ or $\cos^2\theta = 1 - \sin^2\theta$.

- A Pythagorean identity can be used to help simplify trigonometric expressions and equations. For example, if an equation includes the expression $\sin^2\theta + \cos^2\theta$, this could be replaced with 1, and if an equation includes the expression $\sin^2\theta - 1$, this can be replaced with $-\cos^2\theta$.

- The Pythagorean identity $\sin^2\theta + \cos^2\theta = 1$ can be used to find the values of $\sin\theta$, $\cos\theta$, and $\tan\theta$. If you know one of these values, you can find the other two.

- You can solve this Pythagorean identity for one of the trigonometric functions. For example:

$$\sin^2\theta + \cos^2\theta = 1$$

$$\sin^2\theta = 1 - \cos^2\theta$$

$$\sin\theta = \sqrt{1 - \cos^2\theta}$$

- Note that this is similar to the distance formula, which is also derived from the Pythagorean Theorem.

- **Reciprocal identities** are trigonometric identities that define cosecant, secant, and cotangent in terms of sine, cosine, and tangent.

- In the previous lesson, you learned the following reciprocal identities:

$$\csc\theta = \frac{1}{\sin\theta} \qquad \sec\theta = \frac{1}{\cos\theta} \qquad \cot\theta = \frac{1}{\tan\theta}$$

- There are two more identities called **ratio identities** that are useful in simplifying trigonometric expressions:

$$\tan\theta = \frac{\sin\theta}{\cos\theta} \quad \text{and} \quad \cot\theta = \frac{\cos\theta}{\sin\theta}$$

- When solving an application problem, it is helpful to draw a diagram first to see the relationship among the sides and the given angle.

# Guided Practice 5.9.4

## Example 1

Prove the Pythagorean identity $\sin^2\theta + \cos^2\theta = 1$.

---

1. Draw a labeled diagram of a right triangle.

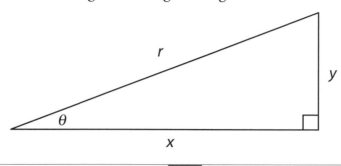

---

2. Apply the Pythagorean Theorem to this triangle.

   The Pythagorean Theorem is $a^2 + b^2 = c^2$.

   Replace the variables in the theorem with the values from the diagram.

   $$x^2 + y^2 = r^2$$

---

3. Divide both sides of this equation by $r^2$.

   $$\frac{x^2}{r^2} + \frac{y^2}{r^2} = 1$$

---

4. Rewrite this equation using the laws of exponents.

   $$\left(\frac{x}{r}\right)^2 + \left(\frac{y}{r}\right)^2 = 1$$

---

5. Find $\sin\theta$ and $\cos\theta$ by looking at the diagram.

$$\sin\theta = \frac{\text{opposite}}{\text{hypotenuse}} = \frac{y}{r}$$

$$\cos\theta = \frac{\text{adjacent}}{\text{hypotenuse}} = \frac{x}{r}$$

6. Substitute $\sin\theta$ and $\cos\theta$ into the equation from step 4.

$$(\cos\theta)^2 + (\sin\theta)^2 = 1$$

7. Rewrite the equation using the standard notation for trigonometric functions with exponents.

$$\cos^2\theta + \sin^2\theta = 1$$

$$\sin^2\theta + \cos^2\theta = 1$$

**Example 2**

If $\sin\theta = \dfrac{2}{5}$ and $0 < \theta < 90$, use the Pythagorean identity $\sin^2\theta + \cos^2\theta = 1$ to find the values of $\cos\theta$ and $\tan\theta$.

1. Substitute the given value of sine into the identity.

$$\sin^2\theta + \cos^2\theta = 1$$

$$\left(\frac{2}{5}\right)^2 + \cos^2\theta = 1$$

2. Solve for $\cos\theta$.

$$\left(\frac{2}{5}\right)^2 + \cos^2\theta = 1$$      Equation with substituted value of $\sin\theta$

$$\frac{4}{25} + \cos^2\theta = 1$$      Square the term.

$$\cos^2\theta = 1 - \frac{4}{25}$$      Isolate $\cos^2\theta$.

$$\cos^2\theta = \frac{25}{25} - \frac{4}{25}$$      Find the common denominator.

$$\cos^2\theta = \frac{21}{25}$$      Simplify.

$$\cos\theta = \sqrt{\frac{21}{25}} = \frac{\sqrt{21}}{5} \approx 0.92$$      Take the square root of both sides of the equation.

The cosine of $\theta$ is approximately 0.92.

3. To find $\tan\theta$, use the ratio identity $\tan\theta = \dfrac{\sin\theta}{\cos\theta}$.

$$\tan\theta = \frac{\sin\theta}{\cos\theta}$$      Tangent ratio identity

$$\tan\theta = \frac{\frac{2}{5}}{\frac{\sqrt{21}}{5}}$$      Substitute the values for $\sin\theta$ and $\cos\theta$.

$$\tan\theta \approx 0.44$$      Simplify.

The value of $\tan\theta$ is approximately 0.44.

4. Summarize your findings.

$$\cos\theta \approx 0.92 \text{ and } \tan\theta \approx 0.44$$

## Example 3

Simplify the expression $\sin^2\theta - \sin^2\theta\cos^2\theta$.

1. Factor the expression.

   Both terms have a common factor of $\sin^2\theta$.

   Factor out $\sin^2\theta$.

   $$\sin^2\theta - \sin^2\theta\cos^2\theta$$

   $$\sin^2\theta\,(1 - \cos^2\theta)$$

2. Analyze the expression for any substitutions that can be made using the Pythagorean identity $\sin^2\theta + \cos^2\theta = 1$.

   Notice that the identity can be rewritten to solve for $\sin^2\theta$ by subtracting $\cos^2\theta$ from both sides.

   $$\sin^2\theta + \cos^2\theta = 1$$

   $$\sin^2\theta = 1 - \cos^2\theta$$

   Also, notice that when the Pythagorean identity $\sin^2\theta + \cos^2\theta = 1$ is rearranged and solved for $\sin^2\theta$, the right side of the equation is equal to the expression inside the parentheses of the factored expression in step 1. Using substitution, the expression can be simplified to write the expression in terms of sine only.

3. Substitute the rearranged Pythagorean identity into the factored expression.

   Since we have determined $\sin^2\theta = 1 - \cos^2\theta$, we can substitute $\sin^2\theta$ into the factored expression, $\sin^2\theta\,(1 - \cos^2\theta)$.

   | | |
   |---|---|
   | $\sin^2\theta\,(1 - \cos^2\theta)$ | Factored expression from step 1 |
   | $\sin^2\theta\,(\sin^2\theta)$ | Substitute $\sin^2\theta$ for $1 - \cos^2\theta$. |
   | $\sin^4\theta$ | Simplify. |

   The expression $\sin^2\theta - \sin^2\theta\cos^2\theta$ can be simplified to $\sin^4\theta$ using the Pythagorean identity $\sin^2\theta + \cos^2\theta = 1$.

## Example 4

Mackenzie is flying a kite. She is standing on the handle of the kite string for a minute while she ties her shoelace. The angle that the kite string makes with the ground is $\theta$. If the length of the kite string is 230 feet when the kite is 190 feet off the ground, find the cosine of $\theta$.

1. Draw a diagram of this situation.

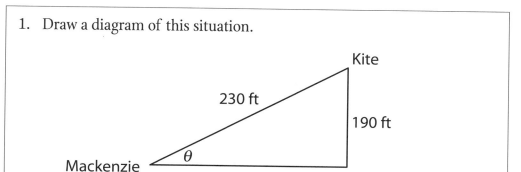

2. Determine which trigonometric ratio to use based on the information in the diagram.

Because the two sides given in the diagram are the side opposite $\theta$ and the hypotenuse, the correct trigonometric ratio to use in order to determine $\cos\theta$ is sine.

Substitute the values from the diagram into the ratio for sine.

$$\sin\theta = \frac{\text{opposite}}{\text{hypotenuse}} = \frac{190}{230} = \frac{19}{23}$$

3. Use the value for $\sin\theta$ to find $\cos\theta$.

Substitute the value from step 2 for sine into the Pythagorean identity $\sin^2\theta + \cos^2\theta = 1$ and solve for $\cos\theta$.

$$\sin^2\theta + \cos^2\theta = 1$$

$$\left(\frac{19}{23}\right)^2 + \cos^2\theta = 1$$

$$0.682 + \cos^2\theta = 1$$

$$\cos^2\theta = 1 - 0.682$$

$$\cos^2\theta = 0.318$$

$$\cos\theta \approx 0.564$$

# UNIT 5 • SIMILARITY, RIGHT TRIANGLE TRIGONOMETRY, AND PROOF
## Lesson 9: Applying Trigonometric Ratios

### Practice 5.9.4: Proving the Pythagorean Identity

Find the value of each given trigonometric function using the Pythagorean identity.

1. Find $\sin\theta$ if $0° < \theta < 90°$ and $\cos\theta = \dfrac{1}{2}$.

2. Find $\cos\theta$ if $0° < \theta < 90°$ and $\sin\theta = \dfrac{\sqrt{3}}{3}$.

3. Find $\sin\theta$ if $0° < \theta < 90°$ and $\cos\theta = \dfrac{3}{4}$.

For problems 4 and 5, one trigonometric function value is given, and $0° < \theta < 90°$. Find the values of the remaining 5 trigonometric functions using identities, then find the value of $\theta$.

4. $\sin\theta = \dfrac{\sqrt{2}}{3}$

5. $\cos\theta = \dfrac{8}{17}$

Use identities to simplify the following expressions.

6. $\dfrac{\sin^2\theta + \cos^2\theta}{\tan\theta}$

7. $\tan^2\theta \sin^2\theta + \tan^2\theta \cos^2\theta$

*continued*

Unit 5: Similarity, Right Triangle Trigonometry, and Proof
5.9.4

Use the given information and identities to solve the following problems.

8. Gao is standing on a hotel balcony. He looks down at an angle of $\theta$ and sees his friend Alysha. The distance from Gao to Alysha is 125 feet. If Alysha is standing 35 feet from the base of the building, find $\sin\theta$ using the Pythagorean identity.

9. The incline of a road going up a hill is $\theta$. The length of the road going up the hill is 200 meters, and the vertical rise of the hill is 24 meters. Find $\cos\theta$.

10. How can you prove or disprove the following identity by manipulating the left side of the equation only?

$$\sin^2\theta + 1 = 2 - \cos^2\theta$$

# Unit 6
## Circles With and Without Coordinates

# Lesson 1: Introducing Circles

## Common Core State Standards

**G–C.1**    Prove that all circles are similar.

**G–C.2**    Identify and describe relationships among inscribed angles, radii, and chords. *Include the relationship between central, inscribed, and circumscribed angles; inscribed angles on a diameter are right angles; the radius of a circle is perpendicular to the tangent where the radius intersects the circle.*

## Essential Questions

1.  Why are all circles similar?

2.  What are the relationships among inscribed angles, radii, and chords of a circle?

3.  What are the relationships among circumscribed angles, central angles, and inscribed angles?

4.  What is the relationship between a tangent line and the radius of a circle?

## WORDS TO KNOW

| | |
|---|---|
| **arc** | part of a circle's circumference |
| **central angle** | an angle with its vertex at the center of a circle |
| **chord** | a segment whose endpoints lie on the circumference of the circle |
| **circle** | the set of all points in a plane that are equidistant from a reference point in that plane, called the center. The set of points forms a 2-dimensional curve that measures 360°. |
| **circumference** | the distance around a circle; $C = 2\pi r$ or $C = \pi d$, for which $C$ represents circumference, $r$ represents the circle's radius, and $d$ represents the circle's diameter |
| **circumscribed angle** | the angle formed by two tangent lines whose vertex is outside of the circle |
| **concentric circles** | coplanar circles that have the same center |

| | |
|---|---|
| **congruent arcs** | two arcs that have the same measure and are either of the same circle or of congruent circles |
| **diameter** | a straight line passing through the center of a circle connecting two points on the circle; equal to twice the radius |
| **inscribed angle** | an angle formed by two chords whose vertex is on the circle |
| **intercepted arc** | an arc whose endpoints intersect the sides of an inscribed angle and whose other points are in the interior of the angle |
| **major arc** | part of a circle's circumference that is larger than its semicircle |
| **minor arc** | part of a circle's circumference that is smaller than its semicircle |
| **pi ($\pi$)** | the ratio of circumference of a circle to the diameter; equal to approximately 3.14 |
| **radius** | the distance from the center to a point on the circle; equal to one-half the diameter |
| **secant line** | a line that intersects a circle at two points |
| **semicircle** | an arc that is half of a circle |
| **tangent line** | a line that intersects a circle at exactly one point and is perpendicular to the radius of the circle |

## Recommended Resources

- Math Open Reference. "Central Angle Theorem."

  http://www.walch.com/rr/00048

  This site describes the Central Angle Theorem and allows users to explore the relationship between inscribed angles and central angles.

- Math Warehouse. "What Is the Tangent of a Circle?"

  http://www.walch.com/rr/00049

  This site reviews the properties of tangent lines, and allows users to interactively explore the idea that a tangent line is perpendicular to a radius at the point of tangency. This site also provides limited practice problems, as well as solutions.

# Lesson 6.1.1: Similar Circles and Central and Inscribed Angles

## Introduction

In the third century B.C., Greek mathematician Euclid, often referred to as the "Father of Geometry," created what is known as Euclidean geometry. He took properties of shape, size, and space and postulated their unchanging relationships that cultures before understood but had not proved to always be true. Archimedes, a fellow Greek mathematician, followed that by creating the foundations for what is now known as calculus. In addition to being responsible for determining things like the area under a curve, Archimedes is credited for coming up with a method for determining the most accurate approximation of *pi*, $\pi$. In this lesson, you will explore and practice applying several properties of circles including proving that all circles are similar using a variation of Archimedes' method.

## Key Concepts

- ***Pi***, $\pi$, is the ratio of the circumference to the diameter of a circle, where the **circumference** is the distance around a circle, the **diameter** is a segment with endpoints on the circle that passes through the center of the circle, and a **circle** is the set of all points that are equidistant from a reference point (the center) and form a 2-dimensional curve.

- A circle measures 360°.

- **Concentric circles** share the same center.

- The diagram below shows circle $A$ $(\odot A)$ with diameter $\overline{BC}$ and radius $\overline{AD}$. The **radius** of a circle is a segment with endpoints on the circle and at the circle's center; a radius is equal to half the diameter.

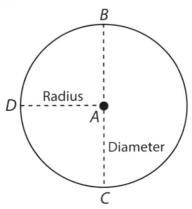

- All circles are similar and measure 360°.

- A portion of a circle's circumference is called an **arc**.

- The measure of a **semicircle**, or an arc that is equal to half of a circle, is 180°.

- Arcs are named by their endpoints.

- The semicircle in the following diagram can be named $\overarc{AB}$.

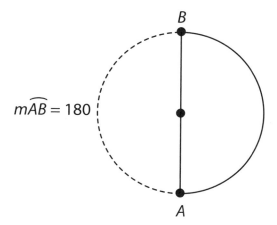

- A part of the circle that is larger than a semicircle is called a **major arc**.

- It is common to identify a third point on the circle when naming major arcs.

- The major arc in the following diagram can be named $\overarc{ABC}$.

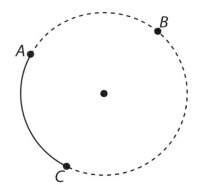

- A **minor arc** is a part of a circle that is smaller than a semicircle.

- The minor arc in the following diagram can be named $\overset{\frown}{AB}$.

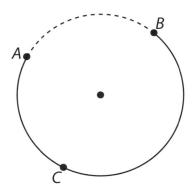

- Two arcs of the same circle or of congruent circles are **congruent arcs** if they have the same measure.

- The measure of an arc is determined by the central angle.

- A **central angle** of a circle is an angle with its vertex at the center of the circle and sides that are created from two radii of the circle.

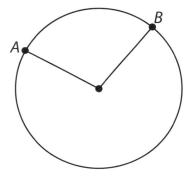

- A **chord** is a segment whose endpoints lie on the circumference of a circle.

- An **inscribed angle** of a circle is an angle formed by two chords whose vertex is on the circle.

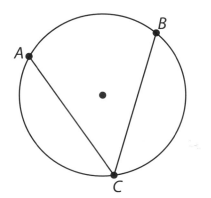

- An inscribed angle is half the measure of the central angle that intercepts the same arc. Conversely, the measure of the central angle is twice the measure of the inscribed angle that intercepts the same arc. This is called the Inscribed Angle Theorem.

---

**Inscribed Angle Theorem**

The measure of an inscribed angle is half the measure of its intercepted arc's angle.

Given $\odot A$, $m\angle C = \dfrac{1}{2} m\overset{\frown}{BD}$.

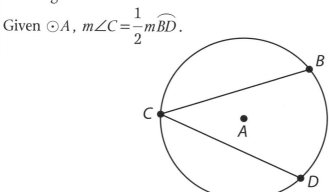

---

- In the following diagram, $\angle BCD$ is the inscribed angle and $\angle BAD$ is the central angle. They both intercept the minor arc $\overset{\frown}{BD}$.

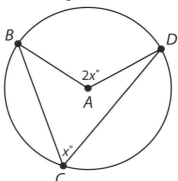

## Corollaries to the Inscribed Angle Theorem

| Corollary 1 | Corollary 2 |
|---|---|
| Two inscribed angles that intercept the same arc are congruent. | An angle inscribed in a semicircle is a right angle. |

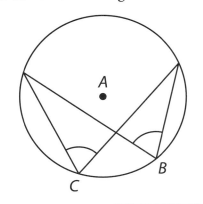

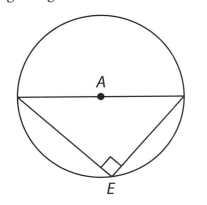

# Guided Practice 6.1.1

**Example 1**

Prove that the measure of a central angle is twice the measure of an inscribed angle that intercepts the same arc.

> Given: $\odot A$ with inscribed $\angle B$ and central $\angle CAD$ intercepting $\overset{\frown}{CD}$.
>
> Prove: $2m\angle B = m\angle CAD$

---

1. Identify the known information.

   Circle $A$ with inscribed $\angle B$ and central $\angle CAD$ intercepts $\overset{\frown}{CD}$.

   Let $\overline{BD}$ be a diameter of the circle.

   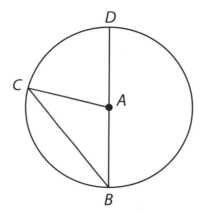

   By definition, $\overline{AB}$ and $\overline{AC}$ are radii of the circle.

   Mark them as $r$.

   Identify $\angle B$ as $x$ and $\angle CAD$ as $y$.

   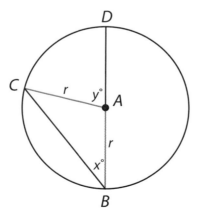

---

2. Identify what information is known about the angles of the triangle.

   $\triangle ABC$ is isosceles since both legs are the same length, $r$.

   By the Isosceles Triangle Theorem, both base angles of the triangle are congruent; therefore, $\angle ABC \cong \angle ACB = x$.

   Also, the vertex angle of the isosceles triangle is a linear pair with $y$ and thus $m\angle CAB = 180 - y$.

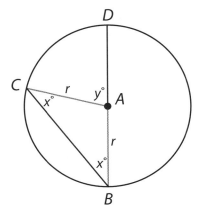

   By the Triangle Sum Theorem:

   $x + x + 180 - y = 180$

   $2x - y = 0$

   $2x = y$

   Substituting the names for $x$ and $y$ yields $2m\angle B = m\angle CAD$.

   Therefore, the measure of a central angle is twice the measure of an inscribed angle that intercepts the same arc.

**Example 2**

Prove that all circles are similar using the concept of similarity transformations.

1.  Create a diagram to help with the proof.

    Draw $\odot A$ with radius $r_1$.

    Draw $\odot B$ with radius $r_2$ such that $r_2 > r_1$.

2. Using properties of rigid motion, translate $\odot B$ so that it is concentric with $\odot A$.

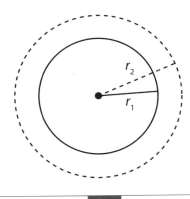

3. Determine the scale factor necessary to dilate $\odot A$ so that it maps to $\odot B$.

To determine the ratio, note that each circle has a radius that by definition is the segment from the center to a point on the circle. To map $\odot A \rightarrow \odot B$, divide $r_2$ by $r_1$. The resulting ratio is the scale factor that produces the following image.

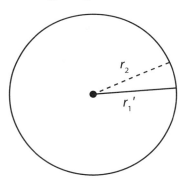

This scale factor, $\dfrac{r_2}{r_1}$, is true for all circles and a similarity transformation of this sort can always be used because all circles are similar.

## Example 3

A car has a circular turning radius of 15.5 feet. The distance between the two front tires is 5.4 feet. To the nearest foot, how much farther does a tire on the outer edge of the turning radius travel than a tire on the inner edge?

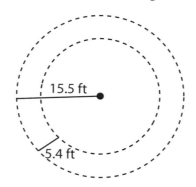

1. Calculate the circumference of the outer tire's turn.

   $C = 2\pi r$          Formula for the circumference of a circle

   $C = 2\pi(15.5)$      Substitute 15.5 for the radius ($r$).

   $C = 31\pi$         Simplify.

2. Calculate the circumference of the inside tire's turn.

   First, calculate the radius of the inner tire's turn.

   Since all tires are similar, the radius of the inner tire's turn can be calculated by subtracting the distance between the two front wheels (the distance between each circle) from the radius of the outer tire's turn.

   $15.5 - 5.4 = 10.1$ ft

   $C = 2\pi r$          Formula for the circumference of a circle

   $C = 2\pi(10.1)$      Substitute 10.1 for the radius ($r$).

   $C = 20.2\pi$        Simplify.

3. Calculate the difference in the circumference of each tire's turn.

Find the difference in the circumference of each tire's turn.

$$31\pi - 20.2\pi = 10.8\pi \approx 33.93$$

The outer tire travels approximately 34 feet farther than the inner tire.

## Example 4

Find the value of each variable.

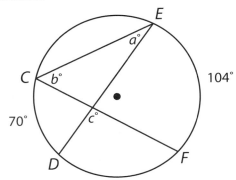

1. Identify the inscribed angle and the intercepted arc and use the proper theorem or corollary to find the value of $a$.

$a$ is the inscribed angle creating the intercepting arc $\overset{\frown}{CD}$.

The measure of the intercepted arc is $70°$.

Use the Inscribed Angle Theorem to find $a$.

$$m\angle E = \frac{1}{2}m\overset{\frown}{CD} \qquad \text{Inscribed Angle Theorem}$$

$$a = \frac{1}{2}(70) \qquad \text{Substitute the given information.}$$

$$a = 35 \qquad \text{Solve for } a.$$

The value of $a$ is $35°$.

2.  Identify the inscribed angle and the intercepted arc and use the proper theorem or corollary to find the value of $b$.

    $b$ is the inscribed angle creating the intercepting arc $\overset{\frown}{EF}$.

    The measure of the intercepted arc is 104°.

    Use the Inscribed Angle Theorem to find $b$.

    $$m\angle C = \frac{1}{2}m\overset{\frown}{EF}$$  Inscribed Angle Theorem

    $$b = \frac{1}{2}(104)$$  Substitute the given information.

    $$b = 52$$  Solve for $b$.

    The value of $b$ is 52°.

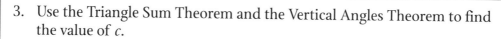

3.  Use the Triangle Sum Theorem and the Vertical Angles Theorem to find the value of $c$.

    Note that $a$ and $b$, in addition to being the measures of inscribed angles, are interior angles of a triangle.

    The third interior angle is a vertical angle to $c$ and is therefore congruent to $c$.

    Finding that third angle will yield the value of $c$.

    $a + b + c = 180$  Triangle Sum Theorem and Vertical Angles Theorem

    $35 + 52 + c = 180$  Substitute the measures of $a$ and $b$.

    $87 + c = 180$  Combine like terms.

    $c = 93$  Solve for $c$.

    The value of $c$ is 93°.

**Example 5**

Find the measures of $\angle BAC$ and $\angle BDC$.

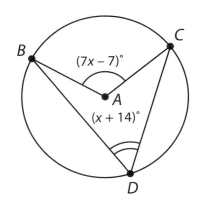

1. Set up an equation to solve for $x$.

   $\angle BAC$ is a central angle and $\angle BDC$ is an inscribed angle in $\odot A$.

   | | |
   |---|---|
   | $m\angle BAC = 2m\angle BDC$ | Central Angle/Inscribed Angle Theorem |
   | $7x - 7 = 2(x + 14)$ | Substitute values for $\angle BAC$ and $\angle BDC$. |
   | $7x - 7 = 2x + 28$ | Distributive Property |
   | $5x = 35$ | Solve for $x$. |
   | $x = 7$ | |

2. Substitute the value of $x$ into the expression for $\angle BDC$ to find the measure of the inscribed angle.

   $m\angle BDC = (x + 14)$

   $m\angle BDC = (7) + 14$

   $m\angle BDC = 21$

   The measure of $\angle BDC$ is 21°.

3. Find the value of the central angle, $\angle BAC$.

By the Inscribed Angle Theorem, $m\angle BAC = 2m\angle BDC$.

   $m\angle BAC = 21(2)$

   $m\angle BAC = 42$

The measure of $\angle BAC$ is 42°.

# UNIT 6 • CIRCLES WITH AND WITHOUT COORDINATES
## Lesson 1: Introducing Circles

## Practice 6.1.1: Similar Circles and Central and Inscribed Angles

Given that all circles are similar, determine the scale factor necessary to map $\odot C \rightarrow \odot D$.

1.  $\odot C$ has a radius of 144 units and $\odot D$ has a radius of 3 units.

2.  $\odot C$ has a diameter of 50 units and $\odot D$ has a diameter of 12 units.

Use your knowledge of similar circles to complete problems 3 and 4.

3.  A circular waterfall is surrounded by a brick wall. The radius of the inner wall is 35 inches. If the bricks are 5 inches wide, what scale factor was used to determine the radius of the outer wall?

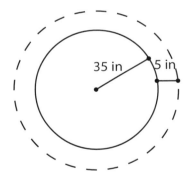

4.  A small car has a tire with a 17-inch diameter. A truck has a tire with a 32-inch diameter. How much farther than the car does the truck have to drive for its tire to complete one revolution?

*continued*

# UNIT 6 • CIRCLES WITH AND WITHOUT COORDINATES
## Lesson 1: Introducing Circles

Use your knowledge of angles to complete the problems that follow.

5. Find the values of $x$, $y$, and $z$.

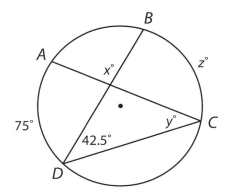

6. Find the value of $x$ and the measure of $\overset{\frown}{AB}$.

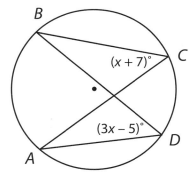

continued

7. Find the values of *x* and *y*.

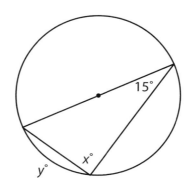

8. Find $m\angle C$ and $m\angle D$.

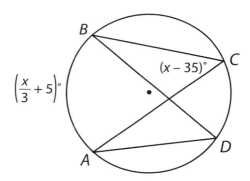

*continued*

9.  Find $m\angle B$ and $m\angle C$.

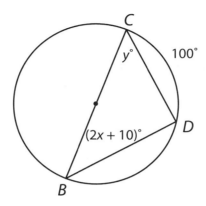

10. Find $m\overset{\frown}{AB}$ and $m\overset{\frown}{CA}$.

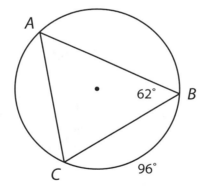

# Lesson 6.1.2: Chord Central Angles Conjecture

## Introduction

Circles have several special properties, conjectures, postulates, and theorems associated with them. This lesson focuses on the relationship between chords and the angles and arcs they create.

## Key Concepts

- Chords are segments whose endpoints lie on the circumference of a circle.

- Three chords are shown on the circle below.

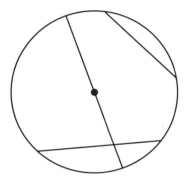

- Congruent chords of a circle create one pair of congruent central angles.

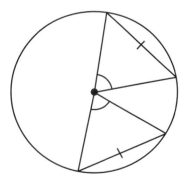

- When the sides of the central angles create diameters of the circle, vertical angles are formed. This creates two pairs of congruent central angles.

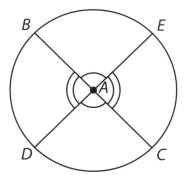

- Congruent chords also intercept congruent arcs.

- An **intercepted arc** is an arc whose endpoints intersect the sides of an inscribed angle and whose other points are in the interior of the angle.

- Remember that the measure of an arc is the same as the measure of its central angle.

- Also, recall that central angles are twice the measure of their inscribed angles.

- In the circle below, chords $\overline{BC}$ and $\overline{DE}$ are congruent chords of $\odot A$.

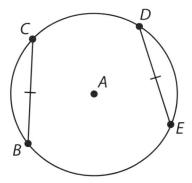

- When the radii are constructed such that each endpoint of the chord connects to the center of the circle, four central angles are created, as well as two congruent isosceles triangles by the SSS Congruence Postulate.

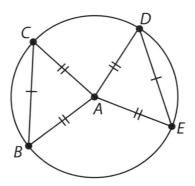

- Since the triangles are congruent and both triangles include two central angles that are the vertex angles of the isosceles triangles, those central angles are also congruent because Corresponding Parts of Congruent Triangles are Congruent (CPCTC).

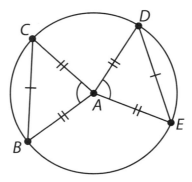

- The measure of the arcs intercepted by the chords is congruent to the measure of the central angle because arc measures are determined by their central angle.

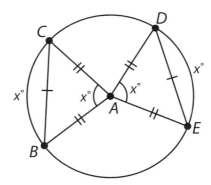

# Guided Practice 6.1.2

**Example 1**

In $\odot A$, $m\angle BAC = 57$. What is $m\overset{\frown}{BDC}$?

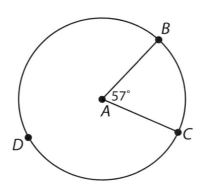

1. Find the measure of $\overset{\frown}{BC}$.

   $m\angle BAC = 57$

   The measure of $\angle BAC$ is equal to the measure of $\overset{\frown}{BC}$ because central angles are congruent to their intercepted arc; therefore, the measure of $\overset{\frown}{BC}$ is also 57°.

2. Find the measure of $\overset{\frown}{BDC}$.

   Subtract the measure of $\overset{\frown}{BC}$ from 360°.

   $360 - 57 = 303$

   $m\overset{\frown}{BDC} = 303$

3. State your conclusion.

   The measure of $\overset{\frown}{BDC}$ is 303°.

## Example 2

$\odot G \cong \odot E$. What conclusions can you make?

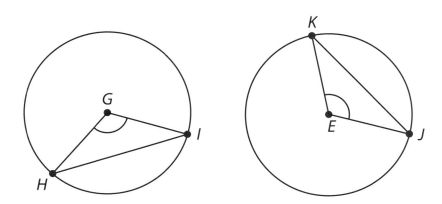

1. What type of angles are $\angle G$ and $\angle E$, and what does that tell you about the chords?

   $\angle G$ and $\angle E$ are congruent central angles of congruent circles, so $\overline{HI}$ and $\overline{JK}$ are congruent chords.

2. Since the central angles are congruent, what else do you know?

   The measures of the arcs intercepted by congruent chords are congruent, so minor arc $HI$ is congruent to minor arc $JK$.

   Deductively, then, major arc $IH$ is congruent to major arc $KJ$.

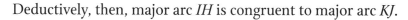

**Example 3**

Find the value of *y*.

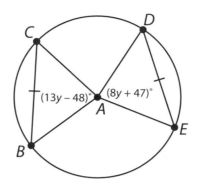

---

1.  Set up an equation to solve for *y*.

    The angles marked are central angles created by congruent chords, and are therefore congruent.

    Set the measure of each angle equal to each other.

    $13y - 48 = 8y + 47$

---

2.  Solve for *y*.

    | | |
    |---|---|
    | $13y - 48 = 8y + 47$ | Central angles created by congruent chords are congruent. |

    $5y = 95$

    $y = 19$

### Practice 6.1.2: Chord Central Angles Conjecture

Use what you've learned about chords and central angles to solve.

1. In $\odot A$, $m\angle BAC = 72$. What is $m\overset{\frown}{BDC}$?

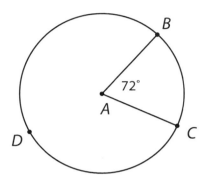

2. In $\odot A$, $\overset{\frown}{BDC} = 315$. What is $m\angle BAC$?

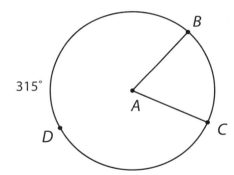

3. What is the value of $w$?

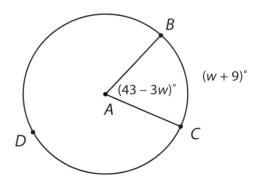

*continued*

4. What can you conclude about $\odot G$ and $\odot E$?

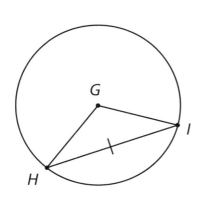
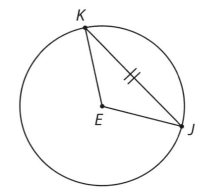

5. $\odot G \cong \odot E$. What is the value of $a$?

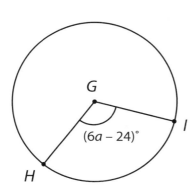
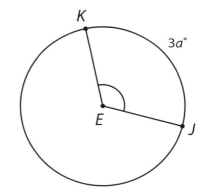

6. Find the value of $b$.

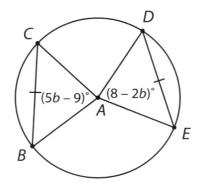

*continued*

7. Find the value of $b$.

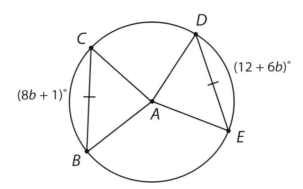

8. Find the value of $b$.

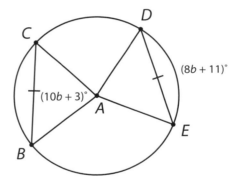

9. If the circumference of one circle is 54 millimeters and the major arc of a second congruent circle measures 182°, what is the length of this major arc of the second circle?

10. You're sewing the seam on a circular lampshade for interior design class. The total circumference of the lampshade is 3 feet. The amount of the seam you've sewn so far measures approximately 23° around the circumference of the lampshade. What length of lampshade still needs to be sewn?

# Lesson 6.1.3: Properties of Tangents of a Circle

## Introduction

Circles and tangent lines can be useful in many real-world applications and fields of study, such as construction, landscaping, and engineering. There are many different types of lines that touch or intersect circles. All of these lines have unique properties and relationships to a circle. Specifically, in this lesson, we will identify what a tangent line is, explore the properties of tangent lines, prove that a line is tangent to a circle, and find the lengths of tangent lines. We will also identify and use secant lines, as well as discuss how they are different from tangent lines.

## Key Concepts

- A **tangent line** is a line that intersects a circle at exactly one point.

- Tangent lines are perpendicular to the radius of the circle at the point of tangency.

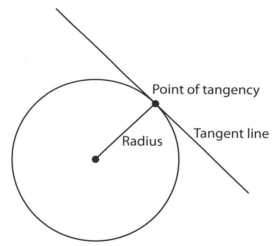

- You can verify that a line is tangent to a circle by constructing a right triangle using the radius, and verifying that it is a right triangle by using the Pythagorean Theorem.

- The slopes of a line and a radius drawn to the possible point of tangency must be negative reciprocals in order for the line to be a tangent.

- If two segments are tangent to the same circle, and originate from the same exterior point, then the segments are congruent.

- The angle formed by two tangent lines whose vertex is outside of the circle is called the **circumscribed angle**.

- $\angle BAC$ is a circumscribed angle.

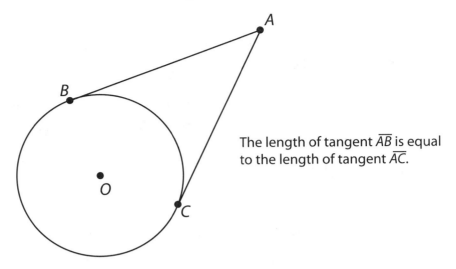

The length of tangent $\overline{AB}$ is equal to the length of tangent $\overline{AC}$.

- The angle formed by two tangents is equal to one half the positive difference of the angle's intercepted arcs.

- A **secant line** is a line that intersects a circle at two points.

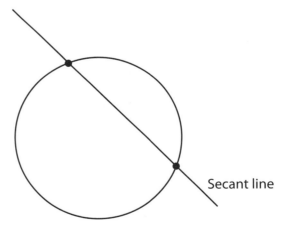

Secant line

- An angle formed by a secant and a tangent is equal to the positive difference of its intercepted arcs.

# Guided Practice 6.1.3

## Example 1

Determine whether $\overline{BC}$ is tangent to $\odot A$ in the diagram below.

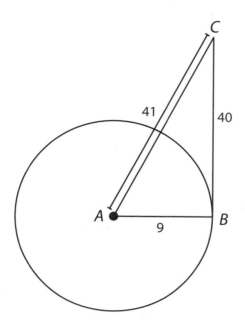

1. Identify the radius.

   The radius of the circle is the segment from the center of the circle to a point on the circle.

   $\overline{AB}$ is the radius of $\odot A$.

2. Determine the relationship between $\overline{AB}$ and $\overline{BC}$ at point $B$ in order for $\overline{BC}$ to be tangent to $\odot A$.

   $\overline{AB}$ must be perpendicular to $\overline{BC}$ at point $B$ in order for $\overline{BC}$ to be tangent to $\odot A$.

3. Show that $\angle ABC$ is a right angle by using the converse of the Pythagorean Theorem.

The converse of the Pythagorean Theorem states that when the sum of the squares of two sides of a triangle is equal to the square of the third side of the triangle, the triangle is a right triangle.

| | |
|---|---|
| $a^2 + b^2 = c^2$ | Pythagorean Theorem |
| $(AB)^2 + (BC)^2 = (AC)^2$ | Substitute segment names for $a$, $b$, and $c$. |
| $9^2 + 40^2 = 41^2$ | Substitute values for $\overline{AB}$, $\overline{BC}$, and $\overline{AC}$. |
| $81 + 1600 = 1681$ | Simplify, then solve. |
| $1681 = 1681$ | |

The result is a true statement; therefore, $\angle ABC$ is a right angle.

4. State your conclusion.

Since the converse of the Pythagorean Theorem is true, $\triangle ABC$ is a right triangle; therefore, $\angle ABC$ is a right angle. This makes $\overline{AB}$ perpendicular to $\overline{BC}$; therefore, $\overline{BC}$ is tangent to $\odot A$.

## Example 2

Each side of $\triangle ABC$ is tangent to circle $O$ at the points $D$, $E$, and $F$. Find the perimeter of $\triangle ABC$.

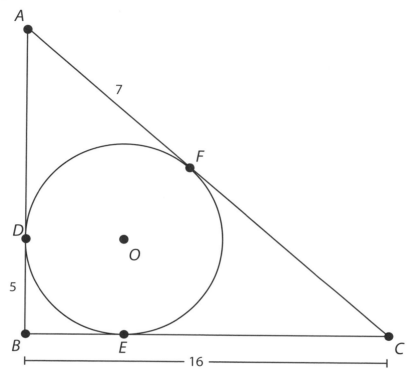

1.  Identify the lengths of each side of the triangle.

    $\overline{AD}$ is tangent to the same circle as $\overline{AF}$ and extends from the same point; therefore, the lengths are equal.

    $AD = 7$ units

    $\overline{BE}$ is tangent to the same circle as $\overline{BD}$ and extends from the same point; therefore, the lengths are equal.

    $BE = 5$ units

    To determine the length of $\overline{CE}$, subtract the length of $\overline{BE}$ from the length of $\overline{BC}$.

    $16 - 5 = 11$

    $CE = 11$ units

    $\overline{CF}$ is tangent to the same circle as $\overline{CE}$ and extends from the same point; therefore, the lengths are equal.

    $CF = 11$ units

2. Calculate the perimeter of $\triangle ABC$.

Add the lengths of $\overline{AD}$, $\overline{AF}$, $\overline{BD}$, $\overline{BE}$, $\overline{CE}$, and $\overline{CF}$ to find the perimeter of the polygon.

$$7 + 7 + 5 + 5 + 11 + 11 = 46 \text{ units}$$

The perimeter of $\triangle ABC$ is 46 units.

## Example 3

A landscaper wants to build a walkway tangent to the circular park shown in the diagram below. The other walkway pictured is a radius of the circle and has a slope of $-\dfrac{1}{2}$ on the grid. If the walkways should intersect at $(4, -2)$ on the grid, what equation can the landscaper use to graph the new walkway on the grid?

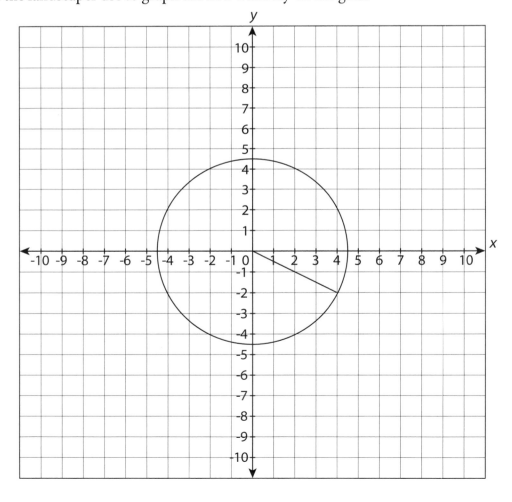

1. Determine the slope of the walkway.

   One of the properties of tangent lines states that if a line is tangent to a circle, then it is perpendicular to the radius at the point of tangency.

   Since the slope of the radius is $-\dfrac{1}{2}$, then the slope of the new walkway will be 2 because perpendicular lines have slopes that are negative reciprocals.

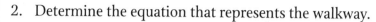

2. Determine the equation that represents the walkway.

   Recall that the point-slope form of a line is $y - y_1 = m(x - x_1)$.

   Since the new walkway is tangent to the circle at (4, –2), then the point (4, –2) is on the tangent line, so it can be used to write the equation.

   $y - (-2) = 2(x - 4)$

   $y + 2 = 2(x - 4)$

   This equation can be rearranged into slope-intercept form, $y = 2x - 10$, for easier graphing.

## Example 4

$\overline{AB}$ is tangent to $\odot C$ at point $B$ as shown below. Find the length of $\overline{AB}$ as well as $m\,\overparen{BD}$.

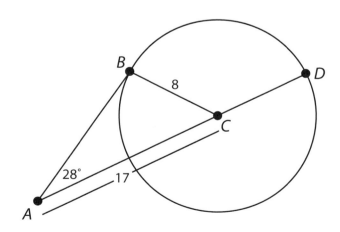

1. Find the length of $\overline{AB}$.

   Since $\overline{AB}$ is tangent to $\odot C$, then $\angle ABC$ is right angle because a tangent and a radius form a right angle at the point of tangency.

   Since $\angle ABC$ is a right angle, $\triangle ABC$ is a right triangle.

   Use the Pythagorean Theorem to find the length of $\overline{AB}$.

   $a^2 + b^2 = c^2$          Pythagorean Theorem

   $8^2 + (AB)^2 = 17^2$      Substitute values for $a$, $b$, and $c$.

   $64 + (AB)^2 = 289$       Simplify.

   $(AB)^2 = 225$

   $AB = 15$

   The length of $\overline{AB}$ is 15 units.

2. Find $m\,\overset{\frown}{BD}$.

   First, determine the unknown measure of $\angle ACB$.

   Recall that the sum of all three angles of a triangle is $180°$.

   $\angle ABC$ is a right angle, so it is $90°$.

   $\angle BAC$ is $28°$, as shown in the diagram.

   Set up an equation to determine the measure of $\angle ACB$.

   $28 + 90 + m\angle ACB = 180$

   $118 + m\angle ACB = 180$

   $m\angle ACB = 62$

   Since $m\angle ACB = 62$, then $m\angle BCD = 118$ because $\angle ACB$ and $\angle BCD$ are a linear pair.

   $\angle BCD$ is a central angle, and recall that the measure of a central angle is the same as its intercepted arc, so $\overset{\frown}{BD}$ is $118°$.

## Practice 6.1.3: Properties of Tangents of a Circle

Use what you have learned about tangent lines and secant lines to answer the questions.

1. $\overline{AB}$ and $\overline{AC}$ are tangent to $\odot L$ in the diagram below. What is the value of $x$?

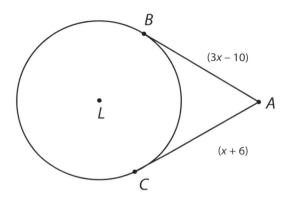

2. You know that $\overline{PR}$ is tangent to $\odot S$ in the diagram below. What must you prove to show that this is true?

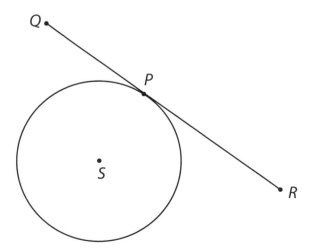

*continued*

3. $\overline{AB}$ is tangent to $\odot C$ at point $B$ in the diagram below. What is the measure of $\angle ACB$?

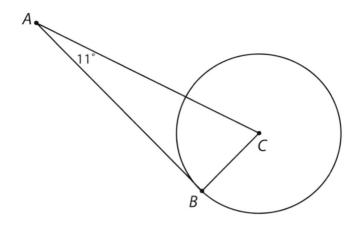

4. A space station orbiting the Earth is sending two signals that are tangent to the Earth. If the intercepted arc of the Earth's surface that is visible to the satellite is 168°, what is the measure of the angle formed by the two signal beams?

5. Is $\overline{XY}$ tangent to $\odot Z$ at point $X$ in the diagram below? Explain.

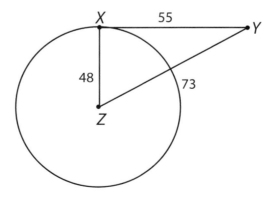

*continued*

6. How many tangents can be drawn that contain a point on a circle? Explain your answer.

7. The slope of radius $\overline{PQ}$ in circle $Q$ is $-\dfrac{2}{3}$. A student wants to draw a tangent to $\odot Q$ at point $P$. What will be the slope of this tangent line?

8. A homeowner is building a square fence around his circular patio so that each side of the fence is tangent to the circle, as shown in the diagram below. The radius of his patio is 18 yards. What is the perimeter of his fence?

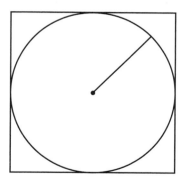

*continued*

# UNIT 6 • CIRCLES WITH AND WITHOUT COORDINATES
## Lesson 1: Introducing Circles

9. You are using binoculars to look at an eagle. The sides of the binoculars seem to extend from the eagle, and are tangent to the circular portion. How far away is the eagle?

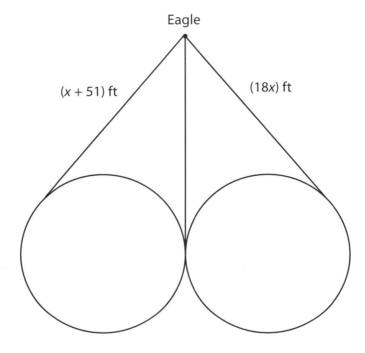

Eagle

$(x + 51)$ ft          $(18x)$ ft

10. Your friend Truman argues that chords and tangents are the same thing. You disagree. What do you tell Truman to convince him that he is incorrect?

# Lesson 2: Inscribed Polygons and Circumscribed Triangles

## Common Core State Standard

**G–C.3**    Construct the inscribed and circumscribed circles of a triangle, and prove properties of angles for a quadrilateral inscribed in a circle.

## Essential Questions

1. What is the purpose of locating the incenter?

2. What is the purpose of locating the circumcenter?

3. Where are an incenter and an inscribed circle used in real life?

4. What types of quadrilaterals can be inscribed in a circle?

## WORDS TO KNOW

| | |
|---|---|
| **angle bisector** | a ray that divides an angle into two congruent angles |
| **circumcenter** | the intersection of the perpendicular bisectors of a triangle |
| **circumscribed circle** | a circle that contains all vertices of a polygon |
| **circumscribed triangle** | triangle whose sides are tangent to an interior circle |
| **equidistant** | the same distance from a reference point |
| **incenter** | the intersection of the angle bisectors of a triangle |
| **inscribed circle** | a circle whose tangents form a triangle |
| **inscribed quadrilateral** | a quadrilateral whose vertices are on a circle |
| **inscribed triangle** | a triangle whose vertices are on a circle |
| **perpendicular bisector** | a line that intersects a segment at its midpoint at a right angle |
| **point of concurrency** | the point where three or more lines intersect |

# Recommended Resources

- Beva.org. "Introduction to Sketchpad: Incenter and Circumcenter of Triangles."

  http://www.walch.com/rr/00051

  This website describes how to construct the incenter in The Geometer's Sketchpad dynamic geometry program.

- IXL Learning. "Angles in inscribed quadrilaterals."

  http://www.walch.com/rr/00052

  This interactive website gives a series of problems and scores them immediately. If the user submits a wrong answer, a description and process for arriving at the correct answer are provided. This activity is meant as practice for inscribed polygons.

- IXL Learning. "Identify medians, altitudes, angle bisectors, and perpendicular bisectors."

  http://www.walch.com/rr/00053

  This interactive website gives a series of problems and scores them immediately. If the user submits a wrong answer, a description and process for arriving at the correct answer are provided. These problems start with a triangle and a construction of a point of concurrency. Users are required to choose which point of concurrency is depicted. This activity is meant as a review of key terms for inscribed polygons and circumscribed triangles.

# Lesson 6.2.1: Constructing Inscribed Circles

## Introduction

In the map of Georgia below, Interstates 475 and 75 form a triangle with Macon as one of the vertices. If a company wants to build a distribution center in the middle of that triangle so that the building will be equidistant from each interstate, where should the distribution center be built? In this lesson, we will investigate the point that solves this problem and the geometry that supports it.

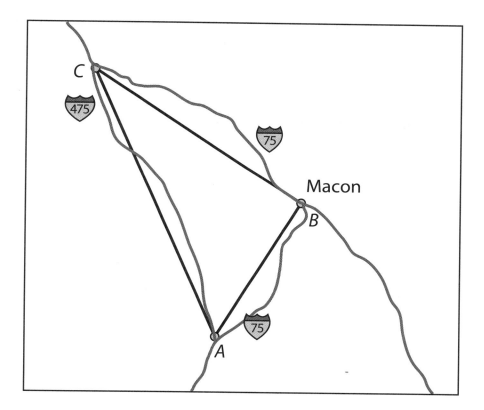

## Key Concepts

- A point that is **equidistant** lies the same distance away from a reference point.

- The company wants its distribution center to be equidistant from the given interstates.

- To determine the location of the distribution center, the company would first need to determine the point at which the distribution center would be equidistant from each of the interstates.

- To determine this point, the company would need to find the angle bisectors of the triangle created by the interstates.

- An **angle bisector** is the ray that divides an angle into two congruent angles.

- When all three angle bisectors of a triangle are constructed, the rays are said to be concurrent, or intersect at one point.

- This point is called the **point of concurrency**, where three or more lines intersect.

- The point of concurrency of the angle bisectors of a triangle is called the **incenter**.

- The incenter is equidistant from the three sides of the triangle and is also the center of the circle tangent to the triangle.

- A circle whose tangents form a triangle is referred to as an **inscribed circle**.

- When the inscribed circle is constructed, the triangle is referred to as a **circumscribed triangle**—a triangle whose sides are tangent to a circle.

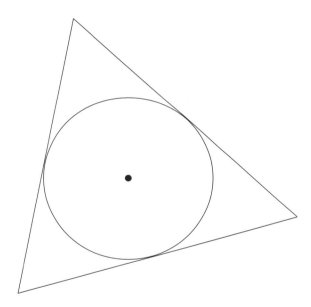

- To construct an inscribed circle, determine the shortest distance from the incenter to each of the sides of the triangle.

- Remember that the shortest distance from a point to a line or line segment is a perpendicular line.

- Follow the steps outlined in the Guided Practice that follows to construct a line perpendicular to a point not on the line.

# Guided Practice 6.2.1

## Example 1

Verify that the angle bisectors of acute △ABC are concurrent and that this concurrent point is equidistant from each side.

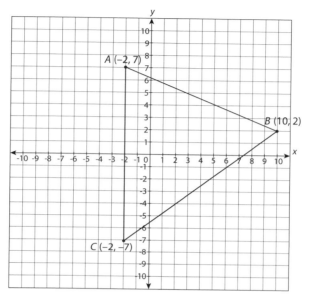

1.  Construct the angle bisector of ∠A.

    First, place the compass on point A and swing an arc that intersects the two sides of the angle.

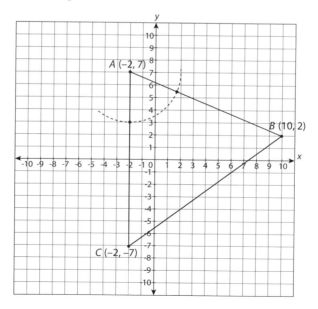

*(continued)*

From each point of intersection, swing an arc in the interior of the angle. These two arcs should intersect. If they do not, increase the radius of the arc. Connect A with the intersections of the two arcs to locate the angle bisector.

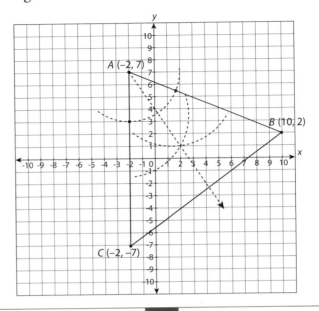

2. Repeat the process for ∠B and ∠C.

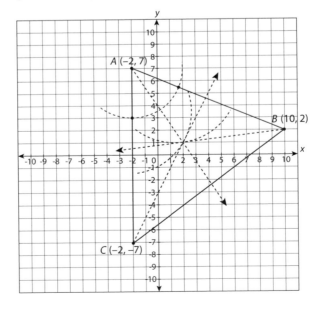

3. Locate the point of concurrency. Label this point as *D*.

The point of concurrency is where all three of the angle bisectors meet.
As seen on the coordinate plane, the point of concurrency is (2, 1).

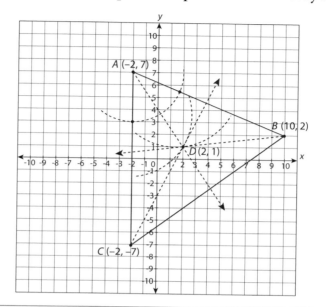

4. Verify that the point of concurrency is equidistant from each side.

Determine the line that is perpendicular to $\overline{AC}$ through point *D* (2, 1).

Find the equation of the line representing $\overline{AC}$.

Use the slope formula to calculate the slope of the line.

$$m = \frac{y_2 - y_1}{x_2 - x_1}$$  Slope formula

$$m = \frac{(-7) - (7)}{(-2) - (-2)}$$  Substitute (–2, 7) and (–2, –7) for $(x_1, y_1)$ and $(x_2, y_2)$.

$$m = \frac{-14}{0}$$

The slope of $\overline{AC}$ is undefined because the line is vertical.

(*continued*)

The equation of a vertical line always has the form $x = a$, where $a$ is the $x$-intercept. In this case, the $x$-intercept is $-2$.

The equation of $\overline{AC}$ is $x = -2$.

The line that is perpendicular to $x = -2$ is horizontal and of the form $y = b$, where $b$ is the $y$-intercept.

The line that is horizontal at $(2, 1)$ intersects the $y$-intercept at 1.

The equation of the line that is perpendicular to $\overline{AC}$ is $y = 1$.

The intersection of the two lines is $(-2, 1)$. Label this point $E$.

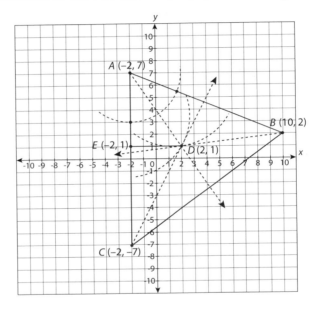

Use the distance formula to calculate the length of $\overline{DE}$.

$d = \sqrt{(x_2 - x_1)^2 + (y_2 - y_1)^2}$     Distance formula

$\sqrt{[(2)-(-2)]^2 + [(1)-(1)]^2}$     Substitute $(-2, 1)$ and $(2, 1)$ for $(x_1, y_1)$ and $(x_2, y_2)$.

$DE = \sqrt{4^2 + 0^2}$     Simplify.

$DE = \sqrt{16}$

$DE = 4$

*(continued)*

Determine the line that is perpendicular to $\overline{AB}$ through point $D$ (2, 1).

Find the equation of the line representing $\overline{AB}$.

The slope of $\overline{AB}$ is $-\dfrac{5}{12}$.

Use the slope-intercept form of a linear equation, $y = mx + b$, to determine the equation of $\overline{AB}$.

The equation of $\overline{AB}$ is $y = -\dfrac{5}{12}x + \dfrac{37}{6}$.

The line that is perpendicular to $\overline{AB}$ has a slope that is the opposite reciprocal of the slope of $\overline{AB}$.

The opposite reciprocal of $-\dfrac{5}{12}$ is $\dfrac{12}{5}$.

Again, use the slope-intercept form of a linear equation to determine the perpendicular line.

The equation of the perpendicular line is $y = \dfrac{12}{5}x - \dfrac{19}{5}$.

The intersection of the two lines can be found by setting the equations equal to each other and solving for $x$.

The intersection of the two lines is at $\left(\dfrac{46}{13}, \dfrac{61}{13}\right)$. Label this point $F$.

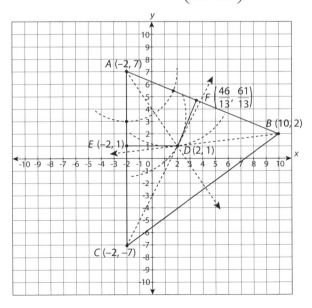

(*continued*)

Use the distance formula to calculate the length of $\overline{DF}$.

$$d=\sqrt{(x_2-x_1)^2+(y_2-y_1)^2}$$  Distance formula

$$DF=\sqrt{\left[(2)-\left(\frac{46}{13}\right)\right]^2+\left[(1)-\left(\frac{61}{13}\right)\right]^2}$$  Substitute $\left(\dfrac{46}{13},\dfrac{61}{13}\right)$ and $(2,1)$ for $(x_1,y_1)$ and $(x_2,y_2)$.

$$DF=\sqrt{\left[\left(\frac{26}{13}\right)-\left(\frac{46}{13}\right)\right]^2+\left[\left(\frac{13}{13}\right)-\left(\frac{61}{13}\right)\right]^2}$$  Simplify.

$$DF=\sqrt{2.37+13.63}$$

$$DF=\sqrt{16}$$

$$DF=4$$

By following these same steps, it can be determined that the point of intersection of $\overline{BC}$ and the line that is perpendicular to $\overline{BC}$ through $D$ (2, 1) is at $\left(\dfrac{22}{5},-\dfrac{11}{5}\right)$.

The midpoint of $BC$ is at (4.4, –2.2). Label this point $G$.

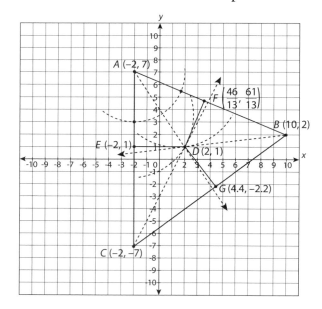

(*continued*)

Use the distance formula to calculate the length of $\overline{DG}$ .

$$d = \sqrt{(x_2 - x_1)^2 + (y_2 - y_1)^2}$$   Distance formula

$$DG = \sqrt{\left[(2) - \left(\dfrac{22}{5}\right)\right]^2 + \left[(1) - \left(-\dfrac{11}{5}\right)\right]^2}$$   Substitute $\left(\dfrac{22}{5}, -\dfrac{11}{5}\right)$ and

$(2, 1)$ for $(x_1, y_1)$ and $(x_2, y_2)$.

$$DG = \sqrt{16}$$   Simplify.

$$DG = 4$$

5. State your conclusion.

The angle bisectors of the triangle are concurrent at point $D$. The three segments perpendicular from point $D$ (the incenter of the triangle) to the sides of the triangle are equal; therefore, the incenter is equidistant from the three sides of the triangle.

## Example 2

Construct a circle inscribed in acute $\triangle ABC$.

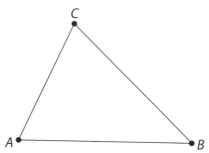

1.  Construct the angle bisectors of each angle.

    Use the same method described in Example 1 to bisect each angle.

    Label the point of concurrency of the angle bisectors as point $D$.

    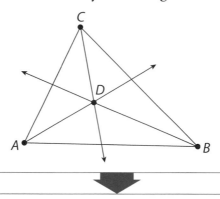

2.  Construct a perpendicular line from $D$ to each side.

    To construct a perpendicular line through $D$, put the sharp point of your compass on point $D$. Open the compass until it extends farther than $\overline{AC}$.

    Make a large arc that intersects $\overline{AC}$ in exactly two places. Without changing your compass setting, put the sharp point of the compass on one of the points of intersection. Make a second arc below the given line.

    Without changing your compass setting, put the sharp point of the compass on the second point of intersection. Make a third arc below the given line. The third arc must intersect the second arc.

    Label the point of intersection $E$.

    Use your straightedge to connect points $D$ and $E$.

    Repeat this process for each of the remaining sides.

3. Verify that the lengths of the perpendicular segments are equal.

Use your compass and carefully measure the length of each perpendicular segment.

Verify that the measurements are the same.

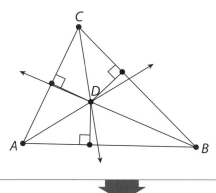

4. Construct the inscribed circle with center $D$.

Place the compass point at $D$ and open the compass to the length of any one of the perpendicular segments.

Use this setting to construct a circle inside of $\triangle ABC$.

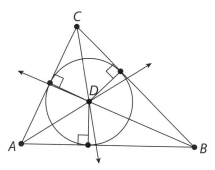

Circle $D$ is inscribed in $\triangle ABC$ and is tangent to each of the sides of the triangle.

## Example 3

Construct a circle inscribed in obtuse $\triangle ABC$.

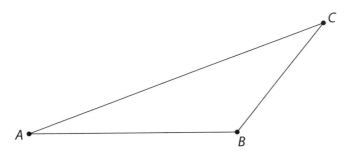

1.  Construct the angle bisectors of each angle.

    Use the same method as described in Example 1 to bisect each angle.

    Label the point of concurrency of the angle bisectors as point $D$.

    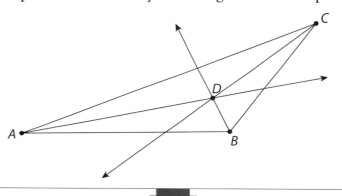

2. Construct a perpendicular line from $D$ to each side.

To construct a perpendicular line through $D$, put the sharp point of your compass on point $D$. Open the compass until it extends farther than $\overline{AC}$.

Make a large arc that intersects $\overline{AC}$ in exactly two places. Without changing your compass setting, put the sharp point of the compass on one of the points of intersection. Make a second arc below the given line.

Without changing your compass setting, put the sharp point of the compass on the second point of intersection. Make a third arc below the given line. The third arc must intersect the second arc.

Label the point of intersection $E$.

Use your straightedge to connect points $D$ and $E$.

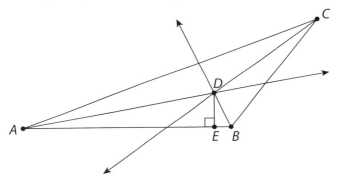

Repeat this process for each of the remaining sides, labeling the points of intersection $F$ and $G$.

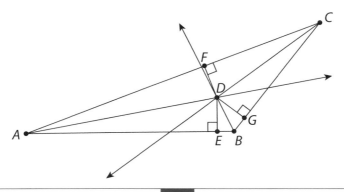

3. Verify that the lengths of the perpendicular segments are equal.

   Use your compass and carefully measure the length of each perpendicular.

   Verify that the measurements are the same.

4. Construct the inscribed circle with center $D$.

   Place the compass point at $D$ and open the compass to the length of any one of the perpendicular segments.

   Use this setting to construct a circle inside of $\triangle ABC$.

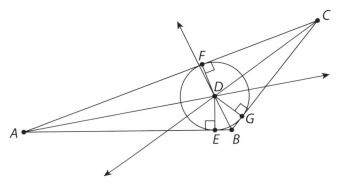

   Circle $D$ is inscribed in $\triangle ABC$ and is tangent to each of the sides of the triangle.

# UNIT 6 • CIRCLES WITH AND WITHOUT COORDINATES
## Lesson 2: Inscribed Polygons and Circumscribed Triangles

## Practice 6.2.1: Constructing Inscribed Circles

Construct the inscribed circle for each of the triangles in problems 1–3.

1.

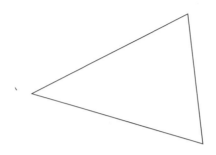

2.

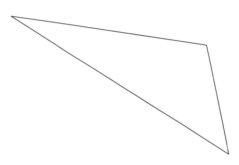

3.

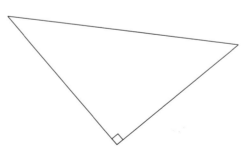

4. Will the incenter ever be located outside of the triangle? Why or why not? Consider your constructions of the previous three problems.

*continued*

# UNIT 6 • CIRCLES WITH AND WITHOUT COORDINATES
## Lesson 2: Inscribed Polygons and Circumscribed Triangles

Use the diagrams provided to solve problems 5–10.

5. In the map of Georgia below, Interstates 16 and 75 and Route 280 form a triangle with Macon as one of the vertices. A company wants to build its new headquarters in the middle of that triangle so that the building is equidistant from each highway. Where should the headquarters be built?

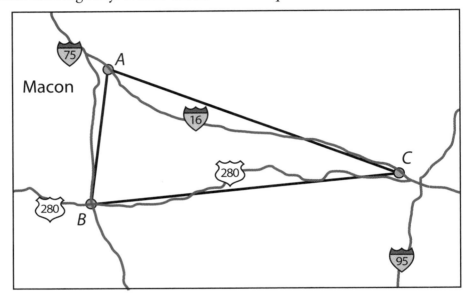

6. Find the length of *BI*. Assume that *I* is the incenter.

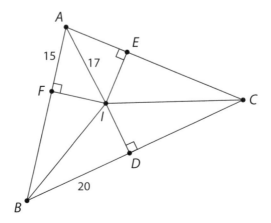

*continued*

# UNIT 6 • CIRCLES WITH AND WITHOUT COORDINATES
## Lesson 2: Inscribed Polygons and Circumscribed Triangles

7. Find the measure of ∠*BIC*. Assume that $\overline{BI}$ and $\overline{CI}$ are angle bisectors.

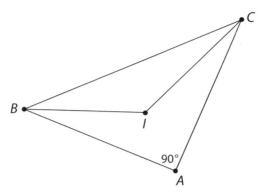

8. Find the measure of ∠*AIB*. Assume that $\overline{BI}$ and $\overline{AI}$ are angle bisectors.

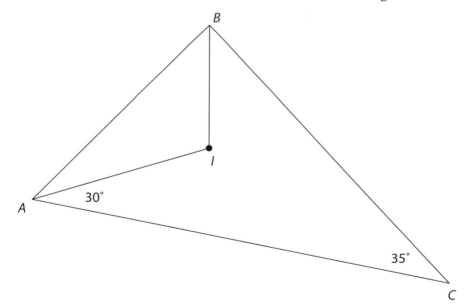

# UNIT 6 • CIRCLES WITH AND WITHOUT COORDINATES
## Lesson 2: Inscribed Polygons and Circumscribed Triangles

9.  Suppose that △*ABC* is equilateral and point *I* is the incenter. What is true about △*ABI* and △*ACI*? Support your answer.

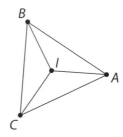

10.  Given the circle shown, construct a circumscribed triangle.

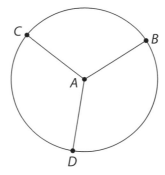

# Lesson 6.2.2: Constructing Circumscribed Circles

## Introduction

The owners of a radio station in Georgia want to build a new broadcasting building located within the triangle formed by the cities of Atlanta, Columbus, and Macon. Where should the station be built so that it is equidistant from each city? In this lesson, we will investigate the point that solves this problem and the geometry that supports it.

## Key Concepts

- To determine the location of the broadcasting building, the station owners would first need to determine the point at which the building would be equidistant from each of the three cities.

- To determine this point, the owners would need to find the perpendicular bisector of each of the sides of the triangle formed by the three cities.

- The **perpendicular bisector** of a segment is the segment that is perpendicular to a given segment and contains the midpoint of that segment.

- When all three perpendicular bisectors of a triangle are constructed, the rays intersect at one point.

- This point of concurrency is called the **circumcenter**.

- The circumcenter is equidistant from the three vertices of the triangle and is also the center of the circle that contains the three vertices of the triangle.

- A circle that contains all the vertices of a polygon is referred to as the **circumscribed circle**.

- When the circumscribed circle is constructed, the triangle is referred to as an **inscribed triangle**, a triangle whose vertices are on a circle.

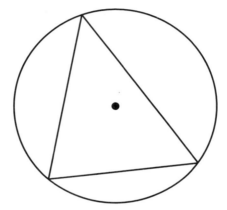

- To construct the circumscribed circle, determine the shortest distance from the circumcenter to each of the vertices of the triangle.

- Remember that the shortest distance from a point to a line or line segment is a perpendicular line.

- Follow the steps in the Guided Practice examples that follow to construct a perpendicular bisector in order to find the circumcenter of the triangle.

# Guided Practice 6.2.2

## Example 1

Verify that the perpendicular bisectors of acute $\triangle ABC$ are concurrent and that this concurrent point is equidistant from each vertex.

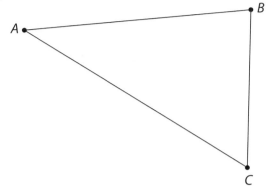

1. Construct the perpendicular bisector of $\overline{AB}$.

   Set the compass at point $A$ and swing an arc.

   Using the same radius, swing an arc from point $B$ so that the two arcs intersect.

   If they do not intersect, lengthen the radius for each arc.

   Connect the two intersections to locate the perpendicular bisector.

   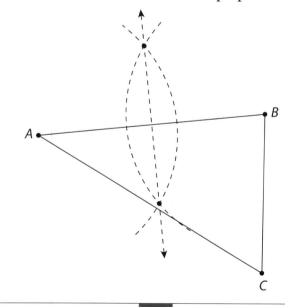

2. Repeat the process for $\overline{BC}$ and $\overline{AC}$.

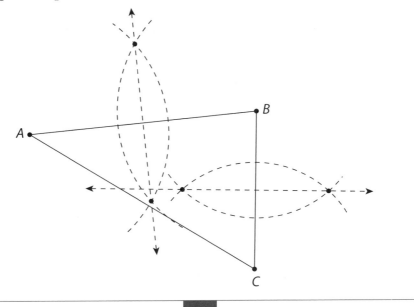

3. Locate the point of concurrency. Label this point $D$.

   The point of concurrency is where all three perpendicular bisectors meet.

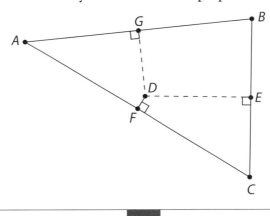

4. Verify that the point of concurrency is equidistant from each vertex.

   Use your compass and carefully measure the length from point $D$ to each vertex.

   The measurements are the same.

**Example 2**

Construct a circle circumscribed about acute $\triangle ABC$.

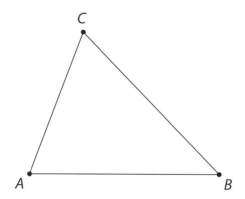

1.  Construct the perpendicular bisectors of each side.

    Use the same method as described in Example 1 to bisect each side.

    Label the point of concurrency of the perpendicular bisectors as point $D$.

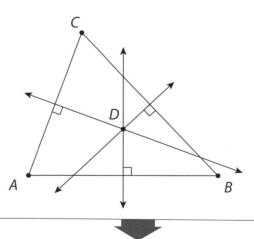

2. Verify that the point of concurrency is equidistant from each of the vertices.

   Use your compass and carefully measure the length of each perpendicular from $D$ to each vertex.

   Verify that the measurements are the same.

3. Construct the circumscribed circle with center $D$.

   Place the compass point at $D$ and open the compass to the distance of $D$ to any vertex.

   Use this setting to construct a circle around $\triangle ABC$.

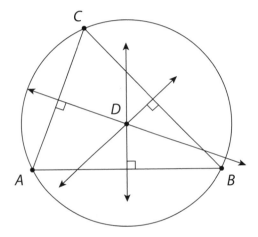

   Circle $D$ is circumscribed about $\triangle ABC$ and each vertex is tangent to the circle.

# Example 3

Construct a circle circumscribed about obtuse $\triangle ABC$.

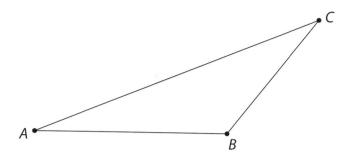

1. Construct the perpendicular bisectors of each side.

   Use the same method as described in Example 1 to bisect each side.

   Label the point of concurrency of the perpendicular bisectors as point $D$.

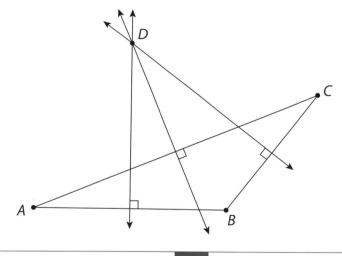

2. Verify that the point of concurrency is equidistant from each of the vertices.

   Use your compass and carefully measure the length of each perpendicular from $D$ to each vertex.

   Verify that the measurements are the same.

3. Construct the circumscribed circle with center $D$.

   Place the compass point at $D$ and open the compass to the distance of $D$ to any vertex.

   Use this setting to construct a circle around $\triangle ABC$.

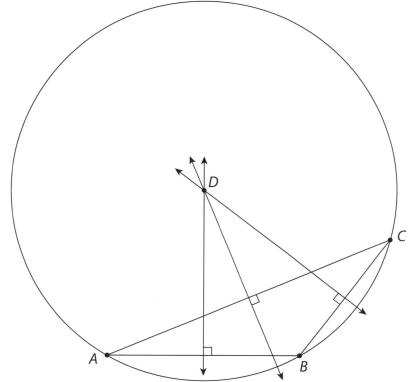

   Circle $D$ is circumscribed about $\triangle ABC$ and each vertex is tangent to the circle.

# UNIT 6 • CIRCLES WITH AND WITHOUT COORDINATES
## Lesson 2: Inscribed Polygons and Circumscribed Triangles

## Practice 6.2.2: Constructing Circumscribed Circles

Construct the circumscribed circle for each of the triangles in problems 1–3.

1.

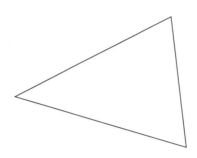

2.

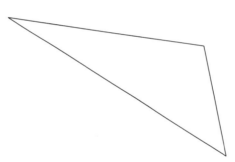

3.

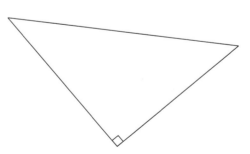

*continued*

# UNIT 6 • CIRCLES WITH AND WITHOUT COORDINATES
## Lesson 2: Inscribed Polygons and Circumscribed Triangles

Use what you've learned and the diagrams, when provided, to complete problems 4–10.

4. Where is the circumcenter in a right triangle? Is this true for all right triangles?

5. Jane, Keith, and Lee are shopping at a mall. The halls are arranged in a star shape, as shown in the diagram. The friends' locations are marked on the diagram. Through texting, they arrange to meet up so they can grab a cinnamon bun. Where should they meet so that each person has the same distance to walk?

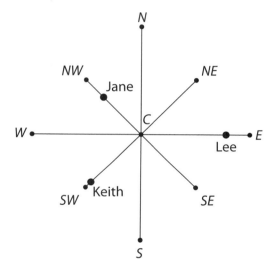

6. Assume that point $C$ is the circumcenter for $\triangle ABD$. What is the length of $\overline{AB}$?

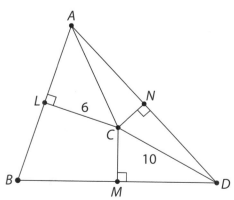

*continued*

# UNIT 6 • CIRCLES WITH AND WITHOUT COORDINATES
## Lesson 2: Inscribed Polygons and Circumscribed Triangles

7.  In planning a new technology building for a college, an architect needs to make sure that the server for the computer network will be in a room that is equidistant from three computer labs. In which room should the server be placed?

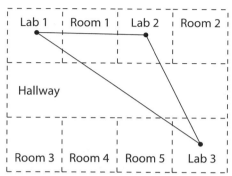

8.  Can the circumcenter of a triangle ever be located outside of the triangle? Explain your reasoning.

9.  Is it possible for the incenter to be the same point as the circumcenter? Why or why not? If it is possible, what type(s) of triangle would fit this criterion? Consider your responses to problems 1 through 3 in determining your answer.

10. Describe a method to verify the center of the circle below. Then, carry out your plan.

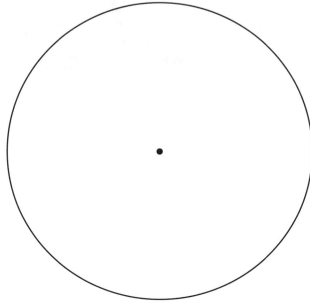

## Lesson 6.2.3: Proving Properties of Inscribed Quadrilaterals

## Introduction

One of the most famous drawings of all time is Leonardo da Vinci's Vitruvian Man. Da Vinci's sketch was of a man enclosed by a circle that touched the man's feet and hands. In this lesson, we will investigate the properties of quadrilaterals inscribed in a circle.

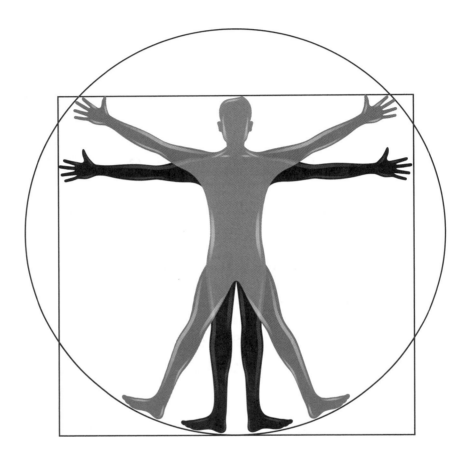

## Key Concepts

- An **inscribed quadrilateral** is a quadrilateral whose vertices are on a circle.

- The opposite angles of an inscribed quadrilateral are supplementary.

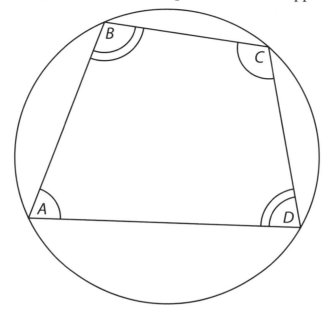

- $m\angle A + m\angle C = 180$

- $m\angle B + m\angle D = 180$

- Remember that the measure of an inscribed angle is half the measure of the intercepted arc.

- Rectangles and squares can always be inscribed within a circle.

# Guided Practice 6.2.3

## Example 1

Consider the inscribed quadrilateral in the following diagram. What are the relationships between the measures of the angles of an inscribed quadrilateral?

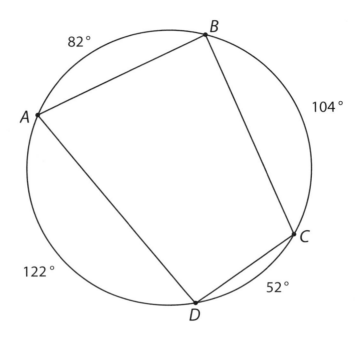

1. Find the measure of $\angle B$.

   $\angle B$ is an inscribed angle. Therefore, its measure will be equal to half the measure of the intercepted arc.

   The intercepted arc $\overset{\frown}{ADC}$ has a measure of $122 + 52$, or $174°$.

   The measure of $\angle B$ is $\dfrac{1}{2}$ of 174, or $87°$.

2. Find the measure of $\angle D$.

The intercepted arc $\overset{\frown}{ABC}$ has a measure of $82 + 104$, or $186°$.

The measure of $\angle D$ is $\dfrac{1}{2}$ of 186, or $93°$.

3. What is the relationship between $\angle B$ and $\angle D$?

Since the sum of the measures of $\angle B$ and $\angle D$ equals $180°$, $\angle B$ and $\angle D$ are supplementary angles.

4. Does this same relationship exist between $\angle A$ and $\angle C$?

The intercepted arc $\overset{\frown}{BCD}$ has a measure of $104 + 52$, or $156°$.

The measure of $\angle A$ is $\dfrac{1}{2}$ of 156, or $78°$.

The intercepted arc $\overset{\frown}{BAD}$ has a measure of $82 + 122$, or $204°$.

The measure of $\angle C$ is $\dfrac{1}{2}$ of 204, or $102°$.

The sum of the measures of $\angle A$ and $\angle C$ also equals $180°$; therefore, $\angle A$ and $\angle C$ are supplementary.

5. State your conclusion.

The opposite angles of an inscribed quadrilateral are supplementary.

## Example 2

Consider the inscribed quadrilateral below. Do the relationships discovered between the angles in Example 1 still hold for the angles in this quadrilateral?

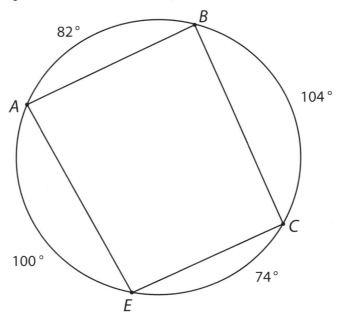

1. Calculate the measures of all four angles of quadrilateral *ABCE*.

   $\angle A$ intercepts $\overset{\frown}{BCE}$, so the measure of $\angle A$ is half the measure of $\overset{\frown}{BCE}$.

   $$m\angle A = \frac{1}{2}(104+74)=89$$

   $\angle B$ intercepts $\overset{\frown}{AEC}$, so the measure of $\angle B$ is half the measure of $\overset{\frown}{AEC}$.

   $$m\angle B = \frac{1}{2}(100+74)=87$$

   $\angle C$ intercepts $\overset{\frown}{BAE}$, so the measure of $\angle C$ is half the measure of $\overset{\frown}{BAE}$.

   $$m\angle C = \frac{1}{2}(100+82)=91$$

   $\angle E$ intercepts $\overset{\frown}{ABC}$, so the measure of $\angle E$ is half the measure of $\overset{\frown}{ABC}$.

   $$m\angle E = \frac{1}{2}(104+82)=93$$

2. Find the sum of the measures of $\angle A$ and $\angle C$.

   The sum of the measures of $\angle A$ and $\angle C$ is equal to $89 + 91 = 180$.

3. State your conclusion.

   The measures of $\angle A$ and $\angle C$ sum to $180°$, as do the measures of $\angle B$ and $\angle E$; therefore, it is still true that opposite angles of an inscribed quadrilateral are supplementary.

## Example 3

Prove that the opposite angles of the given inscribed quadrilateral are supplementary.

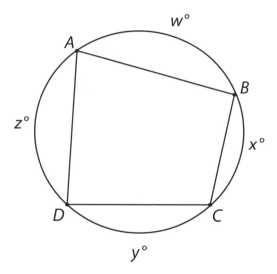

1. What is the sum of $w° + x° + y° + z°$?

   Together, the arcs create a circle that measures $360°$; therefore, the sum of the arc measures is 360.

2. Find the measure of each angle of quadrilateral $ABCD$.

$$m\angle A = \frac{1}{2}(x+y) \qquad m\angle C = \frac{1}{2}(w+z)$$

$$m\angle B = \frac{1}{2}(x+z) \qquad m\angle D = \frac{1}{2}(w+x)$$

3. Find the sum of the measures of $\angle A$ and $\angle C$.

$$m\angle A + m\angle C = \frac{1}{2}(x+y) + \frac{1}{2}(w+z)$$

$$= \frac{1}{2}(x+y+w+z)$$

$$= \frac{1}{2}(360) = 180$$

4. Find the sum of the measures of $\angle B$ and $\angle D$.

$$m\angle B + m\angle D = \frac{1}{2}(y+z) + \frac{1}{2}(w+x)$$

$$= \frac{1}{2}(y+z+w+z)$$

$$= \frac{1}{2}(360) = 180$$

5. State your conclusion.

$m\angle A + m\angle C = 180$ and $m\angle B + m\angle D = 180$. Therefore, each pair of opposite angles of an inscribed quadrilateral is supplementary.

## Practice 6.2.3: Proving Properties of Inscribed Quadrilaterals

Use the provided diagrams and your knowledge of the properties of inscribed quadrilaterals to complete problems 1–5.

1. Find the values of $x$ and $y$.

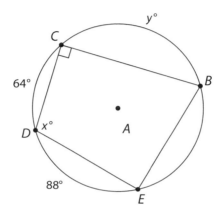

2. Find the values of $k$ and $n$.

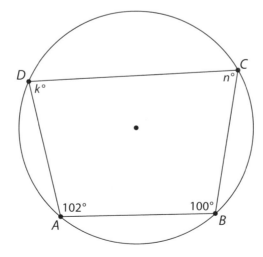

# UNIT 6 • CIRCLES WITH AND WITHOUT COORDINATES
## Lesson 2: Inscribed Polygons and Circumscribed Triangles

3.  Are any two sides of the inscribed quadrilateral parallel? If so, which? Support your answer.

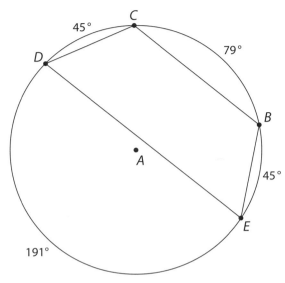

4.  Construct a square inscribed in the innermost circle. Is the new square similar to the original square? Why or why not?

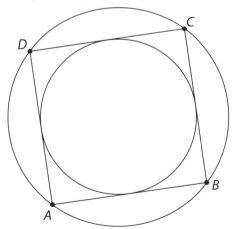

*continued*

5.  Is the quadrilateral below a parallelogram? Why or why not?

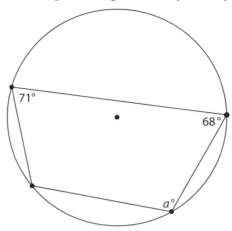

Use the figure below to complete problems 6–8.

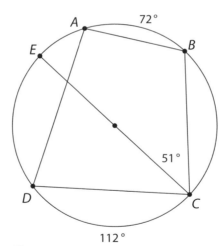

6.  Find the measure of $\overparen{AE}$.

7.  Find the measure of $\angle A$.

8.  Find the measure of $\angle D$.

# UNIT 6 • CIRCLES WITH AND WITHOUT COORDINATES
## Lesson 2: Inscribed Polygons and Circumscribed Triangles

Use your knowledge of inscribed quadrilaterals to complete problems 9 and 10.

9. Is it possible for a kite to be inscribed in a circle? Why or why not?

10. If a rectangle is inscribed in a circle, each diagonal also serves another function. What is this function?

# Lesson 3: Constructing Tangent Lines

## Common Core State Standard

**G–C.4**   (+) Construct a tangent line from a point outside a given circle to the circle.

## Essential Questions

1.  What is the relationship between a line tangent to a circle and the radius at the point of tangency?

2.  If two lines are tangent to the same circle and are drawn from the same exterior point, what must be true about the two lines?

3.  What are some representations of tangent lines in the real world?

## WORDS TO KNOW

| | |
|---|---|
| **common external tangent** | a tangent that is common to two circles and does not intersect the segment joining the radii of the circles |
| **common internal tangent** | a tangent that is common to two circles and intersects the segment joining the radii of the circles |
| **common tangent** | a line tangent to two circles |
| **point of tangency** | the only point at which a line and a circle intersect |
| **tangent line** | a line that intersects a circle at exactly one point and is perpendicular to the radius of the circle |

# Recommended Resources

- IXL Learning. "Circles: Tangent lines."

  http://www.walch.com/rr/00054

  This website provides a user-friendly, interactive review of tangent properties. Immediate scoring is provided and if a wrong answer is submitted, the process for arriving at the correct answer is provided. These problems start with right triangle tangent problems, stressing the importance of knowing that a tangent must be perpendicular to a radius at the point of tangency.

- Math Open Reference. "Tangent to a circle at a point."

  http://www.walch.com/rr/00055

  This site provides step-by-step animated instructions for constructing a tangent to a circle from a point on the circle.

- Math Open Reference. "Tangents through an external point."

  http://www.walch.com/rr/00056

  This site provides step-by-step animated instructions for constructing a tangent to a circle from an external point not on the circle.

# Lesson 6.3.1: Constructing Tangent Lines

## Introduction

Tangent lines are useful in calculating distances as well as diagramming in the professions of construction, architecture, and landscaping. Geometry construction tools can be used to create lines tangent to a circle. As with other constructions, the only tools you are allowed to use are a compass and a straightedge, a reflective device and a straightedge, or patty paper and a straightedge. You may be tempted to measure angles or lengths, but remember, this is not allowed with constructions.

## Key Concepts

- If a line is tangent to a circle, it is perpendicular to the radius drawn to the **point of tangency,** the only point at which a line and a circle intersect.

- Exactly one tangent line can be constructed by using construction tools to create a line perpendicular to the radius at a point on the circle.

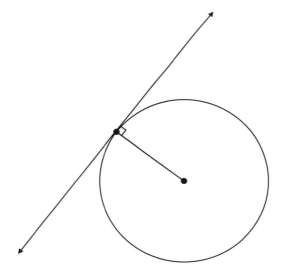

## Constructing a Tangent at a Point on a Circle Using a Compass

1. Use a straightedge to draw a ray from center $O$ through the given point $P$. Be sure the ray extends past point $P$.

2. Construct the line perpendicular to $\overrightarrow{OP}$ at point $P$. This is the same procedure as constructing a perpendicular line to a point on a line.

   a. Put the sharp point of the compass on $P$ and open the compass less wide than the distance of $\overline{OP}$.

   b. Draw an arc on both sides of $P$ on $\overrightarrow{OP}$. Label the points of intersection $A$ and $B$.

   c. Set the sharp point of the compass on $A$. Open the compass wider than the distance of $\overline{AB}$ and make a large arc.

   d. Without changing your compass setting, put the sharp point of the compass on $B$. Make a second large arc. It is important that the arcs intersect each other.

3. Use your straightedge to connect the points of intersection of the arcs.

4. Label the new line $m$.

Do not erase any of your markings.

Line $m$ is tangent to circle $O$ at point $P$.

- It is also possible to construct a tangent line from an exterior point not on a circle.

- Exactly two lines can be constructed that are tangent to the circle through an exterior point not on the circle.

- If two segments are tangent to the same circle, and originate from the same exterior point, then the segments are congruent.

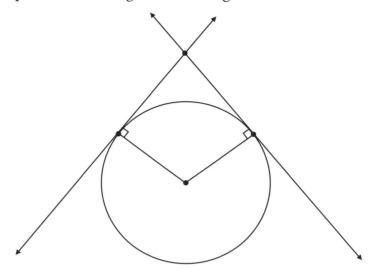

**Constructing a Tangent from an Exterior Point Not on a Circle Using a Compass**

1.  To construct a line tangent to circle $O$ from an exterior point not on the circle, first use a straightedge to draw a ray connecting center $O$ and the given point $R$.

2.  Find the midpoint of $\overline{OR}$ by constructing the perpendicular bisector.

    a.  Put the sharp point of your compass on point $O$. Open the compass wider than half the distance of $\overline{OR}$.

    b.  Make a large arc intersecting $\overline{OR}$.

    c.  Without changing your compass setting, put the sharp point of the compass on point $R$. Make a second large arc. It is important that the arcs intersect each other. Label the points of intersection of the arcs as $C$ and $D$.

    d.  Use your straightedge to connect points $C$ and $D$.

    e.  The point where $\overline{CD}$ intersects $\overline{OR}$ is the midpoint of $\overline{OR}$. Label this point $F$.

3.  Put the sharp point of the compass on midpoint $F$ and open the compass to point $O$.

*(continued)*

4. Without changing the compass setting, draw an arc across the circle so it intersects the circle in two places. Label the points of intersection as $G$ and $H$.

5. Use a straightedge to draw a line from point $R$ to point $G$ and a second line from point $R$ to point $H$.

Do not erase any of your markings.

$\overleftrightarrow{RG}$ and $\overleftrightarrow{RH}$ are tangent to circle $O$.

- If two circles do not intersect, they can share a tangent line, called a **common tangent**.

- Two circles that do not intersect have four common tangents.

- Common tangents can be either internal or external.

- A **common internal tangent** is a tangent that is common to two circles and intersects the segment joining the radii of the circles.

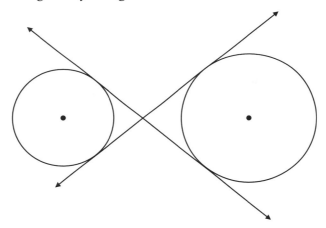

- A **common external tangent** is a tangent that is common to two circles and does not intersect the segment joining the radii of the circles.

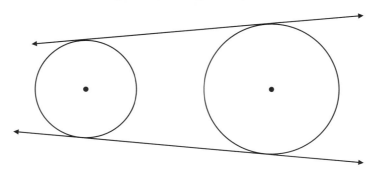

# Guided Practice 6.3.1

## Example 1

Use a compass and a straightedge to construct $\overline{BC}$ tangent to circle $A$ at point $B$.

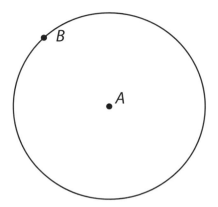

1. Draw a ray from center $A$ through point $B$ and extending beyond point $B$.

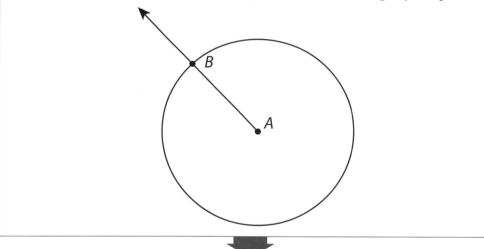

2. Put the sharp point of the compass on point B. Set it to any setting less than the length of $\overline{AB}$, and then draw an arc on either side of B, creating points D and E.

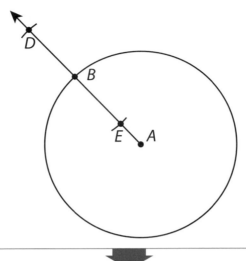

3. Put the sharp point of the compass on point D and set it to a width greater than the distance of $\overrightarrow{DB}$. Make a large arc intersecting $\overrightarrow{AB}$.

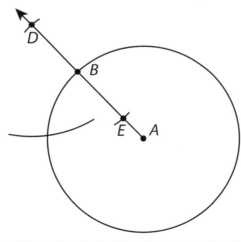

4. Without changing the compass setting, put the sharp point of the compass on point $E$ and draw a second arc that intersects the first. Label the point of intersection with the arc drawn in step 3 as point $C$.

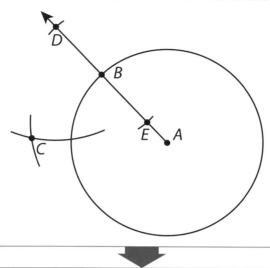

5. Draw a line connecting points $C$ and $B$, creating tangent $\overleftrightarrow{BC}$.

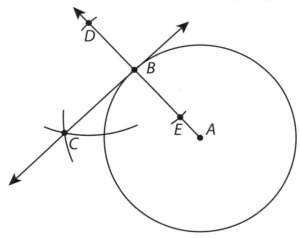

Do not erase any of your markings.

$\overleftrightarrow{BC}$ is tangent to circle $A$ at point $B$.

## Example 2

Using the circle and tangent line from Example 1, construct two additional tangent lines, so that circle A below will be inscribed in a triangle.

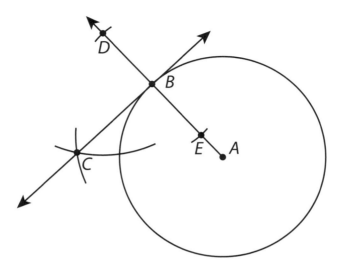

1.  Choose a point, *G*, on circle *A*.

    (*Note*: To highlight the essential ideas of this example, some features of the above diagram have been removed.)

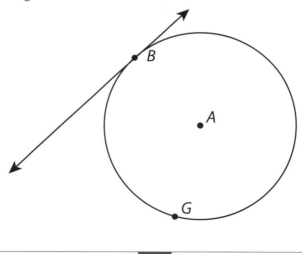

2. Draw a ray from center *A* to point *G*.

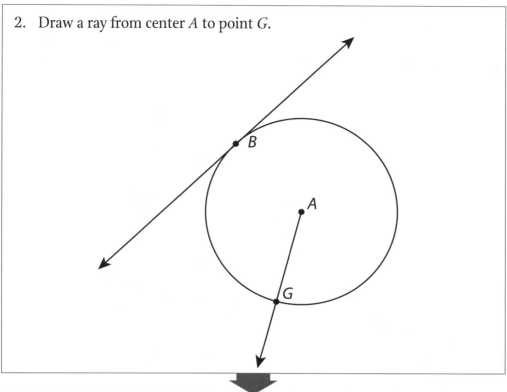

3. Follow the process explained in Example 1 for constructing a tangent line through point *G*.

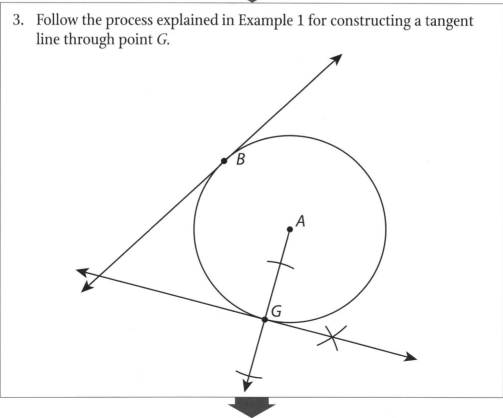

4.  Choose another point, *H*, on circle *A*. Draw a ray from center *A* to point *H*, and follow the process explained in Example 1 to construct the third tangent line. Be sure to draw the tangent lines long enough to intersect one another.

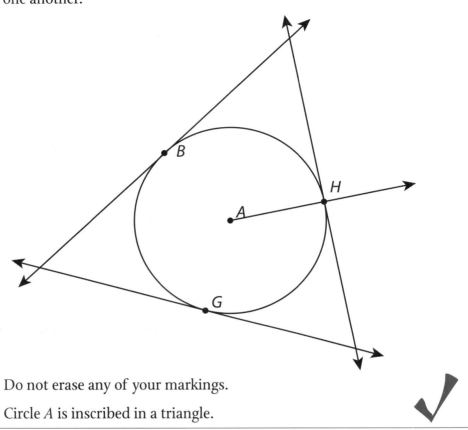

Do not erase any of your markings.

Circle *A* is inscribed in a triangle.

## Example 3

Use a compass and a straightedge to construct the lines tangent to circle $C$ at point $D$.

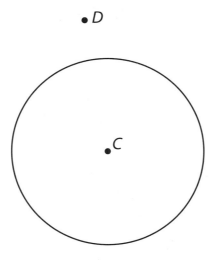

1. Draw a ray connecting center $C$ and the given point $D$.

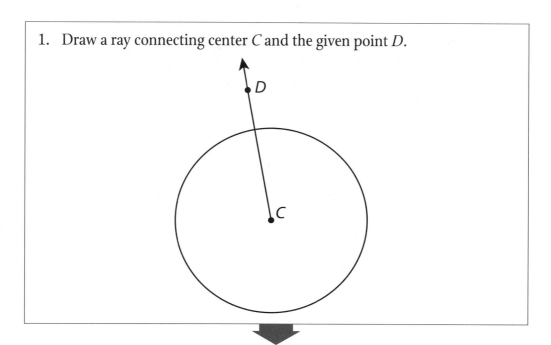

2. Find the midpoint of $\overline{CD}$ by constructing the perpendicular bisector.

Put the sharp point of your compass on point C. Open the compass wider than half the distance of $\overline{CD}$. Make a large arc intersecting $\overline{CD}$.

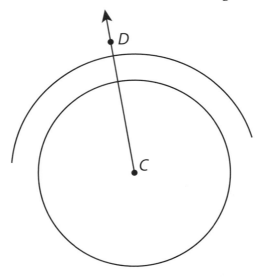

Without changing your compass setting, put the sharp point of the compass on point D. Make a second large arc. It is important that the arcs intersect each other. Label the points of intersection of the arcs as E and F.

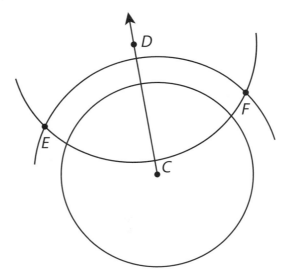

(*continued*)

Use your straightedge to connect points $E$ and $F$. The point where $\overline{EF}$ intersects $\overline{CD}$ is the midpoint of $\overline{CD}$. Label this point $G$.

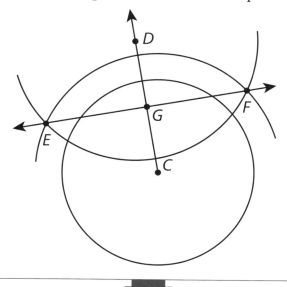

3. Put the sharp point of the compass on midpoint $G$ and open the compass to point $C$. Without changing the compass setting, draw an arc across the circle so it intersects the circle in two places. Label the points of intersection as $H$ and $J$.

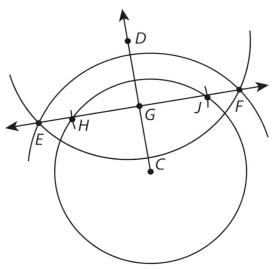

4. Use a straightedge to draw a line from point $D$ to point $H$ and a second line from point $D$ to point $J$.

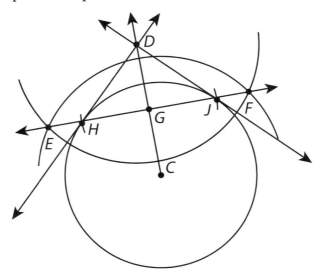

Do not erase any of your markings.

$\overleftrightarrow{DH}$ and $\overleftrightarrow{DF}$ are both tangent to circle $C$.

## Example 4

Circle $A$ and circle $B$ are congruent. Construct a line tangent to both circle $A$ and circle $B$.

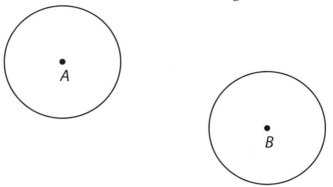

1. Use a straightedge to connect $A$ and $B$, the centers of the circles.

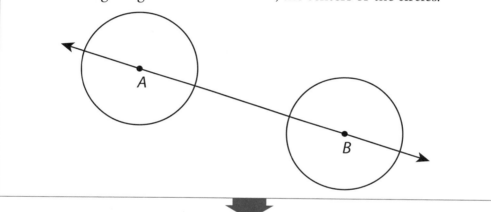

2. At center point $A$, construct a line perpendicular to $\overline{AB}$. Label the point of intersection with circle $A$ as point $D$.

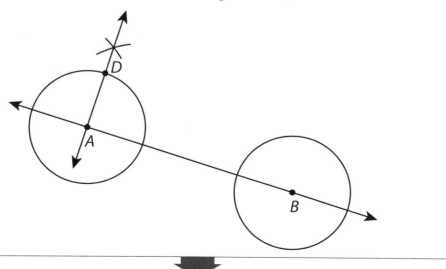

3.  At center point $B$, construct a line perpendicular to $\overline{AB}$. Label the point of intersection with circle $B$ as point $E$.

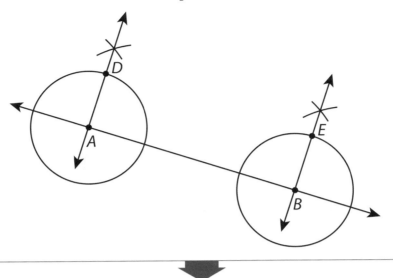

4.  Use a straightedge to connect points $D$ and $E$.

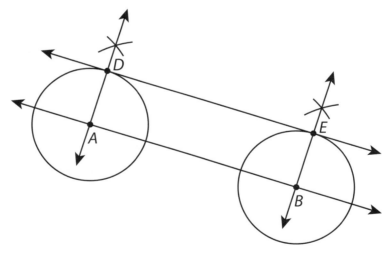

Do not erase any of your markings.

$\overleftrightarrow{DE}$ is tangent to circle $A$ and circle $B$.

# UNIT 6 • CIRCLES WITH AND WITHOUT COORDINATES
## Lesson 3: Constructing Tangent Lines

## Practice 6.3.1: Constructing Tangent Lines

Use your knowledge of constructions to complete each problem that follows.

1. Construct circle *F* given point *G* on the circle. Construct a line tangent to circle *F* at point *G*.

2. Construct circle *H* given point *J* not on the circle. Construct a line tangent to circle *H* through point *J*.

3. Construct two non-intersecting circles with congruent radii. Construct one common interior tangent.

4. $\overline{AB}$ is tangent to circle *G* at point *B*. Point *A* is on circle *G*. What was the first step that had to be completed to construct tangent $\overline{AB}$?

5. $\overline{GH}$ is tangent to circle *F* in the diagram below. In order to construct tangent $\overline{GH}$, a perpendicular bisector first had to be constructed. Describe where the perpendicular bisector was constructed.

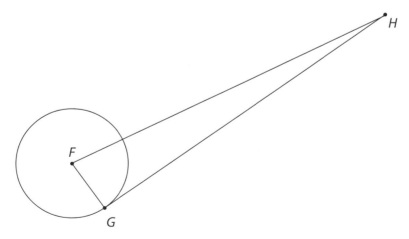

# UNIT 6 • CIRCLES WITH AND WITHOUT COORDINATES
## Lesson 3: Constructing Tangent Lines

6. Quadrilateral *PQRS* is circumscribed about a circle as shown below. Each line of the quadrilateral is tangent to the circle at the points in the diagram. What was the first step in making this construction?

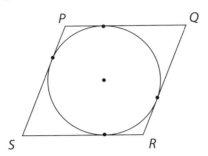

7. A student says $\overline{LM}$ is tangent to circle *N* at point *L* in the diagram below. How can the student use construction tools to verify this?

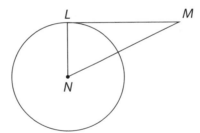

8. $\overline{KL}$ is tangent to circle *J* in the diagram below. Where could the sharp edge of the compass have been positioned to make one of the arcs that formed point *L*?

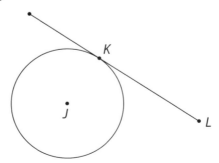

*continued*

# UNIT 6 • CIRCLES WITH AND WITHOUT COORDINATES
## Lesson 3: Constructing Tangent Lines

9. Construct circle $B$. Place three points on circle $B$ and construct the three tangent lines so the circle is inscribed in the triangle.

10. $\triangle ABC$ is a right triangle. What conclusions can you draw about the construction of the diagram below?

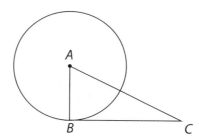

# Lesson 4: Finding Arc Lengths and Areas of Sectors

## Common Core State Standard

**G–C.5** Derive using similarity the fact that the length of the arc intercepted by an angle is proportional to the radius, and define the radian measure of the angle as the constant of proportionality; derive the formula for the area of a sector.

## Essential Questions

1. How is radian measure related to degree measure?
2. How is an arc length related to the circumference of a circle?
3. How is the area of a sector related to the area of a circle?

## WORDS TO KNOW

| | |
|---|---|
| **arc length** | the distance between the endpoints of an arc; written as $m\overset{\frown}{AB}$ |
| **central angle** | an angle with its vertex at the center of a circle |
| **circumference** | the distance around a circle; $C = 2\pi r$ or $C = \pi d$, for which $C$ represents circumference, $r$ represents the circle's radius, and $d$ represents the circle's diameter |
| **radian** | the measure of the central angle that intercepts an arc equal in length to the radius of the circle; $\pi$ radians = 180° |
| **radian measure** | the ratio of the arc intercepted by the central angle to the radius of the circle |
| **sector** | a portion of a circle bounded by two radii and their intercepted arc |

# Recommended Resources

- IXL Learning. "Circles: Arc measure and arc length."

  http://www.walch.com/rr/00057

  This interactive website gives a series of problems and scores them immediately. If the user submits a wrong answer, a description and process for arriving at the correct answer are provided. These problems start with a diagram of a circle with a given radius. Users are given an arc measure in degrees and are asked to find the length of the arc.

- IXL Learning. "Circles: Area of sectors."

  http://www.walch.com/rr/00058

  This interactive website also gives a series of problems and scores them immediately, providing instant feedback if a wrong answer is submitted. These problems start with a diagram of a circle with a given radius. Users are given a sector with a central angle measure in degrees and are asked to find the area of the sector.

- Math Open Reference. "Arc Length."

  http://www.walch.com/rr/00059

  This site gives a brief overview of how to calculate the arc length of a circle and provides a virtual manipulative to experiment with choosing different arc lengths. The equation is updated in real time, allowing users to see what changes in the equation and what remains the same.

- Problems with a Point. "Spinning wheel 1."

  http://www.walch.com/rr/00060

  This sequence of problems introduces the concept of a radian through an application problem about a bicycle wheel. Users are asked a series of questions to explore the meaning of radian measure. Users are then offered hints to discover how to convert between radian measure and degree measure. Answers are provided at the bottom of the webpage.

- TeacherTube. "Geo Screencast: Arc Length."

  http://www.walch.com/rr/00061

  This video explains how to find arc length given the radius of the circle and the degree measure of the central angle.

- TeacherTube. "Geo Screencast: Sector Area."

  http://www.walch.com/rr/00062

  This video offers a tutorial on how to find the area of a sector given the radius of the circle and the degree measure of the central angle.

- Texas Instruments. "Radian Measure."

  http://www.walch.com/rr/00063

  This lesson plan for an activity on the TI-Nspire guides users through a discovery lesson in which they learn how the intercepted arc is related to the central angle and the radius of the circle.

# Lesson 6.4.1: Defining Radians

## Introduction

All circles are similar; thus, so are the arcs intercepting congruent angles in circles. A central angle is an angle with its vertex at the center of a circle. We have measured an arc in terms of the central angle that it intercepts, but we can also measure the length of an arc. **Arc length**, the distance between the endpoints of an arc, is proportional to the radius of the circle according to the central angle that the arc intercepts. The constant of proportionality is the radian measure of the angle. You already know how to measure angles in degrees. Radian measure is another way to measure angles. An angle measure given in degrees includes a degree symbol. An angle measure given in radians does not.

## Key Concepts

- Arc length is the distance between the endpoints of an arc, and is commonly written as $m\overset{\frown}{AB}$.

- The **radian measure** of a central angle is the ratio of the length of the arc intercepted by the angle to the radius of the circle.

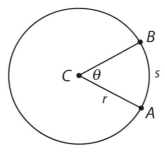

- The definition of radian measure leads us to a formula for the radian measure of a central angle $\theta$ in terms of the intercepted arc length, $s$, and the radius of the circle, $r$: $\theta = \dfrac{s}{r}$.

- When the intercepted arc is equal in length to the radius of the circle, the central angle measures 1 **radian**.

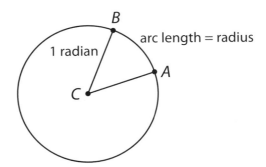

- Recall that the circumference, or the distance around a circle, is given by $C = 2\pi r$ or $C = \pi d$, where $C$ represents circumference, $r$ represents radius, and $d$ represents the circle's diameter.
- Since the ratio of the arc length of the entire circle to the radius of the circle is $\dfrac{2\pi r}{r} = 2\pi$, there are $2\pi$ radians in a full circle.
- We know that a circle contains $360°$ or $2\pi$ radians. We can convert between radian measure and degree measure by simplifying this ratio to get $\pi$ radians $= 180°$.

- To convert between radian measure and degree measure, set up a proportion.

$$\frac{\text{radian measure}}{\pi} = \frac{\text{degree measure}}{180°}$$

- To find the arc length when the central angle is given in radians, use the formula for radian measure to solve for $s$.

- To find arc length $s$ when the central angle is given in degrees, we determine the fraction of the circle that we want to find using the measure of the angle. Set up a proportion with the circumference, $C$.

$$\frac{s}{C} = \frac{\text{degree measure}}{360°}$$

# Guided Practice 6.4.1

## Example 1

Convert 40° to radians.

1. Set up a proportion.

$$\frac{\text{radian measure}}{\pi} = \frac{\text{degree measure}}{180°}$$

$$\frac{x}{\pi} = \frac{40°}{180°}$$

2. Multiply both sides by $\pi$ to solve for $x$.

$$x = \frac{40\pi}{180} = \frac{2\pi}{9} \text{ radians}$$

## Example 2

Convert $\dfrac{3\pi}{4}$ radians to degrees.

1. Set up a proportion.

$$\frac{\text{radian measure}}{\pi} = \frac{\text{degree measure}}{180°}$$

$$\frac{\frac{3\pi}{4}}{\pi} = \frac{x}{180°}$$

$$\frac{3}{4} = \frac{x}{180°}$$

2. Multiply both sides by 180 to solve for $x$.

$$x = \frac{3(180)}{4} = 135°$$

## Example 3

A circle has a radius of 4 units. Find the radian measure of a central angle that intercepts an arc of length 10.8 units.

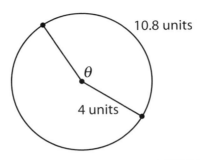

1. Substitute the known values into the formula for radian measure.

$$\theta = \frac{\text{arc length}}{\text{radius}} = \frac{s}{r} = \frac{10.8}{4}$$

2. Simplify.

$\theta = 2.7$ radians

The radian measure is 2.7 radians.

## Example 4

A circle has a radius of 3.8 units. Find the length of an arc intercepted by a central angle measuring 2.1 radians.

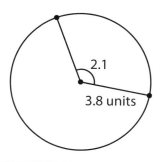

1. Substitute the known values into the formula for radian measure.

$$\theta = \frac{\text{arc length}}{\text{radius}} = \frac{s}{r}$$

$$2.1 = \frac{s}{3.8}$$

2. Multiply both sides by 3.8 to solve for arc length.

$$s = 2.1 \bullet 3.8 = 7.98 \text{ units}$$

The arc length is 7.98 units.

## Example 5

A circle has a diameter of 20 feet. Find the length of an arc intercepted by a central angle measuring 36°.

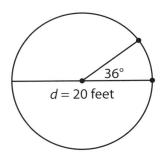

1. Find the circumference of the circle.

   circumference = $\pi$ • diameter

   $C = \pi d = 20\pi$ feet

2. Set up a proportion.

   $$\frac{\text{arc length}}{\text{circumference}} = \frac{\text{degree measure}}{360°}$$

   $$\frac{s}{C} = \frac{\text{degree measure}}{360°}$$

   $$\frac{s}{20\pi} = \frac{36}{360}$$

3. Multiply both sides by $20\pi$ to find the arc length.

   $$s = \frac{36}{360} \bullet 20\pi = \frac{1}{10} \bullet 20\pi = 2\pi \text{ feet} \approx 6.28 \text{ feet}$$

   The length of the arc is approximately 6.28 feet.

## Practice 6.4.1: Defining Radians

Use your knowledge of radian measures to complete the following problems.

1. Convert 260° to radians.

2. Convert 4.9 radians to degrees. Round your answer to the nearest tenth of a degree.

3. A circle has a radius of 2 units. Find the radian measure of a central angle that intercepts an arc length of 5.8 units.

4. A circle has a diameter of 14 units. Find the length of an arc intercepted by a central angle measuring 4 radians.

5. A circle has a radius of 21 units. To the nearest degree, what is the measure of a central angle that intercepts an arc length of 50.4 units?

6. A central angle of 62° intercepts an arc length of 90 units. What is the radius of the circle, rounded to the nearest hundredth?

7. A Ferris wheel has 16 seats and a diameter of 60 feet. The wheel lets off the passengers in one seat, and then revolves until the next seat is at the platform. Approximately how far does each seat travel in this time?

8. How many radians does the hour hand on a clock travel through from 2 to 10?

9. A 20-inch diameter bicycle tire rotates 300 times. How many feet does the bicycle travel?

10. In your own words, what is a radian?

# Lesson 6.4.2: Deriving the Formula for the Area of a Sector

## Introduction

A **sector** is the portion of a circle bounded by two radii and their intercepted arc. Previously, we thought of arc length as a fraction of the circumference of the circle. In a similar way, we can think of a sector as a fraction of the area of the circle. In the same way that we found arc length, we can set up proportions to find the area of a sector.

## Key Concepts

- A sector is the portion of a circle bounded by two radii and their intercepted arc.

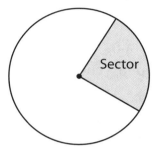

- To find the area of a sector, $A_{sector}$, when the central angle $\theta$ is given in radians, we can set up a proportion using the area of a circle, $A = \pi r^2$.

$$\frac{A_{sector}}{\pi r^2} = \frac{\theta}{2\pi}$$

- We can solve this proportion for the area of the sector and simplify to get a formula for the area of a sector in terms of the radius of the circle and the radian measure of the central angle $\theta$.

$$A_{sector} = \frac{r^2 \theta}{2}$$

- To find the area of a sector when the central angle is given in degrees, we can set up a proportion using the area of a circle.

$$\frac{A_{sector}}{A_{circle}} = \frac{\text{degree measure}}{360°}$$

# Guided Practice 6.4.2

## Example 1

A circle has a radius of 24 units. Find the area of a sector with a central angle of 30°.

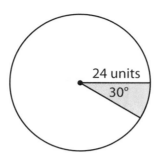

1. Find the area of the circle.

   area = $\pi \cdot$ radius$^2$

   $A = \pi r^2 = \pi \cdot 24^2 = 576\pi$ square units

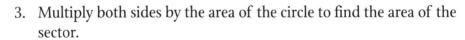

2. Set up a proportion.

   $$\frac{\text{degree measure of sector}}{360°} = \frac{\text{area of sector}}{\text{area of circle}}$$

   $$\frac{30°}{360°} = \frac{\text{area of sector}}{576\pi \text{ square units}}$$

3. Multiply both sides by the area of the circle to find the area of the sector.

   area of sector = $\dfrac{30°}{360°} \cdot 576\pi = 48\pi$ square units $\approx$ 150.80 square units

   The area of the sector is approximately 150.80 units$^2$.

## Example 2

A circle has a radius of 8 units. Find the area of a sector with a central angle of $\dfrac{3\pi}{4}$ radians.

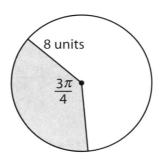

8 units

$\dfrac{3\pi}{4}$

---

1. Substitute radius and radian measure into the formula for the area of a sector.

$$\text{area of sector} = \frac{\text{radius}^2 \bullet \text{radian measure of angle}}{2}$$

$$A_{sector} = \frac{r^2\theta}{2} = \frac{8^2 \bullet \dfrac{3\pi}{4}}{2}$$

---

2. Simplify.

$$A_{sector} = \frac{8^2 \bullet \dfrac{3\pi}{4}}{2} = \frac{64 \bullet \dfrac{3\pi}{4}}{2} = \frac{48\pi}{2} = 24\pi \text{ square units} \approx$$

75.40 square units

The area of the sector is approximately 75.40 units².

---

# Example 3

A circle has a radius of 6 units. Find the area of a sector with an arc length of 9 units.

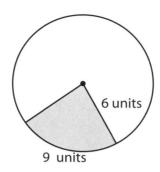

6 units

9 units

1. Use the radian measure formula to find the measure of the central angle.

$$\text{radian measure} = \frac{\text{arc length}}{\text{radius}}$$

$$\theta = \frac{s}{r} = \frac{9}{6} = 1.5 \text{ radians}$$

2. Substitute radius and radian measure into the formula for the area of a sector and simplify.

$$A_{\text{sector}} = \frac{r^2\theta}{2} = \frac{6^2 \cdot 1.5}{2} = \frac{54}{2} = 27 \text{ square units}$$

The area of the sector is 27 units$^2$.

# UNIT 6 • CIRCLES WITH AND WITHOUT COORDINATES
## Lesson 4: Finding Arc Lengths and Areas of Sectors

### Practice 6.4.2: Deriving the Formula for the Area of a Sector

Use your knowledge of the areas of sectors to complete the following problems.

1. Find the area of a sector with a central angle of 7.2 radians and a radius of 14 units.

2. Find the area of a sector with a central angle of $\dfrac{2\pi}{3}$ radians and a radius of 6 units.

3. Find the area of a sector with a central angle of 32° and a radius of 8.5 units.

4. A circle has a radius of 10.6 units. Find the area of a sector with an arc length of 15.9 units.

5. A circle has a radius of 4 units. Find the arc length of a sector with an area of 8 square units.

6. A sector has a central angle of $\dfrac{\pi}{4}$ radians and an area of 47 square units. What is the area of the circle?

7. A small pizza has a diameter of 10 inches. A slice has a central angle of $\dfrac{\pi}{3}$ radians. What is the area of the slice?

8. A pumpkin pie is made in a mini pie pan measuring 5 inches in diameter. It is cut into 4 equal slices. What is the area of 1 piece of pie?

9. A rotating sprinkler sprays a stream of water 32 feet long. The sprinkler rotates 220°. What is the area of the portion of the yard that is watered by the sprinkler?

10. An airplane emits a radar beam that can detect an object up to 70 miles away and covers an angle of 150°. What is the area of the region covered by the radar beam?

# Lesson 5: Explaining and Applying Area and Volume Formulas

## Common Core State Standards

**G–GMD.1**  Give an informal argument for the formulas for the circumference of a circle, area of a circle, volume of a cylinder, pyramid, and cone. *Use dissection arguments, Cavalieri's principle, and informal limit arguments.*

**G–GMD.3**  Use volume formulas for cylinders, pyramids, cones, and spheres to solve problems.★

## Essential Questions

1. How can you prove that the circumference of a circle equals $2\pi r$?

2. How can you prove that the area of a circle equals $\pi r^2$?

3. How can you use the formulas for a circle to solve real-world problems?

4. What is the formula for the volume of a cylinder, and how do you prove the formula?

5. What is the formula for the volume of a pyramid, and how do you prove the formula?

6. What is the formula for the volume of a cone, and how do you prove the formula?

7. What is the formula for the volume of a sphere, and how do you prove the formula?

## WORDS TO KNOW

| | |
|---|---|
| **Archimedes** | a Greek mathematician, physician, engineer, and inventor who lived from 287–212 B.C.; considered to be one of the greatest mathematicians of all time |
| **bisect** | to cut in half |
| **Cavalieri's Principle** | The volumes of two objects of equal height are equal if the areas of their corresponding cross sections are in all cases equal. |

| | |
|---|---|
| **cone** | a solid or hollow object that tapers from a circular or oval base to a point |
| **cylinder** | a solid or hollow object that has two parallel bases connected by a curved surface; the bases are usually circular |
| **dissection** | breaking a figure down into its components |
| **dodecagon** | a 12-sided polygon |
| **irrational number** | a number that cannot be written as $\dfrac{m}{n}$, where $m$ and $n$ are integers and $n \neq 0$; any number that cannot be written as a decimal that ends or repeats |
| **limit** | the value that a sequence approaches as a calculation becomes more and more accurate |
| **polyhedron** | a three-dimensional object that has faces made of polygons |
| **pyramid** | a solid or hollow polyhedron object that has three or more triangular faces that converge at a single vertex at the top; the base may be any polygon |
| **sphere** | a three-dimensional surface that has all its points the same distance from its center |

# Recommended Resources

- CutOutFoldUp.com. "The Volume of a Pyramid is One-Third that of a Prism."

  http://www.walch.com/rr/00065

  This website has many three-dimensional nets and projects for classroom use. The link here is for making prisms to show how a pyramid can contain three prisms.

- Math Open Reference. "Cylinder."

  http://www.walch.com/rr/00066

  At the top, use the interactive diagram of a cylinder to watch the volume change. Transform the right cylinder into an oblique cylinder, and see that the volume stays the same. Farther down the page, use the applet to see that a cylinder is a prism with an infinite number of faces. Click on the "more" link to add more faces and watch the prism transform to a cylinder.

- Math Open Reference. "Volume of a cone."

  http://www.walch.com/rr/00067

  Use the interactive diagram of a cone to see how the volume changes based on changing the height and/or radius of the cone.

- Math Open Reference. "Volume of a pyramid."

  http://www.walch.com/rr/00068

  Use the interactive diagram of a pyramid to see how the volume changes based on the height and base dimensions.

- Math Open Reference. "Volume of a sphere."

  http://www.walch.com/rr/00069

  Use the interactive diagram of a sphere to see how the volume changes based on the length of the sphere's radius.

- Roskes, Bonnie. "Dividing a Cube into Three Identical Pyramids using Google SketchUp."

  http://www.walch.com/rr/00070

  This video shows a cube being constructed with free geometry software. Three congruent pyramids are then created inside the cube.

# Lesson 6.5.1: Circumference and Area of a Circle

## Introduction

You have used the formulas for finding the circumference and area of a circle. In this lesson, you will prove why the formulas for circumference and area work. You will see how the ratio of $\pi$ can be proven.

## Key Concepts

- You know that the circumference of a specific circle divided by its diameter is the ratio *pi*, written as $\pi$.

- *Pi* ($\pi$) is an **irrational number** that cannot be written as a repeating decimal or as a fraction. It has an infinite number of non-repeating decimal places.

- We know that the circumference of a circle $= \pi \bullet$ diameter or $2\pi \bullet$ radius.

- Therefore, $\pi = \dfrac{\text{circumference}}{\text{diameter}} = \dfrac{\text{circumference}}{2 \bullet \text{radius}}$.

- Long ago, mathematicians didn't yet know the value of *pi*. **Archimedes**, a great mathematician from ancient Greece, used inscribed polygons to determine the value of *pi*. He started by inscribing a regular hexagon in a circle.

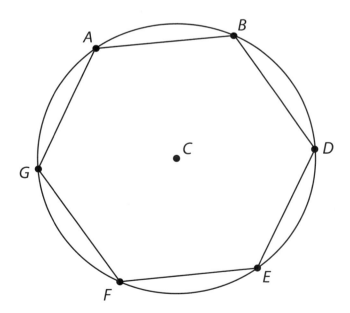

- He determined that each side of the hexagon equals the radius of the circle.

$$AB = BD = DE = EF = FG = GA = CE$$

- Archimedes realized that if the perimeter of the hexagon were equal to the circumference of the circle, then both would equal $6r$. This would mean that $\pi = 3$. However, the circumference is larger than the hexagon; therefore, Archimedes thought, $\pi$ must be larger than 3.

- Next, Archimedes inscribed a regular **dodecagon**—a 12-sided polygon—in the circle. The perimeter of the dodecagon was much closer to the actual perimeter of the circle.

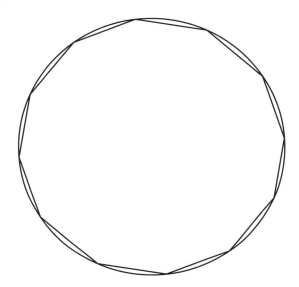

- He calculated the perimeter of the dodecagon to be approximately 6.21166. This means $\pi \approx 3.10583$. However, the circumference of the circle is still larger than the dodecagon, so $\pi$ must be greater than 3.10583.

- Next, Archimedes inscribed a 24-sided regular polygon and calculated its perimeter. This polygon's perimeter is even closer to the circumference of a circle. Archimedes found that the ratio of the perimeter to the diameter is closer to the value of $\pi$.

- Archimedes kept going with this process until he had inscribed a 48-sided polygon. As the number of sides of a polygon increases, the polygon looks more and more like a circle. As he worked, the number for the ratio of $\pi$ became more and more accurate. The more sides an inscribed polygon has, the closer its perimeter is to the actual circumference of the circle.

- Therefore, Archimedes determined that as the number of sides of a polygon inside a circle increases, the calculation approaches the limit for the value of $\pi$.

- A **limit** is the value that a sequence approaches as a calculation becomes more and more accurate. This limit cannot be reached.

- Theoretically, if the polygon had an infinite number of sides, $\pi$ could be calculated. This is the basis for the formula for finding the circumference of a circle.

- Increasing the number of side lengths for the inscribed polygon causes the polygon's perimeter to get closer and closer to the length of the circumference of the circle.

- The area of the circle can be derived similarly using dissection principles. **Dissection** involves breaking a figure down into its components.

- In the diagram that follows, a circle has been divided into four equal sections.

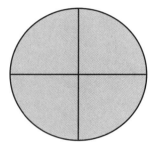

- If you cut the four sections from the circle apart, you can arrange them to resemble a rectangle.

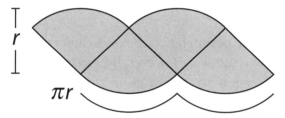

- The width of the "rectangle" equals the radius, $r$, of the original circle. The length is equal to half of the circumference, or $\pi \bullet r$.

- The circle in the diagram below has been divided into 16 equal sections.

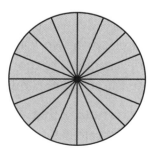

- You can arrange the 16 segments to form a new "rectangle."

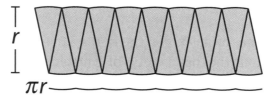

- This figure looks more like a rectangle.

- As the number of sections increases, the rounded "bumps" along its length and the "slant" of its width become less and less distinct. The figure will approach the limit of being a rectangle.

- The formula for the area of a rectangle is $l \cdot w = a$. The length of the rectangle made out of the circle segments is $\pi \cdot r$. The width is $r$. Thus, the area of the circle is $a = r \cdot \pi r = \pi r^2$. This proof is a dissection of the circle.

- Remember that a sector is the part of a circle that is enclosed by a central angle.

- A central angle has its vertex on the center of the circle. A sector will have an angular measure greater than 0° and less than 360°.

# Guided Practice 6.5.1

## Example 1

Show how the perimeter of a hexagon can be used to find an estimate for the circumference of a circle that has a radius of 5 meters. Compare the estimate with the circle's perimeter found by using the formula $C = 2\pi r$.

1. Draw a circle and inscribe a regular hexagon in the circle. Find the length of one side of the hexagon and multiply that length by 6 to find the hexagon's perimeter.

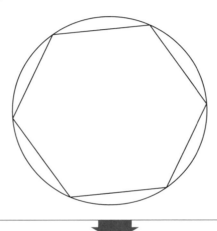

2. Create a triangle with a vertex at the center of the circle. Draw two line segments from the center of the circle to vertices that are next to each other on the hexagon.

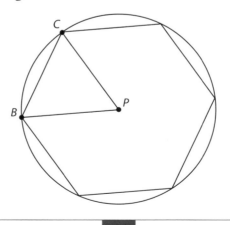

3. To find the length of $\overline{BC}$, first determine the known lengths of $\overline{PB}$ and $\overline{PC}$.

   Both lengths are equal to the radius of circle $P$, 5 meters.

4. Determine $m\angle CPB$.

   The hexagon has 6 sides. A central angle drawn from $P$ will be equal to one-sixth of the number of degrees in circle $P$.

   $$m\angle CPB = \frac{1}{6} \bullet 360 = 60$$

   The measure of $\angle CPB$ is 60°.

5. Use trigonometry to find the length of $\overline{BC}$.

   Make a right triangle inside of $\triangle PBC$ by drawing a perpendicular line, or altitude, from $P$ to $\overline{BC}$.

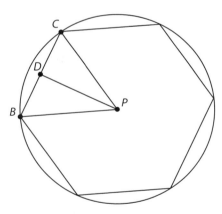

6. Determine $m\angle BPD$.

$\overline{DP}$ **bisects**, or cuts in half, $\angle CPB$. Since the measure of $\angle CPB$ was found to be 60°, divide 60 by 2 to determine $m\angle BPD$.

$$\frac{60}{2} = 30$$

The measure of $\angle BPD$ is 30°.

7. Use trigonometry to find the length of $\overline{BD}$ and multiply that value by 2 to find the length of $\overline{BC}$.

$\overline{BD}$ is opposite $\angle BPD$.

The length of the hypotenuse, $\overline{PB}$, is 5 meters.

The trigonometry ratio that uses the opposite and hypotenuse lengths is sine.

$$\sin BPD = \sin 30° = \frac{BD}{5}$$

$0.5 = \dfrac{BD}{5}$ \qquad Substitute the sine of 30°.

$5 \bullet 0.5 = BD$ \qquad Multiply both sides of the equation by 5.

$BD = 2.5$

The length of $\overline{BD}$ is 2.5 meters.

Since $\overline{BC}$ is twice the length of $\overline{BD}$, multiply 2.5 by 2.

$BC = 2 \bullet 2.5 = 5$

The length of $\overline{BC}$ is 5 meters.

8. Find the perimeter of the hexagon.

   Perimeter $= BC \cdot 6 = 5 \cdot 6 = 30$

   The perimeter of the hexagon is 30 meters.

9. Compare the estimate with the calculated circumference of the circle.

   Calculate the circumference.

   | | |
   |---|---|
   | $C = 2\pi r$ | Formula for circumference |
   | $C = 2\pi \cdot 5$ | Substitute 5 for $r$. |
   | $C \approx 31.416$ meters | |

   Find the difference between the perimeter of the hexagon and the circumference of the circle.

   $31.416 - 30 = 1.416$ meters

   The formula for circumference gives a calculation that is 1.416 meters longer than the perimeter of the hexagon. You can show this as a percentage difference between the two values.

   $$\frac{1.416}{31.416} = 0.0451 = 4.51\%$$

   From a proportional perspective, the circumference calculation is approximately 4.51% larger than the estimate that came from using the perimeter of the hexagon.

   If you inscribed a regular polygon with more side lengths than a hexagon, the perimeter of the polygon would be closer in value to the circumference of the circle.

## Example 2

Show how the area of a hexagon can be used to find an estimate for the area of a circle that has a radius of 5 meters. Compare the estimate with the circle's area found by using the formula $A = \pi r^2$.

1. Inscribe a hexagon into a circle and divide it into 6 equal triangles.

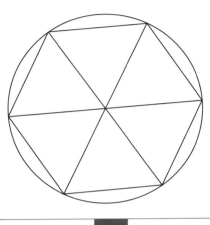

2. Use the measurements from Example 1 to find the area of one of the six triangles.

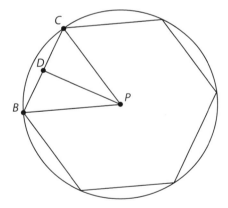

First, determine the formula to use.

$$A = \frac{1}{2}bh$$   Area formula for a triangle

$$A_{\triangle PBC} = \frac{1}{2}BC \bullet PD$$   Rewrite the formula with the base and height of the triangle whose area you are trying to determine.

*(continued)*

From Example 1, the following information is known:

$BC = 5$ meters

$BD = 2.5$ meters

$m\angle BPD = 30°$

You need to find the height, $\overline{PD}$. In $\triangle BPD$, the height, $\overline{PD}$, is the adjacent side length.

Since the hypotenuse, $\overline{BP}$, is a radius of the circle, it is 5 meters. Since the measure of $\angle BPD$ and the hypotenuse are known, use the cosine of 30° to find $\overline{PD}$.

$$\cos 30° = \frac{PD}{5}$$

$0.866054038 = \dfrac{PD}{5}$       Substitute the cosine of 30°.

$5 \cdot 0.866054038 = PD$       Multiply both sides by 5.

$PD \approx 4.33027019$ meters

Now that the length of $\overline{PD}$ is known, use that information to find the area of $\triangle PBC$ using the formula determined earlier.

$A_{\triangle PBC} = \dfrac{1}{2}BC \bullet PD$       Area formula for $\triangle PBC$

$A_{\triangle PBC} = \dfrac{1}{2}(5) \bullet (4.33027019)$       Substitute the values of $BC$ and $PD$.

$A_{\triangle PBC} \approx 10.82567548$ m$^2$

3. Find the area of the hexagon.

Multiply the area of one triangle times 6, the number of triangles in the hexagon.

$6 \bullet 10.82567548 = 64.95405288$ m²

The area of hexagon is about 64.95 m².

4. Compare the area of the hexagon with the area of the circle.

Find the area of the circle.

$$A_{\text{circle } P} = \pi r^2$$     Formula for the area of a circle

$$A_{\text{circle } P} = \pi \cdot 5^2$$     Substitute the value for the radius.

$$A_{\text{circle } P} \approx 78.53981634 \text{ m}^2$$

The actual area of circle $P$ is about 78.54 m².

Find the difference between the area of the hexagon and the area of the circle.

$$78.53981634 - 64.95405288 = 13.58576346$$

The actual area of the circle is approximately 13.59 m² greater than the hexagon's area.

Show the difference as a percentage.

$$\frac{13.59}{78.54} \approx 0.1730 \approx 17.30\%$$

The actual area of the circle is about 17.30% larger than the estimate found by using the area of the hexagon.

The estimate of a circle's area calculated by using an inscribed polygon can be made closer to the actual area of the circle by increasing the number of side lengths of the polygon.

**Example 3**

Find the area of a circle that has a circumference of 100 meters.

1. First, find the measure of the radius by using the formula for circumference.

   $C = 2\pi r$

   $100 = 2\pi r$

   $r = \dfrac{100}{2\pi}$

   $r \approx 15.9155$ m

2. Calculate the area by using the formula for the area of a circle.

   $A = \pi r^2$

   $A \approx \pi(15.9155)^2$

   $A \approx 253.3031\pi \text{ m}^2$

   $A \approx 795.775 \text{ m}^2$

   The area of a circle with a circumference of 100 meters is approximately 796 m².

## Example 4

What is the circumference of a circle that has an area of 1,000 m²?

1. First, find the radius by solving for $r$ in the formula for the area of the circle.

   | | |
   |---|---|
   | $A = \pi r^2$ | Formula for the area of a circle |
   | $1000 = \pi r^2$ | Substitute $A$ into the equation. |
   | $\dfrac{1000}{\pi} = r^2$ | Divide both sides by $\pi$. |
   | $r^2 \approx 318.3099$ | Simplify. |
   | $\sqrt{r^2} = \pm\sqrt{318.3099}$ | Take the square root of both sides. |
   | $r \approx 17.8412$ m | Use only the positive result, as distance is always positive. |

   The radius is approximately 17.8412 meters.

2. Find the circumference using the formula $C = 2\pi r$.

   | | |
   |---|---|
   | $C = 2\pi r$ | Formula for circumference of a circle |
   | $C = 2\pi(17.8412)$ | Substitute 17.8412 for $r$. |
   | $C \approx 112.1$ m | |

   The circumference of a circle with an area of 1,000 m² is approximately 112.1 meters.

# UNIT 6 • CIRCLES WITH AND WITHOUT COORDINATES
## Lesson 5: Explaining and Applying Area and Volume Formulas

## Practice 6.5.1: Circumference and Area of a Circle

Use your knowledge of circumference and area to complete each problem.

1. A circle has a regular decagon (10-sided figure) inscribed in it. The circle has a radius of 1 meter. Find the perimeter of the decagon. Use the formula $2\pi r$ to find the circumference of the circle. Why is the circumference found by using the formula a different length than the perimeter of the decagon?

2. A circle has a regular 20-sided polygon inscribed in it. The circle has a radius of 1 meter. Find the perimeter of the polygon. Then, find the circumference of the circle using $2\pi r$. Why is the circumference found by using the formula a different length than the perimeter of the polygon?

3. Compare the results of problems 1 and 2. Which dissection is a better approximation of the circumference of the circle? Use a 60-sided regular polygon as the inscribed figure in a circle that has a radius of 1 meter. Calculate the polygon's perimeter and compare it with the circle's circumference.

4. A circle has a regular decagon (10-sided figure) inscribed in it. The circle has a radius of 1 meter. Find the area of the circle, then find the area of the decagon. Why is the area of the circle different from the area of the decagon?

5. A circle has a regular 20-sided polygon inscribed in it. The circle has a radius of 1 meter. Find the area of the circle and then of the polygon. Why is the area of the circle different from the area of the polygon?

6.  Compare the results of problems 4 and 5. Which dissection is a better approximation of the area of the circle? Use a 60-sided regular polygon as the inscribed figure in a circle that has a radius of 1 meter. Calculate the polygon's area and compare it with the circle's area.

7.  Enzo paints a large circle on a wall. The circle has a circumference of 35 feet. What is the area of the circle?

8.  What is the area of a pecan pie that has a circumference of 40 inches?

9.  A circular tablecloth has an area of 70 square feet. What is the circumference of the tablecloth?

10. A horse is tied to a post in a grassy field. He can walk in a circle around the post. He has 300 square meters of grass to graze on. What is the circumference of the area that he is grazing on?

# Lesson 6.5.2: Volumes of Cylinders, Pyramids, Cones, and Spheres

## Introduction

Think about the dissection arguments used to develop the area of a circle formula. These same arguments can be used to develop the volume formulas for cylinders, pyramids, cones, and spheres. You have already used volume formulas for prisms, cylinders, pyramids, cones, and spheres, but how are the formulas derived? In this lesson, you will learn how to find the volumes of cylinders, pyramids, cones, and spheres. As part of learning the formulas, you will see proofs of why the formulas work for those objects. The real world is filled with these objects. Using the formulas of volume for these objects expands your problem-solving skills.

## Key Concepts

- The formula for finding the volume of a prism is $V = length \cdot width \cdot height$. This can also be shown as $V = area\ of\ base \cdot height$.

- Remember to use cubic units or volume measures when calculating volume. Some examples are cubic feet ($ft^3$), cubic meters ($m^3$), liters (L), and gallons (gal).

- If the dimensions of an object are all multiplied by a scale factor, $k$, then the volume will be multiplied by a scale factor of $k^3$. For example, if the dimensions are enlarged by a scale factor of 5, then the volume will be enlarged by a scale factor of 125.

### Cylinders

- A cylinder has two bases that are parallel. This is also true of a prism.

- Bonaventura Cavalieri, an Italian mathematician, formulated **Cavalieri's Principle**. This principle states that the volumes of two objects of equal height are equal if the areas of their corresponding cross sections are in all cases equal.

- This principle is illustrated by the diagram below. A rectangular prism has been sliced into six pieces and is shown in three different ways.

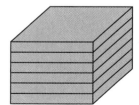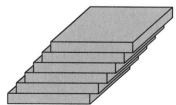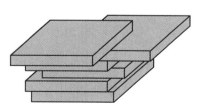

- The six pieces maintain their same volume regardless of how they are moved.

- Cavalieri's Principle describes how each piece is a thin slice in the plane of the prism.

- If each thin slice in each object has the same area, then the volumes of the objects are the same.

- The following diagram shows a prism, a prism at an oblique angle, and a cylinder.

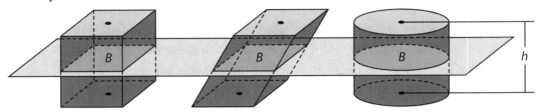

- The three objects meet the two criteria of Cavalieri's Principle. First, the objects have the same height. Secondly, the areas of the objects are the same when a plane slices them at corresponding heights. Therefore, the three objects have the same volume.

- A square prism that has side lengths of $r\sqrt{\pi}$ will have a base area of $r\sqrt{\pi} \bullet r\sqrt{\pi} = \pi r^2$ on every plane that cuts through it. The same is true of a cylinder, which has a radius, $r$.

- The base area of the cylinder will be $\pi r^2$. This shows how a square prism and a cylinder can have the same areas at each plane.

- Another way of thinking about the relationship of a polygonal prism and the cylinder is to remember the earlier proof about the area of a circle.

- A cylinder can be thought of as a prism with an infinite number of sides.

- The diagram below shows a polygonal prism with 200 sides.

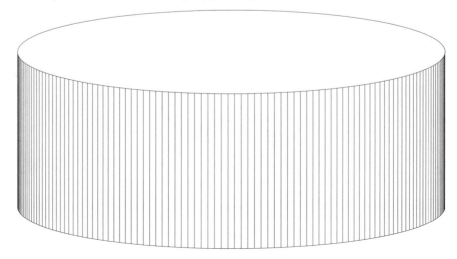

- The area of its base can be calculated by dividing it into quadrilaterals and triangles, but its base is approaching the limit of being a circle.

- If the base area and the height of a prism and a cylinder are the same, the prism and cylinder will have the same volume.

- The formula for finding the volume of a cylinder is $V = \pi r^2 \bullet h$.

## Pyramids

- A **pyramid** is a solid or hollow polyhedron object that has three or more triangular faces that converge at a single vertex at the top; the base may be any polygon.

- A **polyhedron** is a three-dimensional object that has faces made of polygons.

- A triangular prism can be cut into three equal triangular pyramids.

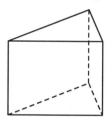

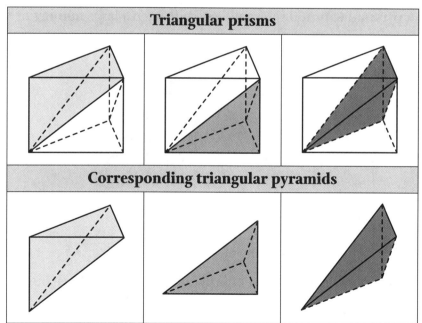

- A cube can be cut into three equal square pyramids.

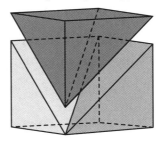

- This dissection proves that the volume of a pyramid is one-third the volume of a prism: $V_{\text{pyramid}} = \dfrac{1}{3}B \bullet h$.

## Cones

- A **cone** is a solid or hollow object that tapers from a circular base to a point.
- A cone and a pyramid use the same formula for finding volume.
- This can be seen by increasing the number of sides of a pyramid.
- The limit approaches that of being a cone.
- A pyramid with 100 sides follows. With such a large number of sides, it looks like a cone.

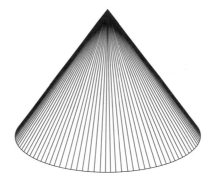

- The formula for the volume of a cone is $V_{\text{cone}} = \dfrac{1}{3}\pi r^2 \bullet h$.
- Cavalieri's Principle shows how pyramids and cones have the same volume.
- The diagram that follows shows cross sections of areas with the same planes.
- Each object has the same area at each cross section.

- Therefore, the volumes of both objects are the same.

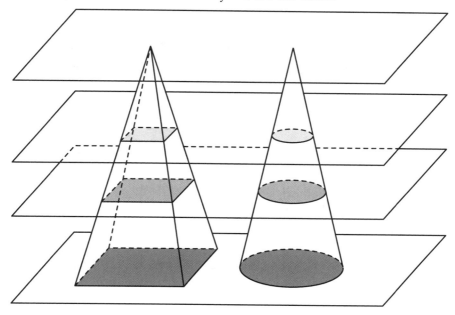

## Spheres

- A **sphere** is a three-dimensional surface that has all its points the same distance from its center.

- The volume of a sphere can be derived in several ways, including by using Cavalieri's Principle and a limit process.

- The formula for the volume of a sphere is $V = \dfrac{4}{3}\pi r^{3}$.

# Guided Practice 6.5.2

## Example 1

Find the dimensions for a cylinder that has the same volume as a square prism with a base area of 9 square meters. The cylinder and the square prism should both have heights of 5 meters.

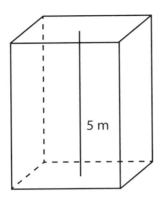 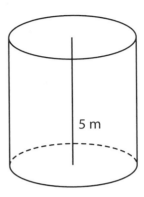

1. Determine the relationship between two objects with the same volume.

   Cavalieri's Principle states that if two objects have the same area in every plane, or cross section, then their volumes are the same. The cylinder and prism have uniform width and length throughout their heights. Both need to have the same height. Therefore, in order for the cylinder and prism to have the same volume, they need to have the same areas for their bases.

2. Set up the formulas for the area of the base of the cylinder and the area of the base of the prism so that they are equal.

   The formula for the area of the circular base of the cylinder is $A = \pi r^2$, where $r$ is the radius of the base of the cylinder.

   The area of the base of the prism is 9 square meters.

   $A_{\text{base of square prism}} = A_{\text{base of cylinder}}$    Set the areas of the bases equal.

   $9 = \pi r^2$    Substitute the known information to form an equation.

3. Solve the equation for $r$.

$$9 = \pi r^2$$

$$\frac{9}{\pi} = r^2 \qquad \text{Divide both sides by } \pi.$$

$$2.864788976 \approx r^2$$

$$\pm\sqrt{2.864788976} \approx r \qquad \text{Take the square root of both sides.}$$

$$r \approx 1.692568751 \qquad \text{The length of the radius must be a positive number.}$$

For the cylinder to have the same volume as the prism, the cylinder's base must have a radius of 1.692568751.

Substitute the value of the radius into the equation to check your work.

$$9 = \pi \bullet r^2$$

$$9 = \pi \bullet (1.692568751)^2$$

$$9 \approx 9.0000000001$$

The difference is infinitesimal. The two objects essentially have bases that have the same area, 9 m².

4. Calculate the volume for each object.

The volume for a prism or a cylinder can be seen as many thin slices or cross sections stacked on top of one another. Thus, their volume formulas are the same: $V = B \bullet h$, where $B$ is the area of the base of the object.

| Prism | Cylinder |
|---|---|
| $V = B \bullet h$ | $V = B \bullet h$ |
| $V = 9 \bullet 5$ | $V \approx 9.0000000001 \bullet 5$ |
| $V = 45$ m³ | $V \approx 45$ m³ |

5. Verify that the two objects will have the same area at a height of 1 meter or any other height.

> Yes, this is true. At every height, both objects have uniform dimensions that are equal to the dimensions of their bases. Therefore, using Cavalieri's Principle, both objects, the prism and the cylinder, have the same volume. ✓

## Example 2

Find the dimensions for a cone that has the same volume as a pyramid of the same height as the cone. Both the cone and the pyramid have a height of 2 meters. The volume of the pyramid is 3 cubic meters. A cone and a pyramid both taper to a point or vertex at the top. The "slant" of the taper is linear, meaning it is a straight line. The dimensions of both the cone and the pyramid change at a constant rate from base to tip.

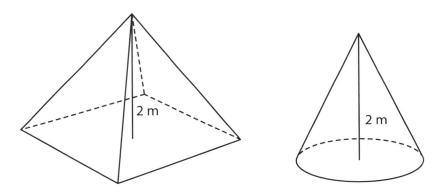

1. Cavalieri's Principle states that the pyramid and cone will have the same volume if the area of each cross section of a plane is the same at every height of the two objects. This means that if the cone and pyramid have bases of equal area, then their volumes will also be equal.

2. Set up an equation to find the radius of the cone.

The volume of the pyramid is 3 m³.

Both objects must have bases of equal area to have the same volume.

The area of the base of the pyramid can be found by solving for $B$ in the formula for the volume of a pyramid.

$V_{\text{pyramid}} = \dfrac{1}{3} B \bullet h$

$3 = \dfrac{1}{3} B \bullet 2$     Substitute the volume and the height of the pyramid.

$3 = \dfrac{2}{3} B$     Simplify.

$\dfrac{3}{2} \bullet 3 = B$     Multiply both sides by $\dfrac{3}{2}$.

$\dfrac{9}{2} = B$     Simplify.

$B = 4.5$

The area of the base of the pyramid is 4.5 square meters.

$A_{\text{pyramid base}} = A_{\text{cone base}} = A_{\text{circle}} = \pi r^2$   Set up the equation.

$4.5 = \pi r^2$     Substitute the value found for the area of the base of the pyramid.

$\dfrac{4.5}{\pi} = r^2$     Divide both sides by $\pi$.

$\pm \sqrt{\dfrac{4.5}{\pi}} = r$     Take the square root of both sides.

$r \approx 1.19682684$

The radius of the cone is approximately 1.197 meters.

## Example 3

A new art museum is being built in the shape of a square pyramid. The height will be 50 meters. The art museum needs 86,400 cubic meters of space inside. What should be the side lengths of the base of the pyramid?

1. Use the formula for the volume of a pyramid to find the unknown side lengths of the base.

$$V = \frac{1}{3} B \bullet h$$

$$86,400 = \frac{1}{3} B \bullet 50 \qquad \text{Substitute the known values.}$$

$$\frac{3 \bullet 86,400}{50} = B \qquad \text{Multiply both sides by } \frac{3}{50}.$$

$$B = 5184$$

The base is 5,184 square meters.

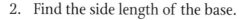

2. Find the side length of the base.

The base is a square. It has an area of *side* • *side*.

Find the length of one side by taking the square root of the area of the base.

$$\pm\sqrt{5184} = 72$$

Take the positive square root since length is a positive number.

The length of each side of the art museum's pyramid base should be 72 meters.

## Example 4

Weston has two round balloons. One balloon has a radius that is 3 times the radius of the other balloon. How much more air will the larger balloon need than the smaller balloon?

1. Use the formula for the volume of a sphere for the smaller balloon.

   $$V = \frac{4}{3}\pi r^3$$

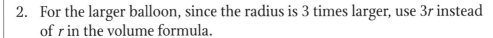

2. For the larger balloon, since the radius is 3 times larger, use $3r$ instead of $r$ in the volume formula.

   $$V = \frac{4}{3}\pi(3r)^3$$

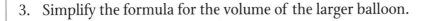

3. Simplify the formula for the volume of the larger balloon.

   $V = \frac{4}{3}\pi(3r)^3$    Formula for the volume of the larger balloon

   $V = \frac{4}{3}\pi(27r^3)$    Distribute the exponent.

   $V = 12\pi r^3$    Multiply the coefficients.

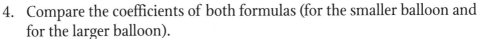

4. Compare the coefficients of both formulas (for the smaller balloon and for the larger balloon).

   The coefficients are 12 and $\frac{4}{3}$.

   Divide to see how many times larger the volume of the larger balloon is.

   $$12 \div \left(\frac{4}{3}\right) = 9$$

   The larger balloon will need 9 times as much air as the smaller balloon.

## Example 5

A teenager buying some chewing gum is comparing packages of gum in order to get the most gum possible. Each package costs the same amount. Package 1 has 20 pieces of gum shaped like spheres. Each piece has a radius of 5 mm. Package 2 has 5 pieces of gum shaped like spheres. Each piece has a radius of 10 mm. Which package should the teenager buy? Round to the nearest millimeter.

1. Find the volume of a piece of gum in package 1 by using the volume formula for a sphere.

   $$V = \frac{4}{3}\pi r^3 \qquad \text{Formula for volume of a sphere}$$

   $$V = \frac{4}{3}\pi (5)^3 \qquad \text{Substitute 5 for } r.$$

   $$V \approx 524 \text{ mm}^3$$

   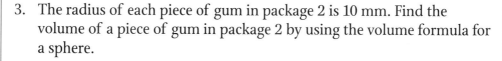

2. Multiply the volume of the single piece of gum in package 1 by 20 to get the total volume of the gum in the package.

   $$(524)(20) = 10{,}480 \text{ mm}^3$$

3. The radius of each piece of gum in package 2 is 10 mm. Find the volume of a piece of gum in package 2 by using the volume formula for a sphere.

   $$V = \frac{4}{3}\pi r^3 \qquad \text{Formula for volume of a sphere}$$

   $$V = \frac{4}{3}\pi (10)^3 \qquad \text{Substitute 10 for } r.$$

   $$V \approx 4189 \text{ mm}^3$$

4. Multiply the volume of a single piece of gum in package 2 by 5 to get the total volume of gum in the package.

   $(4189)(5) = 20,945$ mm$^3$

5. Compare the volumes of the two packages to determine the best purchase.

   $10,480 < 20,945$

   The teenager should buy package 2.

## Practice 6.5.2: Volumes of Cylinders, Pyramids, Cones, and Spheres

Use your knowledge of volume to complete each problem. Round each answer to the nearest hundredth unless otherwise indicated.

1.  A cone has a height of 2 feet and a radius of 1 foot. What is its volume?

2.  A cylinder has a height of 6 cm and a circumference of 10 cm. What is the volume of the cylinder?

3.  A cone and a cylinder are the same height. How will their radii differ if their volumes are the same?

4.  A cylindrical swimming pool has a circumference of 125 feet. The water in the pool is 5 feet deep. What is the volume of the pool? How many hours will it take to fill the pool with water? Assume the water flow is 5 gallons per minute. 1 cubic foot ≈ 7.48052 gallons.

5.  A pyramid in Giza, Egypt has a square base with side lengths of 230 meters. Its height is 146.5 meters. What is its volume?

*continued*

6. A conical cup is 15 cm long. It has a radius of 4 cm. How many liters of water will the cup hold? 1 liter = 1000 cm$^3$.

7. A pyramid-shaped paperweight is made out of solid molded plastic. It is a triangular pyramid with side lengths of 9 cm and a height of 9 cm. What volume of plastic is needed to make one paperweight?

8. The diameter of the moon is approximately 3,476 km. What is the volume of the moon to the nearest kilometer?

9. A child has an ice cream cone with a spherical scoop of ice cream on the top, but the cone is empty. The cone has a diameter of 5 cm and is 7 cm deep. If the ice cream all melts, will it all fit inside the cone or will the cone overflow? Explain.

10. A student has a basketball with a radius that is 4 times larger than a rubber ball. How much more air will the basketball hold than the rubber ball?

# Lesson 6: Deriving Equations

## Common Core State Standards

**G–GPE.1**   Derive the equation of a circle of given center and radius using the Pythagorean Theorem; complete the square to find the center and radius of a circle given by an equation.

**G–GPE.2**   Derive the equation of a parabola given a focus and directrix.

## Essential Questions

1.   How can a circle be described in different ways?

2.   How can a parabola be described in different ways?

3.   How are the definitions of a circle and a parabola similar?

4.   How are the definitions of a circle and a parabola different?

## WORDS TO KNOW

| | |
|---|---|
| **center of a circle** | the point in the plane of the circle from which all points on the circle are equidistant. The center is not part of the circle; it is in the interior of the circle. |
| **circle** | the set of all points in a plane that are equidistant from a reference point in that plane, called the center. The set of points forms a 2-dimensional curve that measures 360°. |
| **directrix of a parabola** | a line that is perpendicular to the axis of symmetry of a parabola and that is in the same plane as both the parabola and the focus of the parabola; the fixed line referenced in the definition of a parabola |
| **distance formula** | a formula that states the distance between points $(x_1, y_1)$ and $(x_2, y_2)$ is equal to $\sqrt{\left(x_2 - x_1\right)^2 + \left(y_2 - y_1\right)^2}$ |
| **focus of a parabola** | a fixed point on the interior of a parabola that is not on the directrix of the parabola but is on the same plane as both the parabola and the directrix; the fixed point referenced in the definition of a parabola |

| | |
|---|---|
| **general form of an equation of a circle** | $Ax^2 + By^2 + Cx + Dy + E = 0$, where $A = B$, $A \neq 0$, and $B \neq 0$ |
| **parabola** | the set of all points that are equidistant from a fixed line, called the directrix, and a fixed point not on that line, called the focus. The parabola, directrix, and focus are all in the same plane. The vertex of the parabola is the point on the parabola that is closest to the directrix. |
| **perfect square trinomial** | a trinomial of the form $x^2 + bx + \left(\dfrac{b}{2}\right)^2$ |
| **Pythagorean Theorem** | a theorem that relates the length of the hypotenuse of a right triangle ($c$) to the lengths of its legs ($a$ and $b$). The theorem states that $a^2 + b^2 = c^2$. |
| **quadratic function** | a function that can be written in the form $f(x) = ax^2 + bx + c$, where $a \neq 0$. The graph of any quadratic function is a parabola. |
| **radius** | the distance from the center to a point on the circle |
| **standard form of an equation of a circle** | $(x - h)^2 + (y - k)^2 = r^2$, where $(h, k)$ is the center and $r$ is the radius |
| **standard form of an equation of a parabola** | $(x - h)^2 = 4p(y - k)$ for parabolas that open up or down; $(y - k)^2 = 4p(x - h)$ for parabolas that open right or left. For all parabolas, $p \neq 0$ and the vertex is $(h, k)$. |
| **vertex of a parabola** | the point on a parabola that is closest to the directrix and lies on the axis of symmetry |

# Recommended Resources

- MathIsFun.com. "Circle Equations."

  http://www.walch.com/rr/00071

  This interactive site reviews the standard form of the equation of a circle and how it is derived. It reminds users that the equation is based on the Pythagorean Theorem, and reviews how to expand binomials and simplify the resulting polynomials to obtain the general form, given the standard form. The site also demonstrates how to use the technique of completing the square to obtain the standard form, given the general form. Questions are provided to assess understanding.

- MathIsFun.com. "Definition of Parabola."

  http://www.walch.com/rr/00072

  An interactive soccer player kicks a ball that follows a parabolic path. Users can change the values of $a$, $b$, and $c$ to obtain equations of the form $y = ax^2 + bx + c$, and see how the graph changes to match the equation. This site might be useful as a review of what has already been learned about quadratic functions and their graphs, which are parabolas.

- MathIsFun.com. "Parabola."

  http://www.walch.com/rr/00073

  This site offers a hands-on activity showing how to use the definition of a parabola to draw one. The only required materials are paper, a pencil, and a ruler. The site explains that rays parallel to the axis of symmetry are reflected from the parabola to its focus, and it lists some devices that use that property, such as a satellite dish. Users can assess understanding by answering quiz questions.

# Lesson 6.6.1: Deriving the Equation of a Circle

## Introduction

The graph of an equation in $x$ and $y$ is the set of all points $(x, y)$ in a coordinate plane that satisfy the equation. Some equations have graphs with precise geometric descriptions. For example, the graph of the equation $y = 2x + 3$ is the line with a slope of 2, passing through the point $(0, 3)$. This geometric description uses the familiar concepts of line, slope, and point. The equation $y = 2x + 3$ is an algebraic description of the line.

In this lesson, we will investigate how to translate between geometric descriptions and algebraic descriptions of circles. We have already learned how to use the Pythagorean Theorem to find missing dimensions of right triangles. Now, we will see how the Pythagorean Theorem leads us to the distance formula, which leads us to the standard form of the equation of a circle.

## Key Concepts

- The standard form of the equation of a circle is based on the distance formula.

- The distance formula, in turn, is based on the Pythagorean Theorem.

- The **Pythagorean Theorem** states that in any right triangle, the square of the hypotenuse is equal to the sum of the squares of the legs.

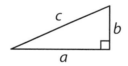

$$a^2 + b^2 = c^2$$

- If $r$ represents the distance between the origin and any point $(x, y)$, then $x^2 + y^2 = r^2$.

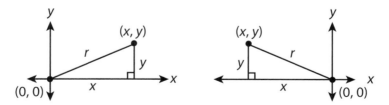

- $x$ can be positive, negative, or zero because it is a coordinate.

- $y$ can be positive, negative, or zero because it is a coordinate.

- $r$ cannot be negative because it is a distance.

- A **circle** is the set of all points in a plane that are equidistant from a reference point in that plane, called the center. The set of points forms a 2-dimensional curve that measures 360°.

- The **center of a circle** is the point in the plane of the circle from which all points on the circle are equidistant. The center is in the interior of the circle.

- The **radius** of a circle is the distance from the center to a point on the circle.

- For a circle with center (0, 0) and radius $r$, any point $(x, y)$ is on that circle if and only if $x^2 + y^2 = r^2$.

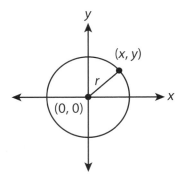

- The distance formula is used to find the distance between any two points on a coordinate plane.

- The **distance formula** states that the distance $d$ between $A\ (x_1, y_1)$ and $B\ (x_2, y_2)$ is $d = \sqrt{(x_2 - x_1)^2 + (y_2 - y_1)^2}$ .

- The distance formula is based on the Pythagorean Theorem.

- Look at this diagram of a right triangle with points $A$, $B$, and $C$. The distance $d$ between points $A$ and $B$ is unknown.

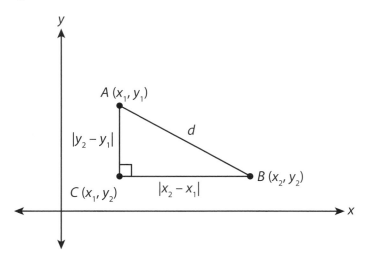

- The worked example that follows shows how the distance formula is derived from the Pythagorean Theorem, using the points from the diagram to find $d$:

  $AB^2 = BC^2 + AC^2$ — Pythagorean Theorem

  $d^2 = \left|x_2 - x_1\right|^2 + \left|y_2 - y_1\right|^2$ — Substitute values for sides $AB$, $BC$, and $AC$ of the triangle.

  $d^2 = \left(x_2 - x_1\right)^2 + \left(y_2 - y_1\right)^2$ — Simplify. All squares are nonnegative.

  $d = \sqrt{\left(x_2 - x_1\right)^2 + \left(y_2 - y_1\right)^2}$ — Take the square of each side of the equation to arrive at the distance formula.

- For a circle with center $(h, k)$ and radius $r$, any point $(x, y)$ is on that circle if and only if $\sqrt{\left(x-h\right)^2 + \left(y-k\right)^2} = r$. Squaring both sides of this equation yields the **standard form of an equation of a circle** with center $(h, k)$ and radius $r$: $(x - h)^2 + (y - k)^2 = r^2$.

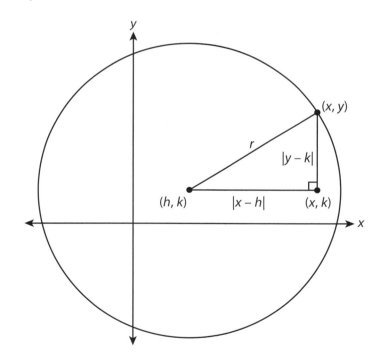

- If a circle has center $(0, 0)$, then its equation is $(x - 0)^2 + (y - 0)^2 = r^2$, or $x^2 + y^2 = r^2$.

- If the center and radius of a circle are known, then either of the following two methods can be used to write an equation for the circle:

  - Apply the Pythagorean Theorem to derive the equation.

- Or, substitute the center coordinates and radius directly into the standard form.

- The **general form of an equation of a circle** is $Ax^2 + By^2 + Cx + Dy + E = 0$, where $A = B$, $A \neq 0$, and $B \neq 0$.

- If any one of the following three sets of facts about a circle is known, then the other two can be determined:

  - center $(h, k)$ and radius $r$

  - standard equation: $(x - h)^2 + (y - k)^2 = r^2$

  - general equation: $Ax^2 + By^2 + Cx + Dy + E = 0$

- The general form of the equation of a circle comes from expanding the standard form of the equation of the circle.

- The standard form of the equation of a circle comes from completing the square from the general form of the equation of a circle.

- Every **perfect square trinomial** has the form $x^2 + bx + \left(\dfrac{b}{2}\right)^2$ because it is the square of a binomial: $x^2 + bx + \left(\dfrac{b}{2}\right)^2 = \left(x + \dfrac{b}{2}\right)^2$.

- Completing the square is the process of determining the value of $\left(\dfrac{b}{2}\right)^2$ and adding it to $x^2 + bx$ to form the perfect square trinomial, $x^2 + bx + \left(\dfrac{b}{2}\right)^2$.

# Guided Practice 6.6.1

## Example 1

Derive the standard equation of the circle with center (0, 0) and radius 5.

1. Sketch the circle.

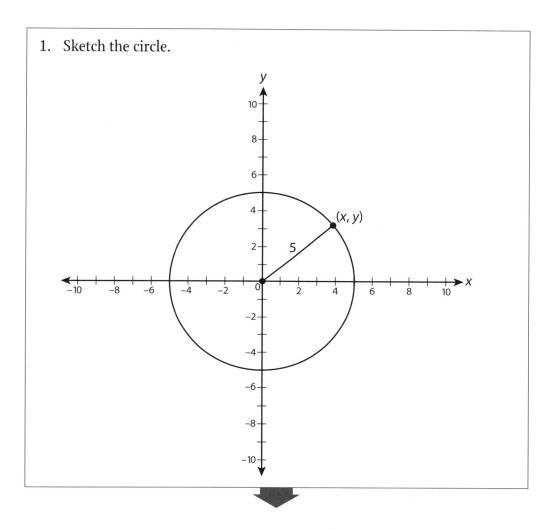

2.  Use the Pythagorean Theorem to derive the standard equation.

In order to use the Pythagorean Theorem, there must be a right triangle.

To create a right triangle, draw a line from point $(x, y)$ that is perpendicular to the horizontal line through the circle. Label the resulting sides of the triangle $x$ and $y$.

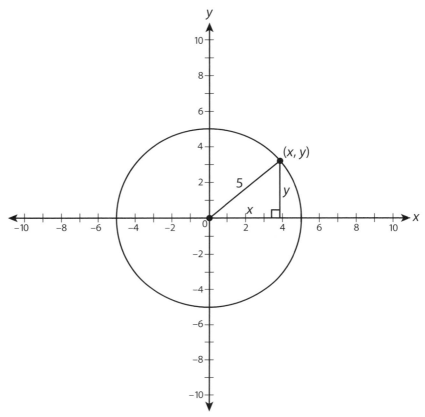

Substitute the values for each side of the triangle into the formula for the Pythagorean Theorem, $a^2 + b^2 + c^2$.

$a^2 + b^2 + c^2$        Pythagorean Theorem

$x^2 + y^2 = 5^2$        Substitute values from the triangle.

$x^2 + y^2 = 25$        Simplify.

The standard equation is $x^2 + y^2 = 25$.

## Example 2

Derive the standard equation of the circle with center (2, 1) and radius 4. Then use a graphing calculator to graph your equation.

1. Sketch the circle.

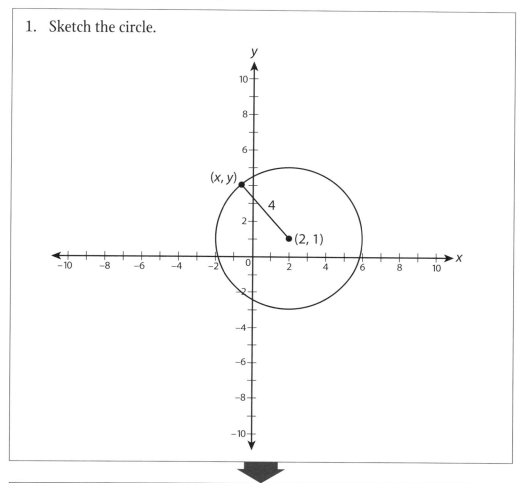

2. Use the Pythagorean Theorem to derive the standard equation.

Create a right triangle. Draw lines from point $(x, y)$ and point $(2, 1)$ that meet at a common point and are perpendicular to each other.

The length of the base of the triangle is equal to the absolute value of the difference of the $x$-coordinates of the endpoints.

The height of the triangle is equal to the absolute value of the difference of the $y$-coordinates of the endpoints.

*(continued)*

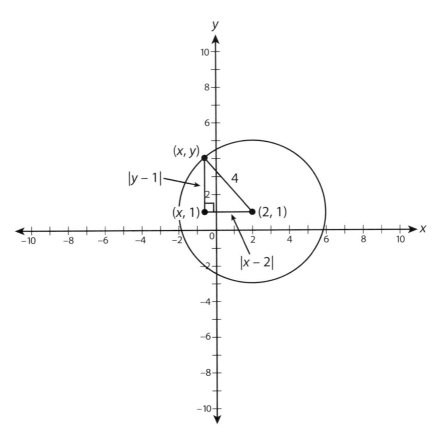

Substitute the resulting values for the sides of the triangle into the Pythagorean Theorem.

$a^2 + b^2 + c^2$                    Pythagorean Theorem

$|x-2|^2 + |y-1|^2 = 4^2$          Substitute values from the triangle.

$(x - 2)^2 + (y - 1)^2 = 4^2$      All squares are nonnegative, so replace the absolute value symbols with parentheses.

$(x - 2)^2 + (y - 1)^2 = 16$       Simplify.

The standard equation is $(x - 2)^2 + (y - 1)^2 = 16$.

3. Solve the standard equation for *y* to obtain functions that can be graphed.

| | |
|---|---|
| $(x-2)^2 + (y-1)^2 = 16$ | Standard equation |
| $(y-1)^2 = 16 - (x-2)^2$ | Subtract $(x-2)^2$ from both sides. |
| $y - 1 = \pm\sqrt{16-(x-2)^2}$ | If $a^2 = b^2$, then $a = \pm\sqrt{b}$. |
| $y = 1 \pm \sqrt{16-(x-2)^2}$ | Add 1 to both sides to solve for *y*. |

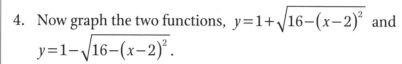

4. Now graph the two functions, $y = 1 + \sqrt{16-(x-2)^2}$ and $y = 1 - \sqrt{16-(x-2)^2}$.

**On a TI-83/84:**

Step 1: Press [Y=].

Step 2: At $Y_1$, type in [1][+][ $\sqrt{\ }$ ][16][–][(][([X, T, θ, n][–][2][)][)][$x^2$][)].

Step 3: At $Y_2$, type in [1][–][ $\sqrt{\ }$ ][16][–][(][([X, T, θ, n][–][2][)][)][$x^2$][)].

Step 4: Press [WINDOW] to change the viewing window.

Step 5: At Xmin, enter [(–)][9].

Step 6: At Xmax, enter [9].

Step 7: At Xscl, enter [1].

Step 8: At Ymin, enter [(–)][6].

Step 9: At Ymax, enter [6].

Step 10: At Yscl, enter [1].

Step 11: Press [GRAPH].

**On a TI-Nspire:**

Step 1: Press the [home] key.

Step 2: Arrow to the graphing icon and press [enter].

Step 3: At the blinking cursor at the bottom of the screen, type [1][+] [ $\sqrt{\ }$ ][16][–][(][($x$][–][2][)][)][$x^2$][enter].

*(continued)*

Step 4: Move the cursor to the bottom left of the screen and click on the double right-facing arrows.

Step 5: At the blinking cursor, type [1][–][ √ ][16][–][(][x][–][2][)][$x^2$] [)][enter].

Step 6: Change the viewing window by pressing [menu], using the arrows to navigate down to number 4: Window/Zoom, and clicking the center button of the navigation pad.

Step 7: Choose 1: Window settings by pressing the center button.

Step 8: Enter in an appropriate XMin value, –9, by pressing [(–)] and [9], then press [tab].

Step 9: Enter in an appropriate XMax value, [9], then press [tab].

Step 10: Leave the XScale set to "Auto." Press [tab] twice to navigate to YMin and enter an appropriate YMin value, –6, by pressing [(–)] and [6].

Step 11: Press [tab] to navigate to YMax. Enter [6]. Press [tab] twice to leave YScale set to "auto" and to navigate to "OK."

Step 12: Press [enter].

Step 13: Press [menu] and select 2: View and 5: Show Grid.

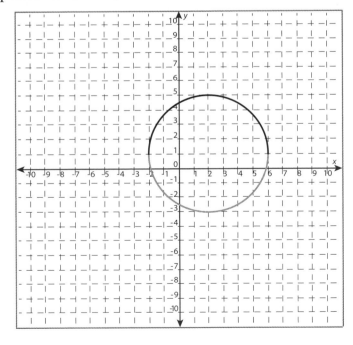

## Example 3

Write the standard equation and the general equation of the circle that has center (–1, 3) and passes through (–5, 5).

1. Sketch the circle.

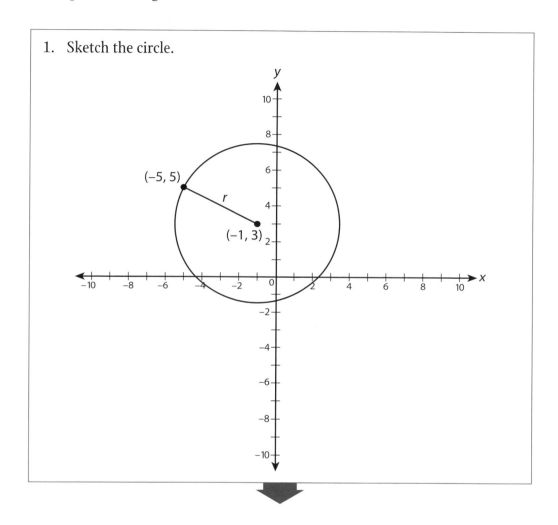

2. Use the distance formula to find the radius, $r$.

$d = \sqrt{(x_2 - x_1)^2 + (y_2 - y_1)^2}$     Distance formula

$r = \sqrt{[(-5)-(-1)]^2 + (5-3)^2}$     Substitute (–1, 3) and (–5, 5) for $(x_1, y_1)$ and $(x_2, y_2)$.

$r = \sqrt{(-4)^2 + (2)^2}$     Simplify.

$r = \sqrt{16 + 4}$

$r = \sqrt{20}$

$r = \sqrt{4 \bullet 5}$     Write 20 as a product with a perfect square factor.

$r = \sqrt{4} \bullet \sqrt{5}$     Apply the property $\sqrt{ab} = \sqrt{a} \bullet \sqrt{b}$ .

$r = 2\sqrt{5}$     Simplify.

3. Substitute the center and radius directly into the standard form.

$(x - h)^2 + (y - k)^2 = r^2$     Standard form

$\left[x-(-1)\right]^2 + (y-3)^2 = (2\sqrt{5})^2$     Substitute values into the equation, using the center (–1, 3), and the radius $2\sqrt{5}$ .

$(x + 1)^2 + (y - 3)^2 = 20$     Simplify to obtain the standard equation.

The standard equation is $(x + 1)^2 + (y - 3)^2 = 20$.

4. Square the binomials and rearrange terms to obtain the general form.

| | |
|---|---|
| $(x + 1)^2 + (y - 3)^2 = 20$ | Standard equation |
| $(x + 1)(x + 1) + (y - 3)(y - 3) = 20$ | Expand the factors. |
| $x^2 + 2x + 1 + y^2 - 6y + 9 = 20$ | Square the binomials to obtain trinomials. |
| $x^2 + 2x + y^2 - 6y + 10 = 20$ | Combine the constant terms on the left side of the equation. |
| $x^2 + 2x + y^2 - 6y - 10 = 0$ | Subtract 20 from both sides to get 0 on the right side. |
| $x^2 + y^2 + 2x - 6y - 10 = 0$ | Rearrange terms in descending order to obtain the general equation. |

The general equation is $x^2 + y^2 + 2x - 6y - 10 = 0$.

# Example 4

Find the center and radius of the circle described by the equation $x^2 + y^2 - 8x + 2y + 2 = 0$.

1. Rewrite the equation in standard form.

   | | |
   |---|---|
   | $x^2 + y^2 - 8x + 2y + 2 = 0$ | General form of the equation |
   | $x^2 + y^2 - 8x + 2y = -2$ | Subtract 2 from both sides to get the constant term on one side. |
   | $x^2 - 8x + y^2 + 2y = -2$ | Group same-variable terms. |

   Next, complete the square for both variables. Add the same values to both sides of the equation as shown:

   $$x^2 - 8x + \left(\frac{-8}{2}\right)^2 + y^2 + 2y + \left(\frac{2}{2}\right)^2 = -2 + \left(\frac{-8}{2}\right)^2 + \left(\frac{2}{2}\right)^2$$

   | | |
   |---|---|
   | $x^2 - 8x + 16 + y^2 + 2y + 1 = -2 + 16 + 1$ | Simplify the equation shown above. |
   | $(x - 4)^2 + (y + 1)^2 = 15$ | Write the perfect square trinomials as squares of binomials. |

   The standard equation is $(x - 4)^2 + (y + 1)^2 = 15$.

2. Determine the center and radius.

   | | |
   |---|---|
   | $(x - 4)^2 + (y + 1)^2 = 15$ | Write the standard equation from step 1. |
   | $\left(x - 4\right)^2 + \left[y - (-1)\right]^2 = \left(\sqrt{15}\right)^2$ | Rewrite to match the form $(x - h)^2 + (y - k)^2 = r^2$. |

   For the equation $(x - h)^2 + (y - k)^2 = r^2$, the center is $(h, k)$ and the radius is $r$, so for the equation $\left(x - 4\right)^2 + \left[y - (-1)\right]^2 = \left(\sqrt{15}\right)^2$, the center is $(4, -1)$ and the radius is $\sqrt{15}$.

## Example 5

Find the center and radius of the circle described by the equation
$4x^2 + 4y^2 + 20x - 40y + 116 = 0$.

1. Rewrite the equation in standard form.

| | |
|---|---|
| $4x^2 + 4y^2 + 20x - 40y + 116 = 0$ | General form of the equation |
| $x^2 + y^2 + 5x - 10y + 29 = 0$ | Divide each term on both sides by 4 to make the leading coefficient 1. |
| $x^2 + y^2 + 5x - 10y = -29$ | Subtract 29 from both sides to get the constant term on one side. |
| $x^2 + 5x + y^2 - 10y = -29$ | Combine like terms. |

Next, complete the square for both variables. Add the same values to both sides of the equation, as shown below:

$$x^2 + 5x + \left(\frac{5}{2}\right)^2 + y^2 - 10y + \left(\frac{-10}{2}\right)^2 = -29 + \left(\frac{5}{2}\right)^2 + \left(\frac{-10}{2}\right)^2$$

| | |
|---|---|
| $x^2 + 5x + \dfrac{25}{4} + y^2 - 10y + 25 = -29 + \dfrac{25}{4} + 25$ | Simplify the equation from above. |
| $\left(x + \dfrac{5}{2}\right)^2 + \left(y - 5\right)^2 = \dfrac{9}{4}$ | Write the perfect square trinomials as squares of binomials. |

The standard equation is $\left(x + \dfrac{5}{2}\right)^2 + \left(y - 5\right)^2 = \dfrac{9}{4}$.

2. Determine the center and radius.

$$\left(x+\frac{5}{2}\right)^2+\left(y-5\right)^2=\frac{9}{4}$$

Write the standard equation from step 1.

$$\left[x-\left(-\frac{5}{2}\right)\right]^2+\left(y-5\right)^2=\left(\frac{3}{2}\right)^2$$

Rewrite to match the form $(x-h)^2+(y-k)^2=r^2$.

For the equation $(x-h)^2+(y-k)^2=r^2$, the center is $(h, k)$ and the radius

is $r$, so for the equation $\left[x-\left(-\frac{5}{2}\right)\right]^2+\left(y-5\right)^2=\left(\frac{3}{2}\right)^2$, the center is

$\left(-\frac{5}{2},5\right)$ and the radius is $\frac{3}{2}$.

# UNIT 6 • CIRCLES WITH AND WITHOUT COORDINATES
## Lesson 6: Deriving Equations

## Practice 6.6.1: Deriving the Equation of a Circle

For problems 1–4, write the standard equation of the circle described.

1. The center is (0, 0) and the radius is $\sqrt{5}$.

2. The center is (3, 3) and the radius is 3.

3. The center is (1.1, –2) and the radius is 1.

4. The center is (5, –2) and the circle passes through (0, –6).

Use the provided information in each problem that follows to solve.

5. Write the general equation of the circle with center (–3.5, 1) and radius 2.4.

6. Find the center and radius of the circle described by the equation
   $x^2 + y^2 - 8x + 10y - 67 = 0$.

# UNIT 6 • CIRCLES WITH AND WITHOUT COORDINATES
## Lesson 6: Deriving Equations

7. Find the center and radius of the circle described by the equation
$$4x^2 + 4y^2 - 10x + 24y + \frac{133}{4} = 0.$$

8. A particular radio station emits a strong signal within a 32-mile radius. The station is located at (10, −12) on a coordinate plane whose units represent miles. What is the standard equation of the outer boundary of the region that receives a strong signal? If Marcy lives at (15, 18), does she receive a strong signal? Explain.

9. A furniture store offers free delivery to homes that are 40 miles or fewer from the store. The store is located at (0, 0) on a coordinate plane whose units represent miles. What is the standard equation of the outer boundary of the free delivery region? Will a customer at $\left(-10\sqrt{7}, 30\right)$ get free delivery? Explain.

10. Mr. Beck is a high school math teacher who coaches the track-and-field team. He makes a drawing of the team's practice field on a coordinate plane, using feet as the distance unit. He draws a quarter-circle on the coordinate plane to represent a boundary of the region for discus-throw practice. He writes the equation $x^2 + y^2 - 160y - 33{,}600 = 0$ to represent the full circle. What are the center and radius of the full circle?

# Lesson 6.6.2: Deriving the Equation of a Parabola

## Introduction

Earlier we studied the circle, which is the set of all points in a plane that are equidistant from a given point in that plane. We have investigated how to translate between geometric descriptions and algebraic descriptions of circles. Now we will investigate how to translate between geometric descriptions and algebraic descriptions of parabolas.

## Key Concepts

- A **quadratic function** is a function that can be written in the form $f(x) = ax^2 + bx + c$, where $a \neq 0$.

- The graph of any quadratic function is a parabola that opens up or down.

- A **parabola** is the set of all points that are equidistant from a given fixed point and a given fixed line that are both in the same plane as the parabola.

- That given fixed line is called the **directrix** of the parabola.

- The fixed point is called the **focus**.

- The parabola, directrix, and focus are all in the same plane.

- The **vertex** of the parabola is the point on the parabola that is closest to the directrix.

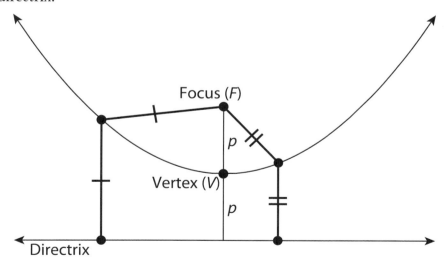

- Parabolas can open in any direction. In this lesson, we will work with parabolas that open up, down, right, and left.

- As with circles, there is a **standard form for the equation of a parabola**; however, that equation differs depending on which direction the parabola opens (right/left or up/down).

## Parabolas That Open Up or Down

- The standard form of an equation of a parabola that opens up or down and has vertex $(h, k)$ is $(x - h)^2 = 4p(y - k)$, where $p \neq 0$.

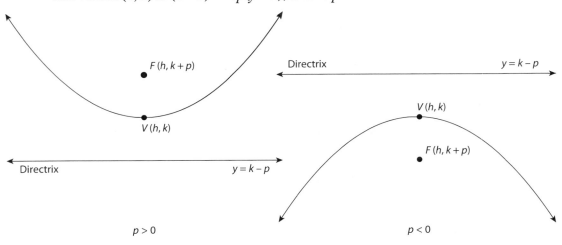

## Parabolas That Open Right or Left

- The standard form of an equation of a parabola that opens right or left and has vertex $(h, k)$ is $(y - k)^2 = 4p(x - h)$, where $p \neq 0$.

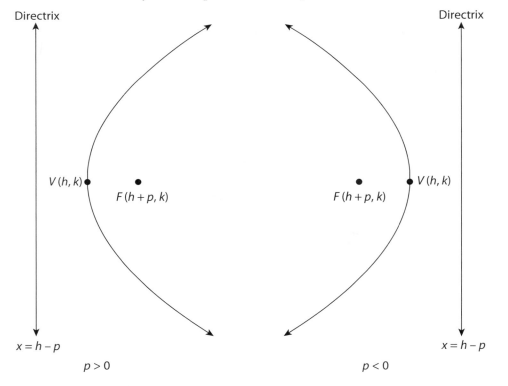

## All Parabolas

- For any parabola, the focus and directrix are each $|p|$ units from the vertex.

- Also, the focus and directrix are $2|p|$ units from each other.

- If the vertex is (0, 0), then the standard equation of the parabola has a simple form.

    - $(x - 0)^2 = 4p(y - 0)$ is equivalent to the simpler form $x^2 = 4py$.

    - $(y - 0)^2 = 4p(x - 0)$ is equivalent to the simpler form $y^2 = 4px$.

- Either of the following two methods can be used to write an equation of a parabola:

    - Apply the geometric definition to derive the equation.

    - Or, substitute the vertex coordinates and the value of $p$ directly into the standard form.

## Guided Practice 6.6.2

### Example 1

Derive the standard equation of the parabola with focus (0, 2) and directrix $y = -2$ from the definition of a parabola. Then write the equation by substituting the vertex coordinates and the value of $p$ directly into the standard form.

1. To derive the equation, begin by plotting the focus. Label it $F(0, 2)$. Graph the directrix and label it $y = -2$. Sketch the parabola. Label the vertex $V$.

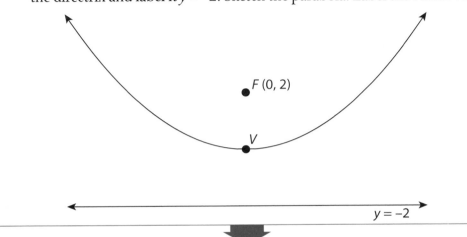

2. Let $A(x, y)$ be any point on the parabola.

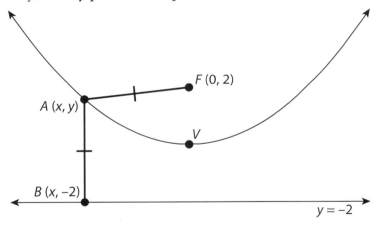

Point $A$ is equidistant from the focus and the directrix. The distance from $A$ to the directrix is the vertical distance $AB$, where $B$ is on the directrix directly below $A$. Since the directrix is at $y = -2$, the $y$-coordinate of $B$ is $-2$. Because $B$ is directly below $A$, it has the same $x$-coordinate as $A$. So $B$ has coordinates $(x, -2)$.

3. Apply the definition of a parabola to derive the standard equation using the distance formula.

Since the definition of a parabola tells us that $AF = AB$, use the graphed points for $AF$ and $AB$ to apply the distance formula to this equation.

$$\sqrt{(x-0)^2 + (y-2)^2} = \sqrt{(x-x)^2 + [y-(-2)]^2}$$

| | |
|---|---|
| $\sqrt{x^2 + (y-2)^2} = \sqrt{(y+2)^2}$ | Simplify. |
| $x^2 + (y-2)^2 = (y+2)^2$ | Square both sides to yield an equivalent equation. (See note.) |
| $x^2 = (y+2)^2 - (y-2)^2$ | Subtract $(y-2)^2$ from both sides to get all $x$ terms on one side and all $y$ terms on the other side. |
| $x^2 = (y^2 + 4y + 4) - (y^2 - 4y + 4)$ | Square the binomials. |
| $x^2 = y^2 + 4y + 4 - y^2 + 4y - 4$ | Distribute the negative sign. |
| $x^2 = 8y$ | Simplify. |

The standard equation is $x^2 = 8y$, or $(x-0)^2 = 8(y-0)$.

*Note*: Squaring both sides of an equation sometimes does not yield an equivalent equation. For example, the only solution to $2x = 6$ is 3, but squaring both sides of that equation yields $4x^2 = 36$, which has two solutions: 3 and −3. Note that if −3 is substituted for $x$ in the equation $2x = 6$, the value of the left side is negative. However, every ordered pair $(x, y)$ that satisfies $x^2 + (y-2)^2 = (y+2)^2$ also satisfies $\sqrt{x^2 + (y-2)^2} = \sqrt{(y+2)^2}$ and vice versa because all terms in both equations are squared terms and therefore nonnegative. Note that if any negative value is substituted for $x$ or $y$ in these equations, both sides of the equation remain nonnegative.

4. To write the equation using the standard form, first determine the coordinates of the vertex and the value of $p$.

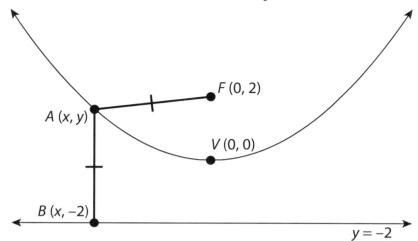

For any parabola, the distance between the focus and the directrix is $2|p|$. In this case, $2|p| = 2 - (-2) = 4$, thus $|p| = 2$. The parabola opens up, so $p$ is positive, and therefore $p = 2$. For any parabola, the distance between the focus and the vertex is $|p|$. Since $|p| = 2$, the vertex is 2 units below the focus. Therefore, the vertex coordinates are (0, 0).

5. Use the results found in step 4 to write the equation.

$(x - h)^2 = 4p(y - k)$      Standard form for a parabola that opens up or down

$(x - 0)^2 = 4(2)(y - 0)$      Substitute the values for $h$, $p$, and $k$.

$x^2 = 8y$      Simplify.

The standard equation is $x^2 = 8y$, or $(x - 0)^2 = 8(y - 0)$.

The results found in steps 3 and 5 match; so, either method of finding the equation (deriving it using the definition or writing the equation using the standard form) will yield the same equation.

## Example 2

Derive the standard equation of the parabola with focus $(-1, 2)$ and directrix $x = 7$ from the definition of a parabola. Then write the equation by substituting the vertex coordinates and the value of $p$ directly into the standard form.

1. To derive the equation, begin by plotting the focus. Label it $F(-1, 2)$. Graph the directrix and label it $x = 7$. Sketch the parabola. Label the vertex $V$.

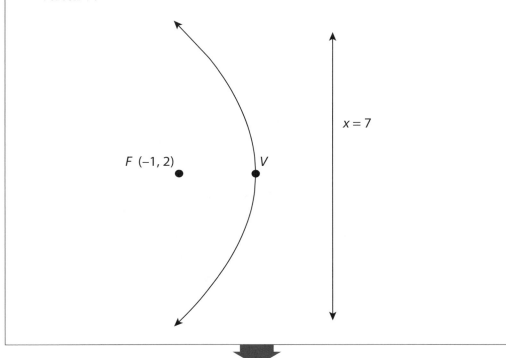

2. Let $A\,(x, y)$ be any point on the parabola.

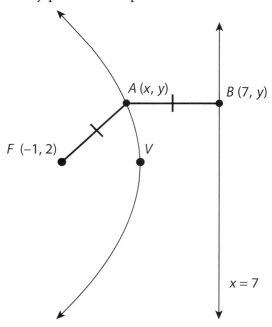

Point $A$ is equidistant from the focus and the directrix. The distance from $A$ to the directrix is the horizontal distance $AB$, where $B$ is on the directrix directly to the right of $A$. The $x$-value of $B$ is 7 because the directrix is at $x = 7$. Because $B$ is directly to the right of $A$, it has the same $y$-coordinate as $A$. So, $B$ has coordinates $(7, y)$.

3. Apply the definition of a parabola to derive the standard equation using the distance formula.

Since the definition of a parabola tells us that $AF = AB$, use the graphed points for $AF$ and $AB$ to apply the distance formula to this equation.

$$\sqrt{\left[x-(-1)\right]^2+\left(y-2\right)^2}=\sqrt{\left(x-7\right)^2+\left(y-y\right)^2}$$

| | |
|---|---|
| $\sqrt{\left(x+1\right)^2+\left(y-2\right)^2}=\sqrt{\left(x-7\right)^2}$ | Simplify. |
| $(x+1)^2+(y-2)^2=(x-7)^2$ | Square both sides. |
| $(y-2)^2=(x-7)^2-(x+1)^2$ | Subtract $(x + 1)^2$ from both sides to get all $x$ terms on one side and all $y$ terms on the other side. |
| $(y-2)^2=(x^2-14x+49)-(x^2+2x+1)$ | Square the binomials on the right side. |
| $(y-2)^2=x^2-14x+49-x^2-2x-1$ | Distribute the negative sign. |
| $(y-2)^2=-16x+48$ | Simplify. |
| $(y-2)^2=-16(x-3)$ | Factor on the right side to obtain the standard form $(y-k)^2=4p(x-h)$. |

The standard equation is $(y-2)^2=-16(x-3)$.

4. Write the equation using standard form.

To write the equation using the standard form, first determine the coordinates of the vertex and the value of $p$.

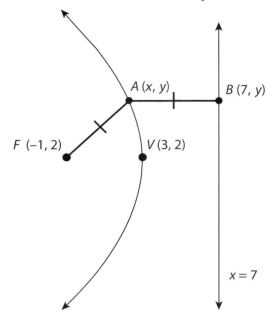

For any parabola, the distance between the focus and the directrix is $2|p|$. In this case, $2|p|=7-(-1)=8$, thus $|p|=4$. The parabola opens left, so $p$ is negative, and therefore $p = -4$. For any parabola, the distance between the focus and the vertex is $|p|$. Since $|p|=4$, the vertex is 4 units right of the focus. Therefore, the vertex coordinates are $(3, 2)$.

5. Use the results found in step 4 to write the equation.

| | |
|---|---|
| $(y - k)^2 = 4p(x - h)$ | Standard form for a parabola that opens right or left |
| $(y - 2)^2 = 4(-4)(x - 3)$ | Substitute the values for $h$, $p$, and $k$. |
| $(y - 2)^2 = -16(x - 3)$ | Simplify. |

The standard equation is $(y - 2)^2 = -16(x - 3)$.

The results shown in steps 3 and 5 match; so, either method of finding the equation (deriving it using the definition or writing the equation using the standard form) will yield the same equation.

## Example 3

Derive the standard equation of the parabola with focus $(0, p)$ and directrix $y = -p$, where $p$ is any real number other than 0.

1. Sketch diagrams showing the two possible orientations of the parabola. Include the focus, directrix, and vertex.

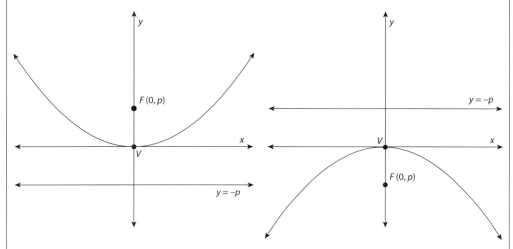

Because the focus is $(0, p)$ and the directrix is $y = -p$, the parabola can open either up or down.

The vertex is the origin because it is equidistant from the focus and directrix.

2. Let $A\,(x, y)$ be any point on the parabola.

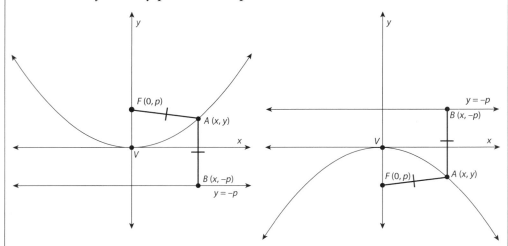

Point $A$ is equidistant from the focus and the directrix. The distance from $A$ to the directrix is the vertical distance $AB$, where $B$ is on the directrix directly above or below $A$. Because $B$ is directly above or below $A$, it has the same $x$-coordinate as $A$. So $B$ has coordinates $(x, -p)$.

3. Apply the definition of a parabola to derive the standard equation using the distance formula.

Since the definition of a parabola tells us that $AF = AB$, use the graphed points for $AF$ and $AB$ to apply the distance formula to this equation.

$$\sqrt{(x-0)^2 + (y-p)^2} = \sqrt{(x-x)^2 + \left[y-(-p)\right]^2}$$

| | |
|---|---|
| $\sqrt{x^2 + (y-p)^2} = \sqrt{(y+p)^2}$ | Simplify. |
| $x^2 + (y-p)^2 = (y+p)^2$ | Square both sides. |
| $x^2 = (y+p)^2 - (y-p)^2$ | Subtract $(y-p)^2$ from both sides to get all $x$ terms on one side and all $y$ terms on the other side. |
| $x^2 = (y^2 + 2py + p^2) - (y^2 - 2py + p^2)$ | Square the binomials on the right side. |
| $x^2 = y^2 + 2py + p^2 - y^2 + 2py - p^2$ | Distribute the negative sign. |
| $x^2 = 4py$ | Simplify. |

The standard equation is $x^2 = 4py$, or $(x-0)^2 = 4p(y-0)$.

## Example 4

Write the standard equation of the parabola with focus (–5, –6) and directrix $y = 3.4$. Then use a graphing calculator to graph your equation.

1. Plot the focus and graph the directrix. Sketch the parabola. Label the vertex $V$.

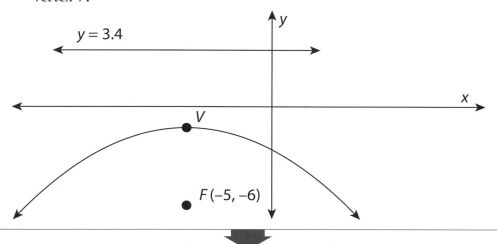

2. To write the equation, first determine the coordinates of the vertex and the value of $p$.

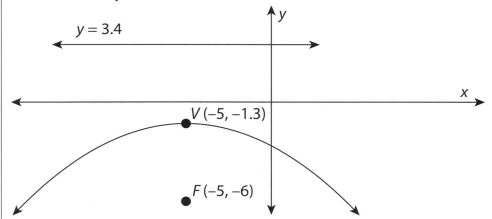

The distance between the focus and the directrix is $2|p|$. So $2|p| = 3.4 - (-6) = 9.4$, and $|p| = 4.7$. The parabola opens down, so $p$ is negative, and therefore $p = -4.7$. The distance between the focus and the vertex is $|p|$, so the vertex is 4.7 units above the focus. Add to find the $y$-coordinate of the vertex: $-6 + 4.7 = -1.3$. The vertex coordinates are (–5, –1.3).

3. Use the results found in step 2 to write the equation.

$(x - h)^2 = 4p(y - k)$        Standard form for a parabola that opens down

$[x - (-5)]^2 = 4(-4.7)[y - (-1.3)]$        Substitute the values for $h$, $p$, and $k$.

$(x + 5)^2 = -18.8(y + 1.3)$        Simplify.

The standard equation is $(x + 5)^2 = -18.8(y + 1.3)$.

4. Solve the standard equation for $y$ to obtain a function that can be graphed.

$(x + 5)^2 = -18.8(y + 1.3)$        Standard equation

$-\dfrac{1}{18.8}(x+5)^2 = y+1.3$        Multiply both sides by $-\dfrac{1}{18.8}$.

$-\dfrac{1}{18.8}(x+5)^2 - 1.3 = y$        Add $-1.3$ to both sides.

5. Graph the function using a graphing calculator.

**On a TI-83/84:**

Step 1: Press [Y=].

Step 2: At Y$_1$, type in [(][(−)][1][ ÷ ][18.8][)][(][X, T, θ, n][+][5][)][$x^2$] [−][1.3].

Step 3: Press [WINDOW] to change the viewing window.

Step 4: At Xmin, enter [(−)][12].

Step 5: At Xmax, enter [12].

Step 6: At Xscl, enter [1].

Step 7: At Ymin, enter [(−)][8].

Step 8: At Ymax, enter [8].

Step 9: At Yscl, enter [1].

Step 10: Press [GRAPH].

*(continued)*

**On a TI-Nspire:**

Step 1: Press the [home] key.

Step 2: Arrow to the graphing icon and press [enter].

Step 3: At the blinking cursor at the bottom of the screen, enter [(] [(−)][1][ ÷ ][18.8][)][(][x][+][5][)][$x^2$][−][1.3].

Step 4: Change the viewing window by pressing [menu], arrowing down to number 4: Window/Zoom, and clicking the center button of the navigation pad.

Step 5: Choose 1: Window settings by pressing the center button.

Step 6: Enter in an appropriate XMin value, −12, by pressing [(−)] and [12], then press [tab].

Step 7: Enter in an appropriate XMax value, [12], then press [tab].

Step 8: Leave the XScale set to "Auto." Press [tab] twice to navigate to YMin and enter an appropriate YMin value, −8, by pressing [(−)] and [8].

Step 9: Press [tab] to navigate to YMax. Enter [8]. Press [tab] twice to leave YScale set to "auto" and to navigate to "OK."

Step 10: Press [enter].

Step 11: Press [menu] and select 2: View and 5: Show Grid.

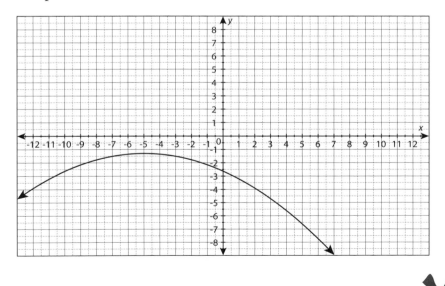

## Example 5

The following diagram shows a plan for a top view of a stage. The back wall is to be on a parabolic curve from $A$ to $B$ so that all sound waves coming from point $F$ that hit the wall are redirected in parallel paths toward the audience. $F$ is the focus of the parabola and $V$ is the vertex.

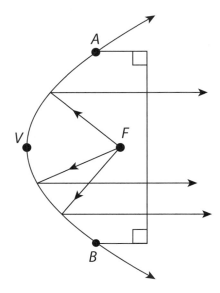

An engineer draws the parabola on a coordinate plane, using feet as the unit of distance. The focus is $(-7, 0)$, the directrix is $x = -25$, and points $A$ and $B$ are on the $y$-axis. What is the equation of the parabola? What is the width of the stage, $AB$?

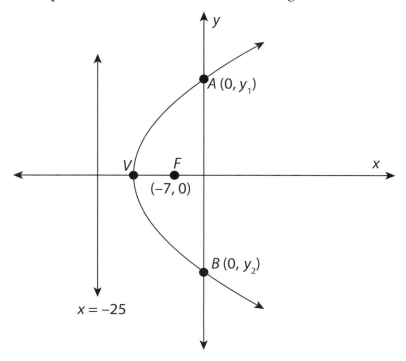

1. To write the equation, first determine the coordinates of the vertex and the value of $p$.

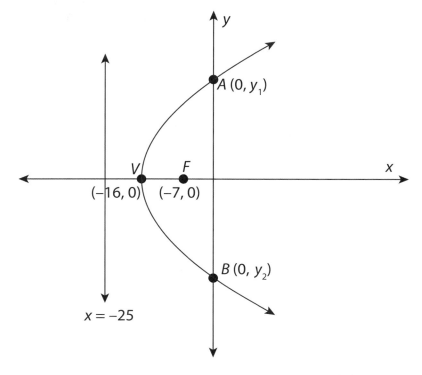

The distance between the focus and the directrix is $2|p|$, so $2|p| = -7 - (-25) = 18$ and $|p| = 9$. The parabola opens right, so $p$ is positive, and therefore $p = 9$. For any parabola, the distance between the focus and the vertex is $|p|$. In this case $|p| = 9$, so the vertex is 9 units left of the focus and therefore the vertex coordinates are (–16, 0).

2. Use the results found in step 1 to write the equation.

$(y - k)^2 = 4p(x - h)$      Standard form for a parabola that opens right or left

$(y - 0)^2 = 4(9)[x - (-16)]$      Substitute the values for $h$, $p$, and $k$.

$y^2 = 36(x + 16)$      Simplify.

The standard equation is $y^2 = 36(x + 16)$.

3. To find the width of the stage, $AB$, first find the $y$-intercepts $y_1$ and $y_2$.

$y^2 = 36(x + 16)$      Equation of the parabola from step 2

$y^2 = 36(0 + 16)$      Substitute 0 for $x$.

$y^2 = 576$      Simplify.

$y = \pm\sqrt{576}$

$y = \pm 24$

So, $y_1 = 24$ and $y_2 = -24$.

$AB = y_1 - y_2 = 24 - (-24) = 48$

The width of the stage is 48 feet.

## Practice 6.6.2: Deriving the Equation of a Parabola

For problems 1–4, derive the standard equation of the parabola with the given focus and directrix. Also, write the equation that shows how you applied the distance formula.

1.  focus: $(0, -3)$; directrix: $y = 3$

2.  focus: $(4, 0)$; directrix: $x = -4$

3.  focus: $(5, 0)$; directrix: $x = 3$

4.  focus: $(4, -8)$; directrix: $y = 4$

For problems 5 and 6, write the standard equation of the parabola with the given focus and directrix.

5.  focus: $(-3, 2)$; directrix: $x = -1$

6.  focus: $(6.2, -1.8)$; directrix: $x = -0.2$

Use what you know about parabolas to solve problems 7–10.

7.  Identify the vertex, focus, and directrix of the parabola whose equation is
    $(y+2)^2 = -\frac{1}{2}(x+4)$.

*continued*

# UNIT 6 • CIRCLES WITH AND WITHOUT COORDINATES
## Lesson 6: Deriving Equations

8.  The diagram below shows a parabolic flashlight reflector. Light rays from the center of the bulb at point *F* are reflected in parallel paths to form a beam of light. A cross section of the reflector is a section of a parabola.

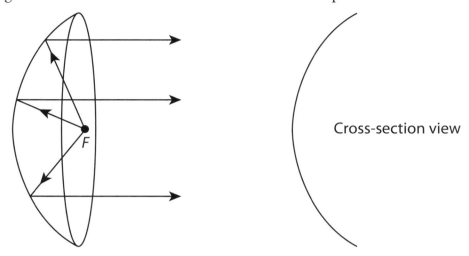

Cross-section view

The parabola is placed on a coordinate plane whose unit of distance is inches. The focus *F* is (0.5, 0) and the directrix is $x = -0.5$. What is the standard equation of the parabola?

9.  The diagram below shows a railroad tunnel opening that is a parabolic curve.

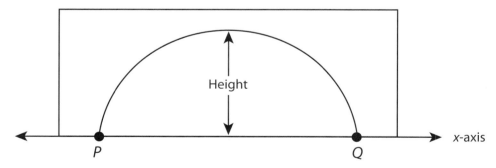

Height

P

Q

*x*-axis

The diagram is placed on a coordinate plane so that points *P* and *Q* are on the *x*-axis, the focus is (15, 10.5), and the directrix is $y = 14.5$. The unit of distance on the grid is feet. What is the standard equation of the parabola? What is the height of the opening? What is *PQ*, the width of the opening at ground level? Sketch the parabola, showing the coordinates of *P*, *Q*, and the vertex.

*continued*

# UNIT 6 • CIRCLES WITH AND WITHOUT COORDINATES
## Lesson 6: Deriving Equations

10. The diagram below shows a radio telescope dish. Incoming light rays reflect off of the dish and toward the feed, located at point $F$. A cross section of the dish is a section of a parabola. The feed is 48 inches above the vertex. The diameter of the dish at the top is 10 feet.

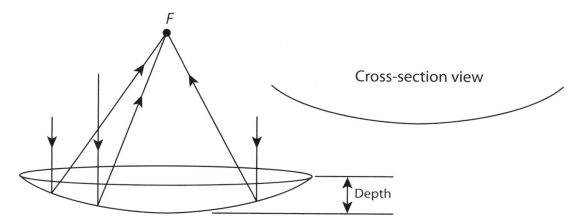

Cross-section view

Depth

An astronomy student draws the parabola on a coordinate plane so that the vertex is at the origin. What is the equation of the parabola on the plane? What is the depth of the dish?

# Lesson 7: Using Coordinates to Prove Geometric Theorems About Circles and Parabolas

**Common Core State Standard**

**G–GPE.4** Use coordinates to prove simple geometric theorems algebraically. *For example, prove or disprove that a figure defined by four given points in the coordinate plane is a rectangle; prove or disprove that the point (1, $\sqrt{3}$) lies on the circle centered at the origin and containing the point (0, 2).*

**Essential Questions**

1. How can you determine whether a point is on a graph?

2. What are some formulas that help describe how points and figures in a coordinate plane are situated with respect to each other?

3. How are equations of quadratic functions related to certain types of parabolas and their equations?

**WORDS TO KNOW**

| | |
|---|---|
| **axis of symmetry of a parabola** | the line through the vertex of a parabola about which the parabola is symmetric. The equation of the axis of symmetry is $x = \dfrac{-b}{2a}$. |
| **circle** | the set of all points in a plane that are equidistant from a reference point in that plane, the center. The set of points forms a 2-dimensional curve that measures 360°. |
| **directrix of a parabola** | a line that is perpendicular to the axis of symmetry of a parabola and that is in the same plane as both the parabola and the focus of the parabola; the fixed line referenced in the definition of a parabola |
| **distance formula** | a formula that states the distance between points $(x_1, y_1)$ and $(x_2, y_2)$ is equal to $\sqrt{(x_2 - x_1)^2 + (y_2 - y_1)^2}$ |

| | |
|---|---|
| **focus of a parabola** | a fixed point on the interior of a parabola that is not on the directrix of the parabola but is on the same plane as both the parabola and the directrix; the fixed point referenced in the definition of a parabola |
| **midpoint formula** | a formula that states the midpoint of the line segment created by connecting $(x_1, y_1)$ and $(x_2, y_2)$ is $\left( \dfrac{x_1 + x_2}{2}, \dfrac{y_1 + y_2}{2} \right)$ |
| **parabola** | the set of all points that are equidistant from a fixed line, called the directrix, and a fixed point not on that line, called the focus. The parabola, directrix, and focus are all in the same plane. The vertex of the parabola is the point on the parabola that is closest to the directrix. |
| **perfect square trinomial** | a trinomial of the form $x^2 + bx + \left( \dfrac{b}{2} \right)^2$ |
| **quadratic function** | a function that can be written in the form $f(x) = ax^2 + bx + c$, where $a \neq 0$. The graph of any quadratic function is a parabola. |
| **slope formula** | a formula that states the slope of the line through (or the line segment connecting) $A\,(x_1, y_1)$ and $B\,(x_2, y_2)$ is $\dfrac{y_2 - y_1}{x_2 - x_1}$ |
| **standard form of an equation of a circle** | $(x - h)^2 + (y - k)^2 = r^2$, where $(h, k)$ is the center and $r$ is the radius |
| **standard form of an equation of a parabola** | $(x - h)^2 = 4p(y - k)$ for parabolas that open up or down; $(y - k)^2 = 4p(x - h)$ for parabolas that open right or left. For all parabolas, $p \neq 0$ and the vertex is $(h, k)$. |
| **theorem** | a statement that is shown to be true |
| **vertex of a parabola** | the point on a parabola that is closest to the directrix and lies on the axis of symmetry |

# Recommended Resources

- IXL Learning. "Lines in the coordinate plane: Slopes of lines."

  http://www.walch.com/rr/00074

  This interactive website gives a series of problems involving slopes of lines and scores them immediately. If the user submits a wrong answer, the correct answer is given and then a thorough explanation is provided, including the slope formula and how it is applied to the problem.

- IXL Learning. "Lines in the coordinate plane: Slopes of parallel and perpendicular lines."

  http://www.walch.com/rr/00075

  This interactive website gives a series of problems involving slopes of lines and whether the lines are parallel, perpendicular, or neither, and scores the problems immediately. If the user submits a wrong answer, the correct answer is given and then a thorough explanation is provided, including the slope conditions required for parallel and perpendicular lines, and how those conditions are applied to the problem.

- IXL Learning. "Points, lines, and segments: Midpoint formula."

  http://www.walch.com/rr/00076

  This interactive website gives a series of problems asking for midpoints of line segments and scores them immediately. If the user submits a wrong answer, the correct answer is given and then a thorough explanation is provided, including the midpoint formula and how it is applied to the problem.

# Lesson 6.7.1: Using Coordinates to Prove Geometric Theorems About Circles and Parabolas

## Introduction

A **theorem** is statement that is shown to be true. Some important theorems have names, such as the Pythagorean Theorem, but many theorems do not have names. In this lesson, we will apply various geometric and algebraic concepts to prove and disprove statements involving circles and parabolas in a coordinate plane. If a statement is proven, it is a theorem. If a statement is disproved, it is not a theorem.

The directions for most problems will have the form "Prove or disprove...," meaning we will work through those problems to discover whether each statement is true or false. Then, at the end of the work, we will state whether we have proved or disproved the statement.

## Key Concepts

- A theorem is any statement that is proven or can be proved to be true.

- The standard form of an equation of a circle with center $(h, k)$ and radius $r$ is $(x-h)^2 + (y-k)^2 = r^2$. This is based on the fact that any point $(x, y)$ is on the circle if and only if $\sqrt{(x-h)^2 + (y-k)^2} = r$.

- Completing the square is the process of determining the value of $\left(\dfrac{b}{2}\right)^2$ and adding it to $x^2 + bx$ to form the perfect square trinomial $x^2 + bx + \left(\dfrac{b}{2}\right)^2$.

- A quadratic function can be represented by an equation of the form $f(x) = ax^2 + bx + c$, where $a \neq 0$.

- The graph of any quadratic function is a parabola that opens up or down.

- A parabola is the set of all points that are equidistant from a fixed line, called the directrix, and a fixed point not on that line, called the focus.

- The parabola, directrix, and focus are all in the same plane.

- The distance between the focus and a point on the parabola is the same as the distance from that point to the directrix.

- The vertex of the parabola is the point on the parabola that is closest to the directrix.

- Every parabola is symmetric about a line called the **axis of symmetry**.

- The axis of symmetry intersects the parabola at the vertex.

- The $x$-coordinate of the vertex is $-\dfrac{b}{2a}$.

- The $y$-coordinate of the vertex is $f\left(-\dfrac{b}{2a}\right)$.

- The standard form of an equation of a parabola that opens up or down and has vertex $(h, k)$ is $(x - h)^2 = 4p(y - k)$, where $p \neq 0$ and $p$ is the distance between the vertex and the focus and between the vertex and the directrix.

- Parabolas that open up or down represent functions, and their equations can be written in either of the following forms: $y = ax^2 + bx + c$ or $(x - h)^2 = 4p(y - k)$. If one form is known, the other can be found.

- The standard form of an equation of a parabola that opens right or left and has vertex $(h, k)$ is $(y - k)^2 = 4p(x - h)$, where $p \neq 0$ and $p$ is the distance between the vertex and the focus and between the vertex and the directrix.

- In any parabola:

    - The focus and directrix are each $|p|$ units from the vertex.

    - The focus and directrix are $2|p|$ units from each other.

# Guided Practice 6.7.1

## Example 1

Given the point $A$ (−6, 0), prove or disprove that point $A$ is on the circle centered at the origin and passing through $\left(-2, -4\sqrt{2}\right)$.

1. Draw a circle on a coordinate plane using the given information.

   You do not yet know if point $A$ lies on the circle, so don't include it in your diagram.

   In the diagram that follows, the name $P$ is assigned to the origin and $G$ is assigned to the known point on the circle.

   To help in plotting points, you can use a calculator to find decimal approximations.

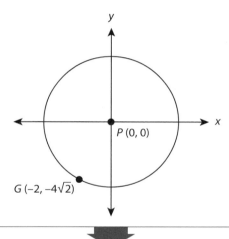

2. Find the radius of the circle using the distance formula.

Use the known points, $P$ and $G$, to determine the radius of the circle.

$r = \sqrt{\left(x_2 - x_1\right)^2 + \left(y_2 - y_1\right)^2}$     Distance formula

$r = \sqrt{\left[(-2) - (0)\right]^2 + \left[\left(-4\sqrt{2}\right) - (0)\right]^2}$  Substitute (0, 0) and $\left(-2, -4\sqrt{2}\right)$ for $(x_1, y_1)$ and $(x_2, y_2)$.

$r = \sqrt{(-2)^2 + \left(-4\sqrt{2}\right)^2}$     Simplify, then solve.

$r = \sqrt{4 + 32}$

$r = \sqrt{36}$

$r = 6$

The radius of the circle is 6 units.

For point $A$ to be on the circle, it must be precisely 6 units away from the center of the circle.

3. Find the distance of point $A$ from the center $P$ to determine whether it is on the circle.

The coordinates of point $P$ are $(0, 0)$.

The coordinates of point $A$ are $(-6, 0)$.

$$AP = \sqrt{\left(x_2 - x_1\right)^2 + \left(y_2 - y_1\right)^2}$$   Distance formula

$$AP = \sqrt{\left[(-6)-(0)\right]^2 + \left[(0)-(0)\right]^2}$$   Substitute $(0, 0)$ and $(-6, 0)$ for $(x_1, y_1)$ and $(x_2, y_2)$.

$$AP = \sqrt{(-6)^2 + (0)^2}$$   Simplify, then solve.

$$AP = \sqrt{(-6)^2}$$

$$AP = \sqrt{36}$$

$$AP = 6$$

Point $A$ is 6 units from the center, and since the radius of the circle is 6 units, point $A$ is on the circle.

The original statement has been proved, so it is a theorem.

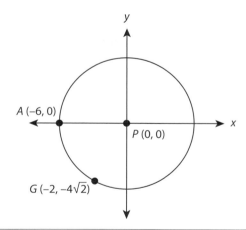

## Example 2

Prove or disprove that the quadratic function graph with vertex (–4, 0) and passing through (0, 8) has its focus at (–4, 1).

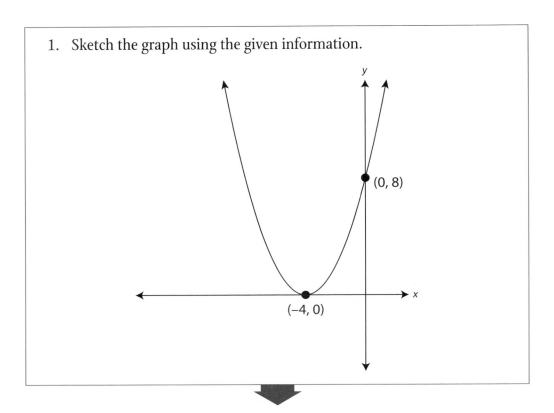

1. Sketch the graph using the given information.

2. Derive an equation of the parabola from its graph.

The parabola opens up, so it represents a function. Therefore, its equation can be written in either of these forms: $y = ax^2 + bx + c$ or $(x - h)^2 = 4p(y - k)$. We were given a vertex and a point on the parabola; therefore, we'll use the form $(x - h)^2 = 4p(y - k)$ and the vertex to begin deriving the equation.

The vertex is $(-4, 0)$, so $h = -4$ and $k = 0$.

| | |
|---|---|
| $(x - h)^2 = 4p(y - k)$ | Standard form of an equation for a parabola that opens up or down |
| $[x - (-4)]^2 = 4p(y - 0)$ | Substitute the vertex $(-4, 0)$ into the equation. |
| $(x + 4)^2 = 4py$ | Simplify, but do not expand the binomial. |

The equation of the parabola is $(x + 4)^2 = 4py$.

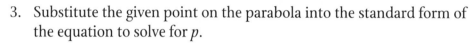

3. Substitute the given point on the parabola into the standard form of the equation to solve for $p$.

The point given is $(0, 8)$.

| | |
|---|---|
| $(x + 4)^2 = 4py$ | Simplified equation from step 2 |
| $(0 + 4)^2 = 4p(8)$ | Substitute the point $(0, 8)$ into the equation. |
| $16 = 32p$ | Simplify and solve for $p$. |
| $p = \dfrac{1}{2}$ | |

4. Use the value of $p$ to determine the focus.

   $p$ is positive, so the focus is directly above the vertex.

   $p = \dfrac{1}{2}$, so the focus is $\dfrac{1}{2}$ unit above the vertex.

   The vertex is $(-4, 0)$, so the focus is $\left(-4, \dfrac{1}{2}\right)$.

   This result disproves the statement that the quadratic function graph with vertex $(-4, 0)$ and passing through $(0, 8)$ has its focus at $(-4, 1)$.

   The statement has been disproved, so it is not a theorem.

   Instead, the following statement has been proved: The quadratic function graph with vertex $(-4, 0)$ and passing through $(0, 8)$ has its focus at $\left(-4, \dfrac{1}{2}\right)$.

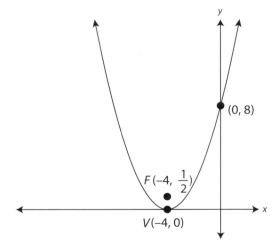

## Example 3

The following information is given about a parabola:

- The vertex $V$ is at $(0, 0)$.

- The focus $F$ is at $(p, 0)$, with $p > 0$.

- The line segment through $F$ is perpendicular to the axis of symmetry and connects two points of the parabola.

Prove that the line segment through $F$ has length $4p$.

1. Make a sketch using the given information.

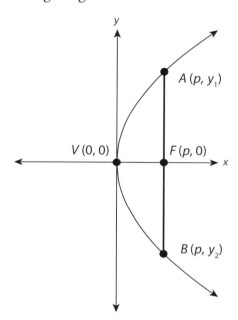

The vertex is $(0, 0)$ and the focus is $F(p, 0)$ with $p > 0$, so $F$ is on the positive $x$-axis. The axis of symmetry is the $x$-axis.

The line segment through $F$, perpendicular to the axis of symmetry, and connecting two points of the parabola is the vertical line segment, $\overline{AB}$. Because the segment is vertical, both $A$ and $B$ have $p$ as their $x$-coordinate, matching the $x$-coordinate of $F$. The $y$-coordinates of $A$ and $B$ are unknown; they are named $y_1$ and $y_2$ in the diagram.

2. Because the parabola opens to the right, its equation has the form $(y - k)^2 = 4p(x - h)$. Use this equation to solve for $y_1$ and $y_2$ in terms of $p$.

| | |
|---|---|
| $(y - k)^2 = 4p(x - h)$ | Standard form of the equation for a parabola that opens right or left |
| $(y - 0)^2 = 4p(x - 0)$ | Substitute $(0, 0)$ for $(h, k)$. |
| $y^2 = 4px$ | Simplify. |
| $(y_1)^2 = 4p \cdot p$ | Substitute the coordinates of point $A$. |
| $(y_1)^2 = 4p^2$ | Simplify. |
| $y_1 = \sqrt{4p^2}$ | $y_1$ is positive, so take the positive square root of $4p^2$. |
| $y_1 = 2p$ | Solve for $y_1$. |
| | |
| $(y_2)^2 = 4p \cdot p$ | Substitute the coordinates of point $B$ into the equation $y^2 = 4px$. |
| $(y_2)^2 = 4p^2$ | Simplify. |
| $y_2 = -\sqrt{4p^2}$ | $y_2$ is negative, so take the negative square root of $4p^2$. |
| $y_2 = -2p$ | Solve for $y_2$. |

3. Use the results from step 2 to find the length of $\overline{AB}$.

$$AB = y_1 - y_2 = 2p - (-2p) = 2p + 2p = 4p$$

For the parabola with vertex $V(0, 0)$ and focus $F(p, 0)$ with $p > 0$, the line segment through $F$ has length $4p$. The original statement has been proved; therefore, it is a theorem.

## Example 4

Prove or disprove that the points $A$ (4, 2), $B$ (–2, 5), $C$ (6, 5), and $D$ (–4, 10) are all on the quadratic function graph with vertex $V$ (2, 1) that passes through $E$ (0, 2).

1. Make a sketch with the given information.

   A quadratic function graph is a parabola. You do not yet know if any of the points $A$, $B$, $C$, or $D$ lie on the parabola, so do not show them in your sketch.

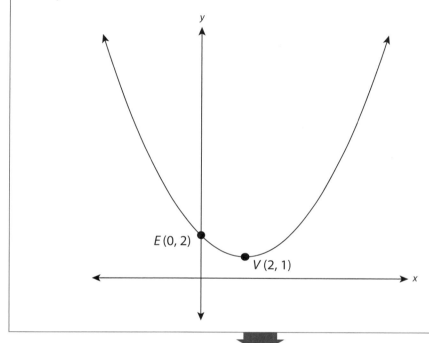

2. Derive an equation of the parabola from its graph.

   The parabola opens up, so it represents a function. Therefore, its equation can be written in either of these forms: $y = ax^2 + bx + c$ or $(x - h)^2 = 4p(y - k)$. We were given a vertex and a point on the parabola, so we'll use the form $(x - h)^2 = 4p(y - k)$ and the vertex to begin deriving the equation.

   The vertex is $(2, 1)$, so $h = 2$ and $k = 1$.

   | | |
   |---|---|
   | $(x - h)^2 = 4p(y - k)$ | Standard form of the equation for a parabola that opens up or down |
   | $(x - 2)^2 = 4p(y - 1)$ | Substitute $(2, 1)$ for $(h, k)$. |

3. Continue to derive the equation of the parabola by finding $p$.

   Use the given point $(0, 2)$ and the equation derived from step 2.

   | | |
   |---|---|
   | $(x - 2)^2 = 4p(y - 1)$ | Derived equation |
   | $[(0) - 2]^2 = 4p[(2) - 1]$ | Substitute point $E\,(0, 2)$ for $(x, y)$. |
   | $(-2)^2 = 4p(1)$ | Simplify, then solve for $p$. |
   | $4 = 4p$ | |
   | $p = 1$ | |

4. Convert the standard form of the equation into the general form of the equation.

Use the value of $p = 1$ and the standard form of the equation derived in step 2.

$(x - 2)^2 = 4p(y - 1)$    Standard form of the equation with the vertex substituted

$(x - 2)^2 = 4(1)(y - 1)$    Standard form of the equation with the value of $p$ substituted

$x^2 - 4x + 4 = 4(y - 1)$    Expand the binomial.

$\dfrac{1}{4}x^2 - x + 1 = y - 1$    Divide both sides of the equation by 4.

$\dfrac{1}{4}x^2 - x + 2 = y$    Add 1 to both sides.

The equation of the parabola is $y = \dfrac{1}{4}x^2 - x + 2$.

5. Determine whether the points $A$, $B$, $C$, and $D$ are on the parabola by substituting their coordinates into the equation.

$A$ (4, 2): $2 = \dfrac{1}{4}(4)^2 - (4) + 2$    Yes, the equation is true, so $A$ is on the parabola.

$B$ (–2, 5): $5 = \dfrac{1}{4}(-2)^2 - (-2) + 2$    Yes, the equation is true, so $B$ is on the parabola.

$C$ (6, 5): $5 = \dfrac{1}{4}(6)^2 - (6) + 2$    Yes, the equation is true, so $C$ is on the parabola.

$D$ (–4, 10): $10 = \dfrac{1}{4}(-4)^2 - (-4) + 2$    Yes, the equation is true, so $D$ is on the parabola.

$A$, $B$, $C$, and $D$ are all on the parabola.

The statement has been proved, so it is a theorem.

## Example 5

Prove or disprove that $P(-2, 1)$, $Q(6, 5)$, $R(8, 1)$, and $S(0, -3)$ are vertices of a rectangle that is inscribed in the circle centered at $C(3, 1)$ and passing through $A\left(1, 1+\sqrt{21}\right)$.

1. Make sketches using the given information.

   You do not yet know if any of the points $P$, $Q$, $R$, or $S$ lie on the circle, so show the polygon on a separate coordinate system. To help in plotting point $A$, you can use a calculator to find a decimal approximation.

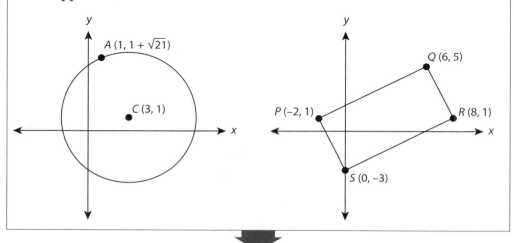

2. Find the radius of the circle.

   $$\text{radius} = AC = \sqrt{(1-3)^2 + \left(1+\sqrt{21}-1\right)^2} = \sqrt{(-2)^2 + \left(\sqrt{21}\right)^2}$$

   $$\text{radius} = AC = \sqrt{4+21} = \sqrt{25} = 5$$

   The radius of the circle is 5 units.

3. Find the distance of points $P$, $Q$, $R$, and $S$ from the center $C$ to determine whether they are on the circle.

$$PC = \sqrt{\left[3-(-2)\right]^2 + (1-1)^2} = \sqrt{(5)^2 + (0)^2} = \sqrt{25} = 5$$

$$QC = \sqrt{(3-6)^2 + (1-5)^2} = \sqrt{(-3)^2 + (-4)^2} = \sqrt{9+16} = \sqrt{25} = 5$$

$$RC = \sqrt{(3-8)^2 + (1-1)^2} = \sqrt{(-5)^2 + (0)^2} = \sqrt{25} = 5$$

$$SC = \sqrt{(3-0)^2 + \left[1-(-3)\right]^2} = \sqrt{(3)^2 + (4)^2} = \sqrt{9+16} = \sqrt{25} = 5$$

$P$, $Q$, $R$, and $S$ are each 5 units from the center, and since the radius is also 5 units, the points are all on the circle.

4. Determine whether $PQRS$ is a rectangle. Use slopes to identify parallel and perpendicular segments.

$$\text{slope of } \overline{PQ} = \frac{5-1}{6-(-2)} = \frac{4}{8} = \frac{1}{2} \qquad \text{slope of } \overline{QR} = \frac{1-5}{8-6} = \frac{-4}{2} = -2$$

$$\text{slope of } \overline{RS} = \frac{-3-1}{0-8} = \frac{-4}{-8} = \frac{1}{2} \qquad \text{slope of } \overline{SP} = \frac{1-(-3)}{-2-0} = \frac{4}{-2} = -2$$

$\overline{PQ}$ is parallel to $\overline{RS}$ and $\overline{QR}$ is parallel to $\overline{SP}$ because they have equal slopes.

Therefore, $PQRS$ is a parallelogram because it has both pairs of opposite sides parallel.

$\overline{PQ}$ is perpendicular to $\overline{QR}$ because the product of their slopes is $-1$:

$$\left(\frac{1}{2}\right)(-2) = -1 \,.$$

Thus, $PQRS$ is a rectangle because it is a parallelogram with a right angle.

5. Steps 2 and 3 allowed us to determine that $P$, $Q$, $R$, and $S$ are all on the circle. Step 4 shows that $PQRS$ is a rectangle. Therefore, $P(-2, 1)$, $Q(6, 5)$, $R(8, 1)$, and $S(0, -3)$ are vertices of a rectangle that is inscribed in the circle centered at $C(3, 1)$ and passing through $A\left(1, 1+\sqrt{21}\right)$.

The statement has been proved, so it is a theorem.

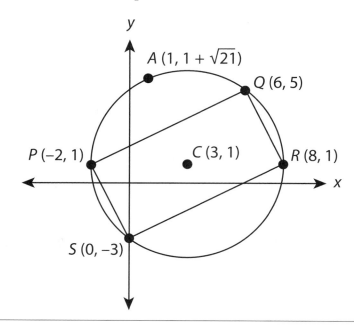

# UNIT 6 • CIRCLES WITH AND WITHOUT COORDINATES

## Lesson 7: Using Coordinates to Prove Geometric Theorems About Circles and Parabolas

### Practice 6.7.1: Using Coordinates to Prove Geometric Theorems About Circles and Parabolas

Use the given information to prove or disprove each statement. Justify your reasoning.

1. Prove or disprove that point $Q\left(-1, -\sqrt{2}\right)$ lies on the circle centered at the origin $R$ and passing through the point $A$ (0, –3).

2. Prove or disprove that point $A$ (0, 7) is on the circle centered at the origin $R$ and passing through the point $P\left(5, 2\sqrt{6}\right)$.

3. Given the points $P$ (–2, 2), $Q$ (4, 8), and $R$ (0, 0), prove or disprove that the points are on the parabola with focus $F\left(0, \dfrac{1}{2}\right)$ and directrix $y = -\dfrac{1}{2}$.

4. Given the points $A$ (–2, –8), $B$ (1, –2), and $C$ (2.25, –10.125), prove or disprove that the points are on the quadratic function graph with focus $F\left(0, -\dfrac{1}{8}\right)$ and directrix $y = \dfrac{1}{8}$.

5. Prove or disprove that the points $A$ (5, 1), $B$ (2, –2), $C$ (6, –2), and $D$ (1, –7) are all on the quadratic function graph with vertex $V$ (4, 2) that passes through $E$ (0, –14).

*continued*

# UNIT 6 • CIRCLES WITH AND WITHOUT COORDINATES
## Lesson 7: Using Coordinates to Prove Geometric Theorems About Circles and Parabolas

6. Prove or disprove that the point $A$ (5, 6) lies on the parabola with focus $F$ (5, 1) and directrix $x = -1$.

7. Prove or disprove that the points $A$ (–5, 12), $B$ (5, 12), and $C$ (0, –13) are the vertices of an isosceles triangle inscribed in the circle centered at the origin $Q$ and passing through the point $P\left(10, \sqrt{69}\right)$.

8. The diagram below shows a target at a carnival dart game. The diagram is on a coordinate system. A player wins a prize by hitting the shaded ring. The ring is formed by two circles. Both circles have center $C$ (12, 12). One circle passes through $P_1$ (6, 20) and the other circle passes through $P_2$ (12, 23). Natasha throws a dart and hits the point $Q$ (19, 4). Does she get a prize? Justify your answer.

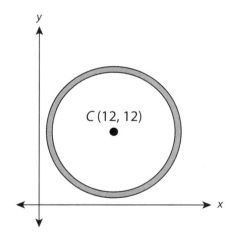

*continued*

# UNIT 6 • CIRCLES WITH AND WITHOUT COORDINATES
## Lesson 7: Using Coordinates to Prove Geometric Theorems About Circles and Parabolas

9. An art student created the following graph to represent the letter $M$. To create the image, she graphed two parabolas intersecting at the point $A$. The parabolas are described as follows:

- a parabola with vertex $V_1$ (6, 8) and focus $F_1$ (6, 5)

- a parabola with vertex $V_2$ (18, 8) and focus $F_2$ (18, 5)

Prove or disprove that point $A$ has coordinates (12, 5).

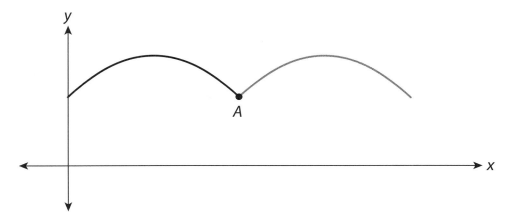

10. The diagram below represents a suspension bridge. The curve is a portion of a parabola. The parabola has vertex $V$ (0, 10) and passes through the point (20, 10.4). Prove or disprove that all points on the parabola are equidistant from the point (0, 260) and the line $y = -240$.

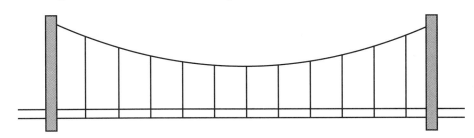

# Answer Key

# Answer Key

## Unit 5: Similarity, Right Triangle Trigonometry, and Proof

### Lesson 1: Line Segments

#### Practice 5.1.1: Midpoints and Other Points on Line Segments, pp. U5-15–U5-16
1. (7, 8)
3. (−6, 4)
5. (4, 10)
7. (8, 7)
9. (7, 5)

### Lesson 2: Investigating Properties of Dilations

#### Practice 5.2.1: Investigating Properties of Parallelism and the Center, pp. U5-30–U5-34
1. The triangle has been dilated. The corresponding sides of the triangle are parallel and the scale factor is consistent ($k = 1/2$). Additionally, the preimage points and image points are collinear with the center of dilation.
3. The rectangle has not been dilated. The scale factor is inconsistent between corresponding sides.
5. $k = 1/3$; reduction
7. $k = 1$; congruency transformation
9. No, because the scale factors of corresponding sides are inconsistent.

#### Practice 5.2.2: Investigating Scale Factors, p. U5-40
1. 10.125
3. 4.6
5. $T'(-3, -1)$, $U'(-2, -2)$, $V'(-2/3, -1)$
7. $N'(-9.6, -3.2)$, $O'(4.8, 8)$, $P'(6.4, -12.8)$
9. $I''(3.375, 2.8125)$, $J''(1.125, 1.125)$, $K''(-1.6875, 2.25)$; $k = 9/16$ or 0.5625

### Lesson 3: Defining and Applying Similarity

#### Practice 5.3.1: Defining Similarity, pp. U5-53–U5-57
1. $\angle C = 44°$, $\angle D = \angle E = 68°$, $CB = 4.5$, $DF = 2.1$
3. The triangles are similar. $\triangle ABC$ can be dilated by a scale factor of 2 with the center at (0, 0) to obtain $\triangle DEF$.
5. Similarity transformations preserve angle measures. The triangles are not similar because the angle measures in each triangle are different.
7. The triangles are similar. $\triangle ABC$ can be dilated by a scale factor of 2/7 with the center at (0, 0) and then rotated 180° clockwise about the origin to obtain $\triangle DEF$.
9. Similarity transformations preserve angle measures. The triangles are not similar because the angle measures in each triangle are different.

#### Practice 5.3.2: Applying Similarity Using the Angle-Angle (AA) Criterion, pp. U5-64–U5-68
1. There is not enough information to determine similarity.
3. Yes, $\triangle ABC \sim \triangle YXZ$ because of the AA Similarity Statement.
5. $\triangle ABC \sim \triangle ZYX$ ; $x = 2$
7. 3 feet
9. 2.16 meters

## Lesson 4: Proving Similarity

### Practice 5.4.1: Proving Triangle Similarity Using Side-Angle-Side (SAS) and Side-Side-Side (SSS) Similarity, pp. U5-79–U5-82

1. $\triangle ABC \sim \triangle FDE$ by SSS
3. $\triangle ABC \sim \triangle DEF$ by SSS
5. $\triangle ABC \sim \triangle EFD$ ; SAS
7. $\triangle ABC \sim \triangle DEF$ ; SSS
9. $x = 5$

### Practice 5.4.2: Working with Ratio Segments, pp. U5-92–U5-95

1. $CD = 12\ 3/8$ units
3. $DE = 8.4$ units
5. $BC = 10$ units; $CD = 12$ units
7. Yes; the sides are proportional.
9. No; the sides are not proportional.

### Practice 5.4.3: Proving the Pythagorean Theorem Using Similarity, pp. U5-105–U5-109

1. $x = 4\sqrt{2} \approx 5.7$ units
3. $x = \sqrt{3} \approx 1.73$ units
5. $a = 2\sqrt{6} \approx 4.9$ units; $e = 1/5; f = 4\ 4/5$
7. $c = 4\sqrt{2} \approx 5.7$ units; $e = f = 2\sqrt{2} \approx 2.8$ units
9. $e = 3.6; f = 6.4$

### Practice 5.4.4: Solving Problems Using Similarity and Congruence, pp. U5-119–U5-124

1. 33 ft
3. 58 1/3 ft
5. 23 m
7. 33.8 ft
9. 7.8 m

## Lesson 5: Proving Theorems About Lines and Angles

### Practice 5.5.1: Proving the Vertical Angles Theorem, pp. U5-145–U5-148

1. Answers may vary. Sample answer: Adjacent angles are $\angle 2$ and $\angle 3$ as well as $\angle 3$ and $\angle 4$. Nonadjacent angles are $\angle 1$ and $\angle 4$ as well as $\angle 5$ and $\angle 2$.
3. $\angle 1$ and $\angle 4$ are vertical angles. Statement: $\angle 1 \cong \angle 4$.
5. $131°$
7. $102°$
9. Since $\overleftrightarrow{AB} \perp \overleftrightarrow{CD}$ as this was given, $\angle 1$ and $\angle 2$, $\angle 2$ and $\angle 3$, and $\angle 1$ and $\angle 4$ all form linear pairs. This means that those pairs of angles are also supplementary by the Supplement Theorem. Therefore, $m\angle 1 + m\angle 2 = 180$, $m\angle 2 + m\angle 3 = 180$, and $m\angle 1 + m\angle 4 = 180$. Given that $\angle 1$ is a right angle, by the definition of right angles, $m\angle 1 = 90$. Use substitution so that $90 + m\angle 2 = 180$, and by the Subtraction Property, $m\angle 2 = 90$. By definition, $\angle 2$ is a right angle. Use substitution so that $90 + m\angle 3 = 180$, and by the Subtraction Property $m\angle 3 = 90$. By definition, $\angle 3$ is a right angle. Use substitution so that $90 + m\angle 4 = 180$, and by the Subtraction Property $m\angle 4 = 90$. By definition, $\angle 4$ is a right angle. Therefore, $\angle 2$, $\angle 3$, and $\angle 4$ are right angles.

## Practice 5.5.2: Proving Theorems About Angles in Parallel Lines Cut by a Transversal, pp. U5-165–U5-169

1. 88°, because alternate interior angles in a set of parallel lines intersected by a transversal are congruent.
3. 86°, because alternate interior angles in a set of lines intersected by a transversal are congruent.
5. 144°, because corresponding angles in a set of lines intersected by a transversal are congruent.
7. 95°
9.

| Statements | Reasons |
|---|---|
| 1. $m \parallel n$ and $\ell$ is the transversal. | 1. Given |
| 2. $\angle 2 \cong \angle 6$ | 2. Corresponding Angles Postulate |
| 3. $\angle 6$ and $\angle 8$ are a linear pair. | 3. Definition of a linear pair |
| 4. $\angle 6$ and $\angle 8$ are supplementary. | 4. If two angles form a linear pair, then they are supplementary. |
| 5. $m\angle 6 + m\angle 8 = 180$ | 5. Supplement Theorem |
| 6. $m\angle 2 + m\angle 8 = 180$ | 6. Substitution |
| 7. $\angle 2$ and $\angle 8$ are supplementary. | 7. Supplement Theorem |

## Lesson 6: Proving Theorems About Triangles

### Practice 5.6.1: Proving the Interior Angle Sum Theorem, pp. U5-186–U5-189

1. $m\angle B = 20$
3. $m\angle B = 81$; $m\angle C = 21$
5. $m\angle A = 92$; $m\angle B = 29$
7. $m\angle CAB = 26$; $m\angle ABC = 24$
9. $m\angle CAB = 10$; $m\angle ABC = 125$

### Practice 5.6.2: Proving Theorems About Isosceles Triangles, pp. U5-203–U5-206

1. $m\angle A = 40$; $m\angle C = 70$
3. $m\angle A = 120$; $m\angle B = m\angle C = 30$
5. $x = 3$
7. $x = 13$
9. $\triangle ABC$ is isosceles; $\angle B \cong \angle C$.

### Practice 5.6.3: Proving the Midsegment of a Triangle, pp. U5-225–U5-231

1. $BC = 12$; $XZ = 7.5$; $m\angle BZX = 55$
3. $XY = 5$
5. $(-9, -2)$, $(5, 8)$, $(5, -2)$
7. Use the slope formula to show that $\overline{EF}$ and $\overline{BC}$ have the same slope equal to $-\frac{3}{4}$. Therefore, $\overline{EF} \parallel \overline{BC}$. Use the distance formula to find $EF = 5$ and $BC = 10$. So, $EF = \frac{1}{2}BC$.
9. The midpoint of $\overline{AC} = (1, 1)$; the midpoint of $\overline{BC} = (4, 2)$; use the slope formula to show that $\overline{EF}$ and $\overline{AB}$ have the same slope equal to $\frac{1}{3}$. Therefore, $\overline{EF} \parallel \overline{AB}$. Use the distance formula to find $EF = \sqrt{10}$ and $AB = 2\sqrt{10}$. So, $EF = \frac{1}{2}AB$.

## Practice 5.6.4: Proving Centers of Triangles, pp. U5-259–U5-261

1. $(-1, -3)$ is the circumcenter of $\triangle ABC$ because the distance from this point to each of the vertices is $\sqrt{10}$.

3. The midpoints of $\triangle ABC$ are $T(7.5, -0.5)$, $U(4, -3)$, and $V(3.5, 0.5)$. The equations of each of the medians of the triangle are $y = 2x - 11$, $y = -x + 4$, and $y = \frac{1}{5}x - 2$. $(5, -1)$ is a solution to the equation of each median.

5. $\triangle ABC$ is an obtuse triangle. The incenter is the intersection of the angle bisectors. The incenter of a triangle is always inside the triangle.

7. It is given that $\triangle ABC$ has perpendicular bisectors $p$, $q$, and $r$ of $\overline{AB}$, $\overline{BC}$, and $\overline{AC}$. $X$ is on the perpendicular bisector of $\overline{AB}$, so it is equidistant from $A$ and $B$. $AX = BX$ by the definition of equidistant. The perpendicular bisector of $\overline{BC}$ also has the point $X$, so $BX = CX$. $AX = CX$ by the Transitive Property of Equality; therefore, $AX = BX = CX$.

9. The incenter should be determined. This center of the triangle is equidistant to the each location within the park. All other locations for the first aid station would create different distances between each location.

## Lesson 7: Proving Theorems About Parallelograms

### Practice 5.7.1: Proving Properties of Parallelograms, pp. U5-281–U5-283

1. No, it's not a parallelogram because opposite sides are not parallel: $m_{\overline{TU}} = 5$, $m_{\overline{VW}} = 2$, $m_{\overline{UV}} = -\frac{2}{3}$, $m_{\overline{WT}} = \frac{1}{3}$.

3. Yes, it's a parallelogram because opposite sides are congruent: $GH = IJ = \sqrt{10}$ and $HI = JG = \sqrt{26}$.

5. Yes, it's a parallelogram because the midpoints of the diagonals are the same, indicating the diagonals bisect each other: $M = \left(3, -\frac{3}{2}\right)$.

7. $m\angle A = m\angle C = 165$ and $m\angle B = m\angle D = 15$; $x = 15$ and $y = 21$

9. Given that $\overline{AB}$ is parallel to $\overline{DE}$, we can use the Alternate Interior Angles Theorem to show that

$m\angle BAH = m\angle DEH$. Given that $\overline{AD}$ is parallel to $\overline{BC}$, the same theorem indicates that

$m\angle ABF = m\angle EAD$. From these pairs of angles, it can be seen that $\triangle ABF \sim \triangle EDA$. Using the full meaning

of the triangles being similar, we can conclude that corresponding sides are in a constant ratio; or, in other words, $\dfrac{AB}{ED} = \dfrac{BF}{DA}$.

### Practice 5.7.2: Proving Properties of Special Quadrilaterals, pp. U5-306–U5-307

1. Quadrilateral $ABCD$ is a parallelogram, a rectangle, a rhombus, and a square. Justification: opposite sides are parallel, consecutive sides are perpendicular, the diagonals bisect each other, and all four sides are congruent.

3. Quadrilateral $JKLM$ is an isosceles trapezoid. Justification: one pair of opposite sides is parallel and the other pair of sides is congruent.

5. Quadrilateral $STUV$ is a parallelogram and a rhombus. Justification: opposite sides are parallel, adjacent sides are not perpendicular, the diagonals are perpendicular, and all four sides are congruent.

7. Quadrilateral $ABCD$ is a kite. Justification: adjacent sides are congruent and the diagonals intersect at a right angle.

9.

| Statements | Reasons |
|---|---|
| 1. Quadrilateral $ABCD$ is a square. | 1. Given |
| 2. $\overline{DP} \cong \overline{PB}$ <br> $\overline{AP} \cong \overline{PC}$ | 2. The diagonals are congruent and bisect each other. |
| 3. $\overline{AC} \perp \overline{DB}$ | 3. The diagonals of a square are perpendicular. |
| 4. $\angle APD \cong \angle APB \cong \angle BPC \cong \angle CPD$, and they are right angles. | 4. Definition of perpendicular lines |
| 5. $\angle APD \cong \angle APB \cong \angle BPC \cong \angle CPD$ | 5. All right angles are congruent. |
| 6. $\triangle APD \cong \triangle APB \cong \triangle CPB \cong \triangle CPD$ | 6. SAS Congruence Statement |

## Lesson 8: Exploring Trigonometric Ratios

### Practice 5.8.1: Defining Trigonometric Ratios, pp. U5-325–U5-329
Answers will vary due to the variation that comes when drawing and measuring or rounding.
1. $\sin A \approx 0.866$; $\cos A = 0.5$; $\tan A \approx 1.732$
3. $\sin B = 0.5$; $\cos B \approx 0.866$; $\tan B \approx 0.577$
5. hypotenuse $= 5$; $m\angle A \approx 37°$; $m\angle B \approx 53°$; $\sin A = 0.6$; $\cos A = 0.8$; $\tan A = 0.75$; $\sin B = 0.8$; $\cos B \approx 0.6$; $\tan B \approx 1.333$
7. The object is 0.288 miles deep; $\tan 30° \approx 0.577$.
9. distance $\approx 0.898$ miles; $\tan 50° \approx 1.192$

### Practice 5.8.2: Exploring Sine and Cosine As Complements, pp. U5-337–U5-339
1. approximately 0.707
3. $\theta = 38°$
5. $\sin 69° \approx 0.934$
7. $\theta = 60°$
9. 640 meters

## Lesson 9: Applying Trigonometric Ratios

### Practice 5.9.1: Calculating Sine, Cosine, and Tangent, pp. U5-356–U5-358
1. $\cos M = \dfrac{21}{29} \approx 0.724$ ; $\tan M = \dfrac{20}{21} \approx 0.952$
3. $72°$
5. 2.812 ft
7. 649.721 ft
9. $YZ = 6.708$ in; $m\angle X = 48.2°$ ; $m\angle Z = 41.8°$

**Practice 5.9.2: Calculating Cosecant, Secant, and Cotangent, pp. U5-368–U5-371**

1. 13.462
3. 102.609
5. $\csc E = \dfrac{5}{3} \approx 1.667$ ; $\sec E = \dfrac{5}{4} \approx 1.25$ ; $\cot E = \dfrac{4}{3} \approx 1.333$
7. 1190.201 ft
9. $\csc B = \dfrac{31}{29} \approx 1.069$ ; $\sec B = \dfrac{29}{11} \approx 2.636$ ; $\cot E = \dfrac{11}{29} \approx 0.379$

**Practice 5.9.3: Problem Solving with the Pythagorean Theorem and Trigonometry, pp. U5-383–U5-385**

1. 31°
3. 7°
5. 29 ft; 41 ft
7. 19°; 15 ft
9. 79°; 226 m

**Practice 5.9.4: Proving the Pythagorean Identity, pp. U5-394–U5-395**

1. $\dfrac{\sqrt{3}}{2}$

3. $\dfrac{\sqrt{7}}{4}$

5. $\sin\theta = \dfrac{5}{17}$ ; $\tan\theta = \dfrac{15}{8}$ ; $\sec\theta = \dfrac{17}{8}$ ; $\csc\theta = \dfrac{17}{15}$ ; $\cot\theta = \dfrac{8}{15}$ ; $\theta \approx 61.93°$

7. $\tan^2\theta$
9. 0.993

# Unit 6: Circles With and Without Coordinates

## Lesson 1: Introducing Circles

### Practice 6.1.1: Similar Circles and Central and Inscribed Angles, pp. U6-18–U6-21
1. 1/48
3. 8/7
5. $x = 100; y = 37.5; z = 85$
7. $x = 90; y = 30$
9. $m\angle B = 50$ ; $m\angle C = 40$

### Practice 6.1.2: Chord Central Angles Conjecture, pp. U6-28–U6-30
1. $m\overgroup{BDC} = 288$
3. $w = 8.5$
5. $a = 8$
7. $b = 5.5$
9. 27.3 mm

### Practice 6.1.3: Properties of Tangents of a Circle, pp. U6-39–U6-42
1. $x = 8$
3. $m\angle ACB = 79$
5. Yes; Sample response: Since the converse of the Pythagorean Theorem is true, $\triangle XYZ$ is a right triangle; therefore, $\angle ZXY$ is a right angle. This makes $\overline{XY}$ perpendicular to $\overline{XZ}$ ; therefore, $\overline{XY}$ is tangent to $\odot Z$ .
7. $\dfrac{3}{2}$
9. 54 feet

## Lesson 2: Inscribed Polygons and Circumscribed Triangles

### Practice 6.2.1: Constructing Inscribed Circles, pp. U6-59–U6-62
1. Students' constructions may vary. Check for accuracy.
3. Students' constructions may vary. Check for accuracy.
5.

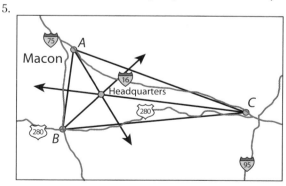

7. 135°
9. $\triangle ABI$ and $\triangle ACI$ are congruent by ASA.

## Practice 6.2.2: Constructing Circumscribed Circles, pp. U6-71–U6-73

1. Students' constructions may vary. Check for accuracy.
3. Students' constructions may vary. Check for accuracy.
5. Construct the circumcenter to find the location where the friends should meet, point $X$.

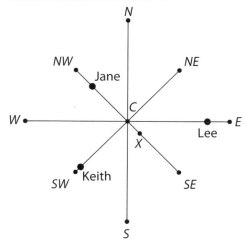

7. The circumcenter is in Room 4; the server should be placed there.

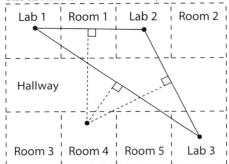

9. Yes, it is possible if the triangle is equilateral. In an equilateral triangle, the angle bisector is the same as the perpendicular bisector.

## Practice 6.2.3: Proving Properties of Inscribed Quadrilaterals, pp. U6-81–U6-84

1. $x = 104; y = 116$
3. Yes, $\overline{BC} \parallel \overline{DE}$ because $m\overarc{CD} = m\overarc{BE}$; these equal arcs have equal chords.
5. No, the consecutive angles are not supplementary.
7. $m\angle A = 95$
9. Yes, but only if one pair of opposite angles are right angles.

## Lesson 3: Constructing Tangent Lines

## Practice 6.3.1: Constructing Tangent Lines, pp. U6-103–U6-105

1. Answers will vary; check students' work for accuracy.
3. Answers will vary; check students' work for accuracy.
5. It was constructed at the midpoint of point $F$ and point $H$.
7. Check that point $M$ was properly constructed using the steps to construct a tangent at point $L$ on the diagram.
9. Answers will vary; check students' work for accuracy.

## Lesson 4: Finding Arc Lengths and Areas of Sectors

### Practice 6.4.1: Defining Radians, p. U6-115

1. $13\pi/9$ radians
3. 2.9 radians
5. 138°
7. 11.78 feet
9. $\approx 1{,}570.80$ feet

### Practice 6.4.2: Deriving the Formula for the Area of a Sector, p. U6-120

1. 705.6 square units
3. $289\pi/45 \approx 20.18$ square units
5. 4 units
7. $25\pi/6 \approx 13.09$ square inches
9. $\approx 1{,}965.94$ square feet

## Lesson 5: Explaining and Applying Area and Volume Formulas

### Practice 6.5.1: Circumference and Area of a Circle, pp. U6-137–U6-138

1. Circumference $\approx 6.28318$ m; perimeter $\approx 6.18$ m. The circumference is larger than the perimeter of the polygon because the circle is larger than the inscribed polygon.
3. The 20-sided polygon gave the closest approximation. Perimeter $\approx 6.2803$ m; the perimeter of the 60-sided polygon is very close to the actual circumference.
5. Area of circle $\approx 3.1416$ m²; area of polygon $\approx 3.09$ m². Some of the area of the circle is not included in the polygon's area.
7. $\approx 97.5$ square feet
9. $\approx 29.66$ feet

### Practice 6.5.2: Volumes of Cylinders, Pyramids, Cones, and Spheres, pp. U6-152–U6-153

1. $\approx 2.09$ cubic feet
3. The cone must have a radius that is $\sqrt{3}$ times larger than the cylinder.
5. $\approx 2{,}583{,}283.33$ m³
7. $\approx 105.22$ cubic centimeters
9. It will overflow because there is more ice cream than space in the cone. The volume of the cone is 45.79 cm³, and the volume of the ice cream is 65.42 cm³.

## Lesson 6: Deriving Equations

### Practice 6.6.1: Deriving the Equation of a Circle, pp. U6-173–U6-174

1. $x^2 + y^2 = 5$
3. $(x - 1.1)^2 + (y + 2)^2 = 1$
5. $x^2 + y^2 + 7x - 2y + 7.49 = 0$
7. center: (5/4, −3); radius = 3/2
9. Standard equation: $x^2 + y^2 = 1600$. Yes, a customer at $\left(-10\sqrt{7}, 30\right)$ will get free delivery because the distance from $\left(-10\sqrt{7}, 30\right)$ to (0, 0) is 40 miles.

**Practice 6.6.2: Deriving the Equation of a Parabola, pp. U6-193–U6-195**

1. $x^2 = -12y$; $\sqrt{(x-0)^2 + (y+3)^2} = \sqrt{(x-x)^2 + (y-3)^2}$

3. $y^2 = 4(x-4)$; $\sqrt{(x-5)^2 + (y-0)^2} = \sqrt{(x-3)^2 + (y-y)^2}$

5. $(y-2)^2 = -4(x+2)$

7. focus: $(-4\,1/8, -2)$; vertex: $(-4, -2)$; directrix: $x = -3\,7/8$

9. equation: $(x-15)^2 = -8(y-12.5)$; height = 12.5 ft; width of $PQ$ = 20 ft

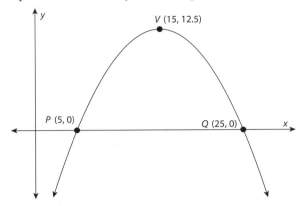

## Lesson 7: Using Coordinates to Prove Geometric Theorems About Circles and Parabolas

### Practice 6.7.1: Using Coordinates to Prove Geometric Theorems About Circles and Parabolas, pp. U6-215–U6-217

1. The statement has been disproved. Justification: The radius = $AR = 3$ and
   $QR = \sqrt{(-1-0)^2 + (-\sqrt{2}-0)^2} = \sqrt{1+2} = \sqrt{3}$. Since $\sqrt{3} \neq 3$, $Q$ does not lie on the circle.

3. The statement has been proved. Justification: $p = 1/2$, the vertex is $R\,(0, 0)$, and the equation is $x^2 = 2y$. $P$, $Q$, and $R$ are all on the parabola.

5. The statement has been proved. Justification: Use the form $y = ax^2 + bx + c$. The point $(0, -14)$ is on the graph, so $c = -14$ and $y = ax^2 + bx - 14$. The vertex is $(4, 2)$, so $-b/2a = 4$, $b = -8a$, and $y = ax^2 - 8ax - 14$. The point $(4, 2)$ is on the graph, so $2 = a(4)^2 - 8a(4) - 14$, $a = -1$, and the equation is $y = -x^2 + 8x - 14$. $A$, $B$, $C$, and $D$ are all on the parabola.

7. The statement has been proved. Justification: The radius =
   $PQ = \sqrt{(10-0)^2 + (\sqrt{69}-0)^2} = \sqrt{100+69} = \sqrt{169} = 13$; $A$, $B$, and $C$ are all on the circle.
   $AC = \sqrt{[0-(-5)]^2 + (-13-12)^2} = \sqrt{25+625} = \sqrt{650} = 5\sqrt{26}$ and
   $BC = \sqrt{(0-5)^2 + (-13-12)^2} = \sqrt{25+625} = \sqrt{650} = 5\sqrt{26}$; therefore, $ABC$ is an isosceles triangle.

9. The statement has been proved. Justification: The left parabola has an equation of the form $(x-h)^2 = 4p(y-k)$ with $p = -3$ and vertex $(h, k) = (6, 8)$, so its equation is $(x-6)^2 = -12(y-8)$. The right parabola has an equation of the form $(x-h)^2 = 4p(y-k)$ with $p = -3$ and vertex $(h, k) = (18, 8)$, so its equation is $(x-18)^2 = -12(y-8)$. The point $A\,(12, 5)$ is on both parabolas because it satisfies both equations.

# Glossary

# Glossary

| English | | Español |
|---|---|---|
| | **A** | |

**absolute value** a number's distance from 0 on a number line; the positive value of a quantity — U2-91 — **valor absoluto** distancia de un número a partir del 0 en una recta numérica; valor positivo de una cantidad

**absolute value function** a function with a variable inside an absolute value — U2-91 — **función de valor absoluto** función con una variable dentro de un valor absoluto

**acute triangle** a triangle in which all of the angles are acute (less than 90°) — U5-170 — **triángulo agudo** triángulo en el que todos los ángulos son agudos (menos de 90°)

**Addition Rule** If $A$ and $B$ are any two events, then the probability of $A$ or $B$, denoted $P(A$ or $B)$, is given by: $P(A$ or $B) = P(A) + P(B) - P(A$ and $B)$. Using set notation, the rule is $P(A \cup B) = P(A) + P(B) - P(A \cap B)$. — U4-1 — **Regla de la suma** Si $A$ y $B$ son dos eventos cualquiera, entonces la probabilidad de $A$ o $B$, que se indica con $P(A$ o $B)$, está dada por: $P(A$ o $B) = P(A) + P(B) - P(A$ y $B)$. Con el uso de notación de conjuntos, la regla es $P(A \cup B) = P(A) + P(B) - P(A \cap B)$.

**adjacent angles** angles that lie in the same plane and share a vertex and a common side. They have no common interior points. — U5-125 — **ángulos adyacentes** ángulos en el mismo plano que comparten un vértice y un lado común. No tienen puntos interiores comunes.

**adjacent side** the leg next to an acute angle in a right triangle that is not the hypotenuse — U5-308 — **lado adyacente** el cateto junto a un ángulo agudo en un triángulo rectángulo que no es la hipotenusa

**alternate exterior angles** angles that are on opposite sides of the transversal and lie on the exterior of the two lines that the transversal intersects — U5-125 — **ángulos exteriores alternos** ángulos en lados opuestos de la transversal que se sitúan en el exterior de las dos líneas que corta la transversal

| English | | Español |
|---------|---|---------|
| **alternate interior angles** angles that are on opposite sides of the transversal and lie within the interior of the two lines that the transversal intersects | U5-125 | **ángulos interiores alternos** ángulos que están en los lados opuestos de la transversal y se ubican en el interior de las dos líneas que corta la transversal |
| **altitude** the perpendicular line from a vertex of a figure to its opposite side; height | U5-69 U5-340 | **altitud** línea perpendicular desde el vértice de una figura hasta su lado opuesto; altura |
| **Angle-Angle (AA) Similarity Statement** If two angles of one triangle are congruent to two angles of another triangle, then the triangles are similar. | U5-41 | **Criterio de semejanza ángulo-ángulo (AA)** Si dos ángulos de un triángulo son congruentes con dos ángulos de otro triángulo, entonces los triángulos son similares. |
| **angle bisector** a ray that divides an angle into two congruent angles | U5-69 U6-43 | **bisectriz del ángulo** semirrecta que divide un ángulo en dos ángulos congruentes |
| **angle of depression** the angle created by a horizontal line and a downward line of sight to an object that is below the observer | U5-340 | **ángulo de depresión** ángulo creado por una línea horizontal y una línea de mira descendente en relación a un objeto que se encuentra por debajo del observador |
| **angle of elevation** the angle created by a horizontal line and an upward line of sight to an object that is above the observer | U5-340 | **ángulo de elevación** ángulo creado por una línea horizontal y una línea de mira ascendente en relación a un objeto que se encuentra por encima del observador |
| **arc** part of a circle's circumference | U6-1 | **arco** parte de la circunferencia de un círculo |
| **arc length** the distance between the endpoints of an arc; written as $m\overset{\frown}{AB}$ | U6-106 | **longitud de arco** distancia entre los extremos de un arco; se expresa como $m\overset{\frown}{AB}$ |
| **arccosine** the inverse of the cosine function, written $\cos^{-1}\theta$ or $\arccos\theta$ | U5-340 | **arcocoseno** inversa de la función coseno; se expresa $\cos^{-1}\theta$ o $\arccos\theta$ |

| English | | Español |
|---|---|---|
| **Archimedes** a Greek mathematician, physician, engineer, and inventor who lived from 287–212 B.C.; considered to be one of the greatest mathematicians of all time | U6-121 | **Arquímedes** fue un matemático, físico, ingeniero e inventor griego que vivió entre 287 y 212 A.C.; se lo considera uno de los matemáticos más importantes de todos los tiempos |
| **arcsine** the inverse of the sine function, written $\sin^{-1}\theta$ or $\arcsin\theta$ | U5-340 | **arcoseno** inversa de la función seno; se expresa $\operatorname{sen}^{-1}\theta$ o $\operatorname{arcsen}\theta$ |
| **arctangent** the inverse of the tangent function, written $\tan^{-1}\theta$ or $\arctan\theta$ | U5-341 | **arcotangente** inversa de la función tangente; se expresa $\tan^{-1}\theta$ o $\arctan\theta$ |
| **asymptote** a line that a function gets closer and closer to as one of the variables increases or decreases without bound | U3-144 | **asíntota** una línea que una función se acerca cada vez más cerca de una de las variables aumenta o disminuye sin límite |
| **average rate of change** the ratio of the difference of output values to the difference of the corresponding input values: $\dfrac{f(b)-f(a)}{b-a}$; a measure of how a quantity changes over some interval | U2-35 | **tasa de cambio promedio** proporción de la diferencia de valores de salida a la diferencia de valores correspondientes de entrada: $\dfrac{f(b)-f(a)}{b-a}$; medida de cuánto cambia una cantidad en cierto intervalo |
| **axis of symmetry of a parabola** the line through the vertex of a parabola about which the parabola is symmetric. The equation of the axis of symmetry is $x=\dfrac{-b}{2a}$. | U2-1 U3-57 U6-196 | **eje de simetría de una parábola** línea que atraviesa el vértice de una parábola sobre la que la parábola es simétrica. La ecuación del eje de simetría es $x=\dfrac{-b}{2a}$. |

| English | | Español |
|---|---|---|
| | **B** | |
| **base** the quantity that is being raised to an exponent in an exponential expression; in $a^x$, $a$ is the base. Also, the side that is opposite the vertex angle of an isosceles triangle. | U1-1 U5-170 | **base** cantidad elevada a un exponente en una expresión exponencial; en $a^x$, $a$ es la base. También, el lado que es opuesto al ángulo vértice de un triángulo isósceles. |
| **base angle** an angle formed by the base and one congruent side of an isosceles triangle | U5-170 | **ángulo base** ángulo formado por la base y un lado congruente de un triángulo isósceles |
| **binomial** a polynomial with two terms | U3-1 | **binomio** polinomio con dos términos |
| **bisect** to cut in half | U6-121 | **bisecar** cortar por la mitad |
| | **C** | |
| **Cavalieri's Principle** The volumes of two objects of equal height are equal if the areas of their corresponding cross sections are in all cases equal. | U6-121 | **Principio de Cavalieri** Los volúmenes de dos objetos de igual altura son iguales si las superficies de sus correspondientes secciones transversales son en todos los casos iguales. |
| **ceiling function** also known as the least integer function; a function represented as $y = \lceil x \rceil$. For any input $x$, the output is the smallest integer greater than or equal to $x$; for example, $\lceil -3 \rceil = -3$, $\lceil 2.1 \rceil = 3$, and $\lceil -2.1 \rceil = -2$. | U2-91 | **función techo** también conocida como función del mínimo entero; función representada como $y = \lceil x \rceil$. Para cualquier entrada $x$, la salida es el entero más pequeño mayor que o igual a $x$; por ejemplo, $\lceil -3 \rceil = -3$, $\lceil 2.1 \rceil = 3$, y $\lceil -2.1 \rceil = -2$. |
| **center of a circle** the point in the plane of the circle from which all points on the circle are equidistant. The center is not part of the circle; it is in the interior of the circle. | U6-154 | **centro de un círculo** punto en el plano del círculo desde el cual son equidistantes todos los puntos del círculo. El centro no es parte del círculo: se encuentra en el interior del círculo. |

| English | | Español |
|---|---|---|
| **center of dilation** a point through which a dilation takes place; all the points of a dilated figure are stretched or compressed through this point | U5-17 | **centro de dilatación** punto a través del cual se produce una dilatación; todos los puntos de una figura dilatada se alargan o comprimen a través de este punto |
| **central angle** an angle with its vertex at the center of a circle | U6-1 U6-121 | **ángulo central** ángulo con su vértice en el centro de un círculo |
| **centroid** the intersection of the medians of a triangle | U5-170 | **centroide** intersección de las medianas de un triángulo |
| **chord** a segment whose endpoints lie on the circumference of the circle | U6-1 | **cuerda** segmento cuyos extremos se ubican en la circunferencia del círculo |
| **circle** the set of all points in a plane that are equidistant from a reference point in that plane, called the center. The set of points forms a two-dimensional curve that measures 360°. | U6-1 U6-154 U6-196 U3-242 | **círculo** conjunto de todos los puntos de un plano equidistantes desde un punto de referencia en ese plano, denominado centro. El conjunto de puntos forma una curva bidimensional que mide 360°. |
| **circumcenter** the intersection of the perpendicular bisectors of a triangle | U5-170 U6-43 | **circuncentro** intersección de las bisectrices perpendiculares de un triángulo |
| **circumference** the distance around a circle; $C = 2\pi r$ or $C = \pi d$, for which $C$ represents circumference, $r$ represents the circle's radius, and $d$ represents the circle's diameter. | U6-1 U6-106 | **circunferencia** distancia alrededor de un círculo; $C = 2\pi r$ o $C = \pi d$, en donde $C$ representa la circunferencia, $r$ representa el radio del círculo y $d$, su diámetro. |
| **circumscribed angle** the angle formed by two tangent lines whose vertex is outside of the circle | U6-1 | **ángulo circunscrito** ángulo formado por dos líneas tangentes cuyo vértice está fuera del círculo |
| **circumscribed circle** a circle that contains all vertices of a polygon | U5-170 U6-43 | **círculo circunscrito** círculo que contiene todos los vértices de un polígono |

| English | | Español |
|---|---|---|
| **circumscribed triangle** triangle whose sides are tangent to an interior circle | U6-43 | **triángulo circunscrito** triángulo cuyos lados son tangentes a un círculo interior |
| **closed interval** an interval that includes its endpoints | U3-144 | **intervalo cerrado** intervalo que incluye sus extremos |
| **closure** a system is closed, or shows closure, under an operation if the result of the operation is within the system | U1-18 | **cierre** un sistema es cerrado, o tiene cierre, en una operación si el resultado de la misma está dentro del sistema |
| **coefficient** the number multiplied by a variable in an algebraic expression | U3-1 | **coeficiente** número multiplicado por una variable en una expresión algebraica |
| **cofunction** a trigonometric function whose ratios have the same values when applied to the two acute angles in the same right triangle. The sine of one acute angle is the cofunction of the cosine of the other acute angle. | U5-308 | **cofunción** función trigonométrica cuyas proporciones tienen los mismos valores cuando se aplican a los dos ángulos agudos en el mismo triángulo rectángulo. El seno de un ángulo agudo es la cofunción del coseno del otro ángulo agudo. |
| **collinear points** points that lie on the same line | U5-17 | **puntos colineales** puntos que se ubican en la misma línea |
| **combination** a subset of a group of objects taken from a larger group of objects; the order of the objects does not matter, and objects may be repeated. A combination of size $r$ from a group of $n$ objects can be represented using the notation $_nC_r$, where $_nC_r = \dfrac{n!}{(n-r)!r!}$. | U4-99 | **combinación** subconjunto de un grupo de objetos tomado de un grupo de objetos más grande; el orden de los objetos no importa y los objetos pueden repetirse. Una combinación de tamaño $r$ de un grupo de $n$ objetos puede representarse con la notación $_nC_r$, donde $_nC_r = \dfrac{n!}{(n-r)!r!}$. |

| English | | Español |
|---|---|---|
| **common external tangent** a tangent that is common to two circles and does not intersect the segment joining the radii of the circles | U6-85 | **tangente común externa** tangente común a dos círculos que no corta el segmento que une los radios de los círculos |
| **common internal tangent** a tangent that is common to two circles and intersects the segment joining the radii of the circles | U6-85 | **tangente común interna** tangente común a dos círculos que corta el segmento que une los radios de los círculos |
| **common tangent** a line tangent to two circles | U6-85 | **tangente común** recta tangente a dos círculos |
| **complement** a set whose elements are not in another set, but are in some universal set being considered. The complement of set $A$, denoted by $\overline{A}$, is the set of elements that are in the universal set, but not in $A$. The event does not occur. The probability of an event not occurring is 1 minus the probability of the event occurring, $P(\overline{A}) = 1 - P(A)$. | U4-1 | **complemento** conjunto cuyos elementos no se encuentran en otro conjunto, pero están en algún conjunto universal que se considera. El complemento del conjunto $A$, que se indica con $\overline{A}$, es el conjunto de elementos que se encuentran en el conjunto universal, pero no en $A$. El evento no se produce. La probabilidad de que un evento no se produzca es 1 menos la probabilidad de que se produzca, $P(\overline{A}) = 1 - P(A)$. |
| **complementary angles** two angles whose sum is 90° | U5-125 U5-308 | **ángulos complementarios** dos ángulos cuya suma es 90° |
| **complex conjugate** the complex number that when multiplied by another complex number produces a value that is wholly real; the complex conjugate of $a + bi$ is $a - bi$ | U1-34 | **conjugado de número complejo** número complejo que cuando se multiplica por otro número complejo produce un valor totalmente real; el conjugado complejo de $a + bi$ es $a - bi$ |
| **complex conjugates** two complex numbers of the form $a + bi$ and $a - bi$ | U3-108 | **conjugados de números complejos** dos números complejos de la forma $a + bi$ y $a - bi$ |

| English | | Español |
|---|---|---|
| **complex number** a number in the form $a + bi$, where $a$ and $b$ are real numbers, and $i$ is the imaginary unit | U1-34 U3-108 | **número complejo** número en la forma $a + bi$, donde $a$ y $b$ son números reales e $i$ es la unidad imaginaria |
| **complex number system** all numbers of the form $a + bi$, where $a$ and $b$ are real numbers, including complex numbers (neither $a$ nor $b$ equal 0), real numbers ($b = 0$), and imaginary numbers ($a = 0$) | U1-34 | **sistema de números complejos** todos los números de la forma $a + bi$, donde $a$ y $b$ son números reales, incluidos los números complejos (ni $a$ ni $b$ son iguales a 0), reales ($b = 0$) e imaginarios ($a = 0$) |
| **compound event** the combination of two or more simple events | U4-48 | **evento compuesto** combinación de dos o más eventos simples |
| **compound interest** interest earned on both the initial amount and on previously earned interest | U3-221 | **interés compuesto** interés devengado tanto de la cantidad inicial como del interés previamente devengado |
| **compound probability** the probability of compound events | U4-48 | **probabilidad compuesta** probabilidad de eventos compuestos |
| **compression** a transformation in which a figure becomes smaller; compressions may be horizontal (affecting only horizontal lengths), vertical (affecting only vertical lengths), or both | U5-17 | **compresión** transformación en la que una figura se hace más pequeña; las compresiones pueden ser horizontales (cuando afectan sólo la longitud horizontal), verticales (cuando afectan sólo la longitud vertical), o en ambos sentidos |
| **concave down** a graph of a curve that is bent downward, such as a quadratic function with a maximum value | U2-36 | **cóncavo hacia abajo** gráfico de una curva que se inclina hacia abajo, tal como una función cuadrática con un valor máximo |
| **concave polygon** a polygon with at least one interior angle greater than 180° and at least one diagonal that does not lie entirely inside the polygon | U5-262 | **polígono cóncavo** polígono con al menos un ángulo interior de más de 180° y con al menos una diagonal que no se ubica por completo dentro de él |

| English | | Español |
|---|---|---|
| **concave up** a graph of a curve that is bent upward, such as a quadratic function with a minimum value | U2-36 | **cóncavo hacia arriba** gráfico de una curva que se inclina hacia arriba, tal como una función cuadrática con un valor mínimo |
| **concavity** with respect to a curve, the property of being arched upward or downward. A quadratic with positive concavity will increase on either side of the vertex, meaning that the vertex is the minimum or lowest point of the curve. A quadratic with negative concavity will decrease on either side of the vertex, meaning that the vertex is the maximum or highest point of the curve. | U2-36 U2-69 | **concavidad** con respecto a una curva, la propiedad de ser arqueado hacia arriba o hacia abajo. Una función cuadrática con concavidad positiva se incrementará en ambos lados del vértice, lo que significa que el vértice es el punto mínimo o más bajo de la curva. Una función cuadrática con concavidad negativa disminuirá a cada lado del vértice, lo que significa que el vértice es el punto máximo o más alto de la curva. |
| **concentric circles** coplanar circles that have the same center | U6-1 | **círculos concéntricos** círculos coplanares que tienen el mismo centro |
| **concurrent lines** lines that intersect at one point | U5-171 | **rectas concurrentes** rectas con intersección en un punto |
| **conditional probability of $B$ given $A$** the probability that event $B$ occurs, given that event $A$ has already occurred. If $A$ and $B$ are two events from a sample space with $P(A) \neq 0$, then the conditional probability of $B$ given $A$, denoted $P(B|A)$, has two equivalent expressions: $$P(B|A) = \frac{P(A \text{ and } B)}{P(A)} =$$ $$\frac{\text{number of outcomes in } (A \text{ and } B)}{\text{number of outcomes in } A}.$$ | U4-48 | **probabilidad condicional de $B$ dado $A$** la probabilidad de que el evento $B$ se produzca, dado que el evento $A$ ya se ha producido. Si $A$ y $B$ son dos eventos de un espacio muestral con $P(A) \neq 0$, entonces la probabilidad condicional de $B$ dado $A$, indicado $P(B|A)$ tiene dos expresiones equivalentes: $$P(B|A) = \frac{P(A \text{ y } B)}{P(A)} =$$ $$\frac{\text{numero de resultados en } (A \text{ y } B)}{\text{numero de resultados en } A}.$$ |

| English | | Español |
|---|---|---|
| **cone** a solid or hollow object that tapers from a circular or oval base to a point | U6-122 | **cono** objeto sólido o hueco que se estrecha desde una base circular u ovalada hasta un punto |
| **congruency transformation** a transformation in which a geometric figure moves but keeps the same size and shape; a dilation where the scale factor is equal to 1 | U5-17 | **transformación de congruencia** transformación en la cual una figura geométrica se mueve pero mantiene el mismo tamaño y la misma forma; dilatación en la que el factor de escala es igual a 1 |
| **congruent arcs** two arcs that have the same measure and are either of the same circle or of congruent circles | U6-2 | **arcos congruentes** dos arcos que tienen la misma medida y son parte del mismo círculo o de círculos congruentes |
| **consecutive angles** angles that lie on the same side of a figure | U5-262 | **ángulos consecutivos** ángulos ubicados en el mismo lado de una figura |
| **constant term** a term whose value does not change | U3-1 | **término constante** término cuyo valor no cambia |
| **converse of the Pythagorean Theorem** If the sum of the squares of the measures of two sides of a triangle equals the square of the measure of the longest side, then the triangle is a right triangle. | U5-69 | **conversa del teorema de Pitágoras** Si la suma de los cuadrados de las medidas de dos lados de un triángulo equivale al cuadrado de la medida del lado más largo, entonces el triángulo es rectángulo. |
| **convex polygon** a polygon with no interior angle greater than 180°; all diagonals lie inside the polygon | U5-262 | **polígono convexo** polígono sin ángulo interior de más de 180°; todas las diagonales están dentro del polígono |
| **coordinate proof** a proof that involves calculations and makes reference to the coordinate plane | U5-171 | **prueba de coordenadas** prueba que involucra cálculos y hace referencia al plano de coordenadas |

| English | | Español |
|---|---|---|

| | | |
|---|---|---|
| **corollary** a theorem that accompanies another theorem and is usually easily deduced from the other theorem | U3-108 | **corolario** teorema que acompaña a otro teorema y por lo general se deduce con facilidad del primero |
| **Corollary to the Fundamental Theorem of Algebra** If $P(x)$ is a polynomial function of degree $n \geq 1$ with complex coefficients, then the related equation $P(x) = 0$ has exactly $n$ complex solutions (roots), if a double solution is counted as two separate solutions. | U3-108 | **Corolario del teorema fundamental del álgebra** Si $P(x)$ es una función polinómica de grado $n \geq 1$ con coeficientes complejos, entonces la ecuación relacionada $P(x) = 0$ tiene exactamente $n$ soluciones complejas (raíces), si una solución doble se cuenta como dos soluciones individuales. |
| **corresponding angles** angles in the same relative position with respect to the transversal and the intersecting lines | U5-125 | **ángulos correspondientes** ángulos en la misma posición relativa con respecto a las líneas transversal y de intersección |
| **corresponding sides** sides of two figures that lie in the same position relative to the figure. In transformations, the corresponding sides are the preimage and image sides, so $\overline{AB}$ and $\overline{A'B'}$ are corresponding sides and so on. | U5-17 | **lados correspondientes** lados de dos figuras que están en la misma posición relativa a la figura. En las transformaciones, los lados correspondientes son los de preimagen e imagen, entonces $\overline{AB}$ y $\overline{A'B'}$ son los lados correspondientes, etc. |
| **cosecant** the reciprocal of the sine ratio, $\csc\theta = \dfrac{1}{\sin\theta}$; the cosecant of $\theta = \csc\theta = \dfrac{\text{length of hypotenuse}}{\text{length of opposite side}}$ | U5-308 U5-341 | **cosecante** razón inversa del seno, $\csc\theta = \dfrac{1}{\operatorname{sen}\theta}$; la cosecante de $\theta = \csc\theta = \dfrac{\text{longitud de la hipotenusa}}{\text{longitud del lado opuesto}}$ |

| English | | Español |
|---|---|---|
| **cosine** a trigonometric function of an acute angle in a right triangle that is the ratio of the length of the side adjacent to the length of the hypotenuse; the cosine of $\theta =$ $$\cos \theta = \frac{\text{length of adjacent side}}{\text{length of hypotenuse}}$$ | U5-308 | **coseno** función trigonométrica de un ángulo agudo en un triángulo rectángulo que es la proporción de la longitud de lado adyacente a la longitud de la hipotenusa; el coseno de $\theta = \cos \theta =$ $$\frac{\text{longitud del lado adyacente}}{\text{longitud de la hipotenusa}}$$ |
| **cotangent** the reciprocal of tangent, $\cot \theta = \dfrac{1}{\tan \theta}$; the cotangent of $\theta = \cot \theta =$ $$\frac{\text{length of adjacent side}}{\text{length of opposite side}}$$ | U5-309 U5-341 | **cotangente** recíproco de la tangente, $\cot \theta = \dfrac{1}{\tan \theta}$; la cotangente de $\theta = \cot \theta =$ $$\frac{\text{longitud del lado adyacente}}{\text{longitud del lado opuesto}}$$ |
| **critical number of a polynomial inequality** an $x$-value that makes $f(x) = 0$, where $f(x)$ is a polynomial function and the inequality is written in any of these forms: $f(x) < 0, f(x) \leq 0, f(x) > 0,$ or $f(x) \geq 0$ | U3-144 | **número crítico de una desigualdad polinómica** valor de $x$ que hace $f(x) = 0$, donde $f(x)$ es una función polinómica y la desigualdad se expresa en cualquiera de estas formas: $f(x) < 0, f(x) \leq 0, f(x) > 0,$ o $f(x) \geq 0$ |
| **critical number of a rational inequality** an $x$-value that makes $f(x) = 0$ or makes $f(x)$ undefined, where $f(x)$ is a rational function and the inequality is written in any of these forms: $f(x) < 0,$ $f(x) \leq 0, f(x) > 0,$ or $f(x) \geq 0$ | U3-144 | **número crítico de una desigualdad racional** valor de $x$ que hace $f(x) = 0$ o $f(x)$ indefinido, donde $f(x)$ es una función racional y la desigualdad se expresa en cualquiera de estas formas: $f(x) < 0, f(x) \leq 0, f(x) > 0,$ o $f(x) \geq 0$ |

| English | | Español |
|---|---|---|
| **cube root** For any real numbers $a$ and $b$, if $a^3 = b$, then $a$ is a cube root of $b$. The cube root of $b$ is written using a radical: $\sqrt[3]{b}$ . | U2-91 | **raíz cúbica** para cualquiera de los números reales $a$ y $b$, si $a^3 = b$, entonces $a$ es la raíz cúbica de $b$. La raíz cúbica de $b$ se escribe con un radical: $\sqrt[3]{b}$ . |
| **cube root function** a function that contains the cube root of a variable. The general form is $y = a\sqrt[3]{(x-h)} + k$, where $a$, $h$, and $k$ are real numbers. | U2-91 | **función raíz cúbica** función que contiene la raíz cúbica de una variable. La forma general es $y = a\sqrt[3]{(x-h)} + k$, donde $a$, $h$, y $k$ son números reales. |
| **curve** the graphical representation of the solution set for $y = f(x)$. In the special case of a linear equation, the curve will be a line. | U2-69 | **curva** representación gráfica del conjunto de soluciones para $y = f(x)$. En el caso especial de una ecuación lineal, la curva será una recta. |
| **cylinder** a solid or hollow object that has two parallel bases connected by a curved surface; the bases are usually circular | U6-122 | **cilindro** objeto sólido o hueco que tiene dos bases paralelas conectadas por medio de una superficie curva; las bases por lo general son circulares |

**D**

| English | | Español |
|---|---|---|
| **decay factor** $1 - r$ in the exponential decay model $f(t) = a(1 - r)^t$, or $b$ in the exponential function $f(t) = ab^t$ if $0 < b < 1$; the multiple by which a quantity decreases over time. The general form of an exponential function modeling decay is $f(t) = a(1 - r)^t$. | U2-153 U3-221 | **factor de decaimiento** $1 - r$ en el modelo de decaimiento exponencial $f(t) = a(1 - r)^t$, o $b$ en la función exponencial $f(t) = ab^t$ si $0 < b < 1$; el múltiplo por el que una cantidad disminuye con el tiempo. La forma general de una función exponencial que determina decaimiento es $f(t) = a(1 - r)^t$. |
| **decay rate** $r$ in the exponential decay model $f(t) = a(1 - r)^t$ | U2-153 U3-221 | **tasa de decaimiento** $r$ en el modelo de decaimiento exponencial $f(t) = a(1 - r)^t$ |

| English | | Español |
|---|---|---|
| **decreasing** the interval of a function for which the output values are becoming smaller as the input values are becoming larger | U2-36 | **decreciente** intervalo de una función por el que los valores de salida se hacen más pequeños a medida que los valores de entrada se hacen más grandes |
| **decreasing function** a function such that as the independent values increase, the dependent values decrease | U2-91 | **función decreciente** función en la que a medida que aumentan los valores independientes, disminuyen los dependientes |
| **degree of a one-variable polynomial** the greatest exponent attached to the variable in the polynomial | U3-108 | **grado de un polinomio de una variable** el mayor exponente anexado a la variable en el polinomio |
| **dependent events** events that are not independent. The outcome of one event affects the probability of the outcome of another event. | U4-1 U4-48 | **eventos dependientes** eventos que no son independientes. El resultado de un evento afecta la probabilidad del resultado de otro. |
| **dependent variable** labeled on the *y*-axis; the quantity that is based on the input values of the independent variable; the output variable of a function | U3-144 | **variable dependiente** designada en el eje de *y*; cantidad que se basa en los valores de entrada de la variable independiente; variable de salida de una función |
| **diagonal** a line that connects nonconsecutive vertices | U5-262 | **diagonal** línea que conecta vértices no consecutivos |
| **diameter** a straight line passing through the center of a circle connecting two points on the circle; equal to twice the radius | U6-2 | **diámetro** línea recta que atraviesa el centro de un círculo y conecta dos puntos en él; equivale a dos veces del radio |
| **dilation** a transformation in which a figure is either enlarged or reduced by a scale factor in relation to a center point | U5-18 | **dilatación** transformación en la que una figura se amplía o se reduce por un factor de escala en relación con un punto central |

| English | | Español |
|---|---|---|
| **directrix of a parabola** a line that is perpendicular to the axis of symmetry of a parabola and that is in the same plane as both the parabola and the focus of the parabola; the fixed line referenced in the definition of a parabola | U6-154 U6-196 | **directriz de una parábola** línea perpendicular al eje de simetría de una parábola que está en el mismo plano tanto de la parábola como de su foco; línea fija mencionada en la definición de parábola |
| **discriminant** an expression whose solved value indicates the number and types of solutions for a quadratic. For a quadratic equation in standard form ($ax^2 + bx + c = 0$), the discriminant is $b^2 - 4ac$. | U3-18 | **discriminante** expresión cuyo valor resuelto indica la cantidad y los tipos de soluciones para una ecuación cuadrática. En una ecuación cuadrática en forma estándar ($ax^2 + bx + c = 0$), el discriminante es $b^2 - 4ac$. |
| **disjoint events** events that have no outcomes in common. If $A$ and $B$ are disjoint events, then they cannot both occur. Disjoint events are also called mutually exclusive events. | U4-2 | **eventos disjuntos** eventos que no tienen resultados en común. Si $A$ y $B$ son eventos disjuntos, entonces no pueden producirse ambos. También se denominan eventos mutuamente excluyentes. |
| **dissection** breaking a figure down into its components | U6-122 | **disección** desglose de una figura en sus componentes |
| **distance formula** a formula that states the distance between points $(x_1, y_1)$ and $(x_2, y_2)$ is equal to $\sqrt{\left(x_2 - x_1\right)^2 + \left(y_2 - y_1\right)^2}$ | U5-1 U6-154 U6-196 | **fórmula de distancia** fórmula que señala la distancia entre puntos $(x_1, y_1)$ y $(x_2, y_2)$ es igual a $\sqrt{\left(x_2 - x_1\right)^2 + \left(y_2 - y_1\right)^2}$ |
| **dodecagon** a 12-sided polygon | U6-122 | **dodecágono** polígono de 12 lados |
| **domain** the set of all input values ($x$-values) that satisfy the given function without restriction | U2-36 U2-92 U3-144 | **dominio** conjunto de todos los valores de entrada (valores de $x$) que satisfacen la función dada sin restricciones |
| **double root** two roots that are equal | U3-109 | **raíz doble** dos raíces que son iguales |
| **double solution** two solutions that are equal | U3-109 | **solución doble** dos soluciones que son iguales |

| English | | Español |
|---|---|---|
| | **E** | |
| **element** an item in a set; also called a member | U4-2 | **elemento** ítem en un conjunto; también se denomina miembro |
| **empty set** a set that has no elements, denoted by $\varnothing$. The empty set is also called the null set. | U4-2 | **conjunto vacío** conjunto que no contiene elementos, indicado con $\varnothing$. También se denomina conjunto nulo. |
| **end behavior** the behavior of the graph as $x$ approaches positive infinity and as $x$ approaches negative infinity | U2-36 U3-145 | **comportamiento final** el comportamiento de la gráfica al aproximarse $x$ a infinito positivo o a infinito negativo |
| **enlargement** a dilation of a figure where the scale factor is greater than 1 | U5-18 | **ampliación** dilatación de una figura en la que el factor de escala es mayor que 1 |
| **equal sets** sets with all the same elements | U4-2 | **conjuntos iguales** conjuntos con todos los mismos elementos |
| **equiangular** having equal angles | U5-171 | **equiangular** que tiene ángulos iguales |
| **equidistant** a point or points that lie the same distance away from a given object | U5-125 U6-43 | **equidistante** punto o puntos que están a la misma distancia de un determinado objeto |
| **equilateral triangle** a triangle with all three sides equal in length | U5-171 | **triángulo equilátero** triángulo que tiene los tres lados de la misma longitud |
| **even function** a function that, when evaluated for $-x$, results in a function that is the same as the original function; $f(-x) = f(x)$ | U2-36 | **función par** función que, cuando se la evalúa para $-x$, tiene como resultado una función que es igual a la original; $f(-x) = f(x)$ |
| **event** an outcome or set of outcomes of an experiment. An event is a subset of the sample space. | U4-2 | **evento** resultado o conjunto de resultados de un experimento. Un evento es un subconjunto del espacio de muestral. |
| **expected value** an estimate of value that is determined by finding the product of a total value and a probability of a given event | U4-120 | **valor esperado** estimación de valor que se determina al encontrar el producto de un valor total y una probabilidad de un evento determinado |

| English | | Español |
|---|---|---|
| **experiment** a process or action that has observable results. The results are called outcomes. | U4-2 | **experimento** proceso o acción con consecuencias observables. Las consecuencias se denominan resultados. |
| **exponent** the number which tells how many times a number is multiplied by itself; in the expression $a^x$, the exponent is $x$ | U1-1 | **exponente** el número que indica cuántas veces un número se multiplica por sí mismo; en la expresión $a^x$, $x$ es el exponente |
| **exponential decay** an exponential equation with a base, $b$, that is between 0 and 1 ($0 < b < 1$); can be represented by the formula $y = a(1 - r)^t$, where $a$ is the initial value, $(1 - r)$ is the decay rate, $t$ is time, and $y$ is the final value | U2-154 U3-221 | **decaimiento exponencial** ecuación exponencial con una base, $b$, que está entre 0 y 1 ($0 < b < 1$); puede representarse con la fórmula $y = a(1 - r)^t$, en la que $a$ es el valor inicial, $(1 - r)$ es la tasa de decaimiento, $t$ es el tiempo y $y$ es el valor final |
| **exponential decay model** an exponential function, $f(t) = a(1 - r)^t$, where $f(t)$ is the final output value at the end of $t$ time periods, $a$ is the initial value, $r$ is the percent decrease per time period (expressed as a decimal), and $t$ is the number of time periods | U2-154 U3-222 | **modelo de decaimiento exponencial** función exponencial, $f(t) = a(1 - r)^t$, en la que $f(t)$ es el valor de salida final despues de $t$ períodos de tiempo, $a$ es el valor inicial, $r$ es el porcentaje de disminución por período (expresado como decimal), y $t$ es la cantidad de períodos |
| **exponential equation** an equation that has a variable in the exponent | U1-1 | **ecuación exponencial** una ecuación que tiene una variable en el exponente |
| **exponential expression** an expression that contains a base and a power/exponent | U1-2 U3-222 | **expresión exponencial** expresión que incluye una base y una potencia o exponente |
| **exponential function** a function with the general form $f(t) = ab^t$, where $a$ is the initial value, $b$ is the growth or decay factor, $t$ is the time, and $f(t)$ is the final output value | U2-154 U3-222 | **función exponencial** función con la forma general $f(t) = ab^t$, en la que $a$ es el valor inicial, $b$ es el factor de crecimiento o decaimiento, $t$ es el tiempo, y $f(t)$ es el valor de salida final |

| English | | Español |
|---|---|---|
| **exponential growth** an exponential function with a base, $b$, greater than 1 ($b > 1$); can be represented by the formula $f(t) = a(1 + r)^t$, where $a$ is the initial value, $(1 + r)$ is the growth rate, $t$ is time, and $f(t)$ is the final value | U2-154 U3-222 | **crecimiento exponencial** función exponencial con una base, $b$, mayor que 1 ($b > 1$); puede representarse la fórmula $f(t) = a(1 + r)^t$, en la que $a$ es el valor inicial, $(1 + r)$ es la tasa de crecimiento, $t$ es el tiempo, y $f(t)$ es el valor final |
| **exponential growth model** an exponential function, $f(t) = a(1 + r)^t$, where $f(t)$ is the final output value at the end of $t$ time periods, $a$ is the initial value, $r$ is the percent increase per time period (expressed as a whole number or decimal), and $t$ is the number of time periods | U2-154 U3-222 | **modelo de crecimiento exponencial** función exponencial, $f(t) = a(1 - r)^t$, en la que $f(t)$ es el valor de salida final despues de $t$ períodos de tiempo, $a$ es el valor inicial, $r$ es el porcentaje de aumento por período (expresado como entero o decimal), y $t$ es la cantidad de períodos |
| **exterior angle of a polygon** an angle formed by one side of a polygon and the extension of another side | U5-171 | **ángulo exterior de un polígono** ángulo formado por un lado de un polígono y la extensión de otro lado |
| **exterior angles** angles that lie outside a pair of parallel lines | U5-125 | **ángulos exteriores** ángulos que están fuera de un par de líneas paralelas |
| **extraneous solution (extraneous root) of an equation** a solution of an equation that arises during the solving process, but which is not a solution of the original equation | U3-145 | **solución extraña (raíz extraña) de una ecuación** solución de una ecuación que surge durante el proceso de resolución pero que no es una solución de la ecuación original |
| **extrema** the minima or maxima of a function | U2-1 U2-36 U2-92 | **extremos** los mínimos o máximos de una función |

| | **F** | |
|---|---|---|
| **factor (noun)** one of two or more numbers or expressions that when multiplied produce a given product | U3-1 | **factor** uno de dos o más números o expresiones que al multiplicarse dan un producto determinado |

| English | | Español |
|---|---|---|
| **factor (verb)** to write an expression as the product of its factors | U3-19 | **factorizar** escribir una expresión como el producto de sus factores |
| **factored form of a quadratic function** the intercept form of a quadratic equation, written as $f(x) = a(x - p)(x - q)$, where $p$ and $q$ are the $x$-intercepts of the function; also known as the *intercept form of a quadratic function* | U2-1 | **forma factorizada de una función cuadrática** forma de intercepto de una ecuación cuadrática, se expresa como $f(x) = a(x - p)(x - q)$, en la que $p$ y $q$ son los interceptos de $x$ de la función; también se conoce como la *forma de intercepto de una función cuadrática* |
| **factorial** the product of an integer and all preceding positive integers, represented using a ! symbol; $n! = n \bullet (n - 1) \bullet (n - 2) \bullet \ldots \bullet 1$. For example, $5! = 5 \bullet 4 \bullet 3 \bullet 2 \bullet 1$. By definition, $0! = 1$. | U4-99 | **factorial** producto de un entero y todos los enteros positivos anteriores, que se representa con el símbolo !; $n! = n \bullet (n - 1) \bullet (n - 2) \bullet \ldots \bullet 1$. Por ejemplo, $5! = 5 \bullet 4 \bullet 3 \bullet 2 \bullet 1$. Por definición, $0! = 1$. |
| **family of functions** a set of functions whose graphs have the same general shape as their parent function. The parent function is the function with a simple algebraic rule that represents the family of functions. | U3-145 | **familia de funciones** conjunto de funciones cuyos gráficos tienen la misma forma general que su función principal. La función principal es la función con una regla algebraica simple que representa la familia de funciones. |
| **first difference** in a set of data, the change in the $y$-value when the $x$-value is increased by 1 | U2-154 | **primera diferencia** en un conjunto de datos, el cambio en el valor $y$ cuando el valor $x$ aumenta por 1 |
| **floor function** also known as the greatest integer function; a function represented as $y = \lfloor x \rfloor$. For any input $x$, the output is the largest integer less than or equal to $x$; for example, $\lfloor -3 \rfloor = -3$, $\lfloor 2.1 \rfloor = 2$, and $\lfloor -2.1 \rfloor = -3$. | U2-92 | **función piso** también conocida como la función del mayor entero; función representada como $y = \lfloor x \rfloor$. Para cualquier entrada $x$, la salida es el entero más grande que es menor que o igual a $x$; por ejemplo, $\lfloor -3 \rfloor = -3$, $\lfloor 2.1 \rfloor = 2$, y $\lfloor -2.1 \rfloor = -3$. |

| English | | Español |
|---|---|---|
| **flow proof** a graphical method of presenting the logical steps used to show an argument. In a flow proof, the logical statements are written in boxes and the reason for each statement is written below the box. | U5-69 | **prueba de flujo** método gráfico para presentar los pasos lógicos utilizados para mostrar un argumento. En una prueba de flujo, las declaraciones lógicas se expresan en casillas y la razón de cada declaración se escribe debajo de la casilla. |
| **focus of a parabola** a fixed point on the interior of a parabola that is not on the directrix of the parabola but is on the same plane as both the parabola and the directrix; the fixed point referenced in the definition of a parabola | U6-154<br>U6-197 | **foco de una parábola** punto fijo en el interior de una parábola que no está en la directriz de la parábola sino en el mismo plano que la parábola y la directriz; punto fijo mencionado en la definición de parábola |
| **function** a relation in which every element of the domain is paired with exactly one element of the range; that is, for every value of $x$, there is exactly one value of $y$. | U2-69<br>U2-204 | **función** relación en la que cada elemento del dominio se empareja con un único elemento del rango; es decir, para cada valor de $x$, existe exactamente un valor de $y$. |
| **function notation** the use of $f(x)$, which means "function of $x$," instead of $y$ or another dependent variable in an equation of a function; $f(x) = 2x + 1$ and $y = 2x + 1$ are equivalent functions | U2-204 | **notación de funciones** el uso de $f(x)$, que significa "función de $x$", en lugar de $y$ u otra variable dependiente en la ecuación de una función; $f(x) = 2x + 1$ e $y = 2x + 1$ son funciones equivalentes |
| **Fundamental Theorem of Algebra** If $P(x)$ is a polynomial function of degree $n \geq 1$ with complex coefficients, then the related equation $P(x) = 0$ has at least one complex solution (root). | U3-109 | **Teorema fundamental del álgebra** Si $P(x)$ es una función polinómica de grado $n \geq 1$ con coeficientes complejos, entonces la ecuación relacionada $P(x) = 0$ tiene al menos una solución compleja (raíz). |

| English | | Español |
|---|---|---|
| | **G** | |
| **general form of an equation of a circle** $Ax^2 + By^2 + Cx + Dy + E = 0$, where $A = B$, $A \neq 0$, and $B \neq 0$ | U6-155 | **forma general de ecuación de un círculo** $Ax^2 + By^2 + Cx + Dy + E = 0$, en la que $A = B$, $A \neq 0$, y $B \neq 0$ |
| **greatest common factor (GCF)** the largest factor that two or more terms share | U3-19 | **máximo común divisor (GCF)** el factor más grande que comparten dos o más términos |
| **greatest integer function** also known as the floor function; a function represented as $y = \lfloor x \rfloor$. For any input $x$, the output is the largest integer less than or equal to $x$; for example, $\lfloor -3 \rfloor = -3$, $\lfloor 2.1 \rfloor = 2$, and $\lfloor -2.1 \rfloor = -3$. | U2-92 | **función del mayor entero** también conocida como función piso; función que se representa como $y = \lfloor x \rfloor$. Para cualquier entrada $x$, la salida es el entero más grande que es menor que o igual a $x$; por ejemplo, $\lfloor -3 \rfloor = -3$, $\lfloor 2.1 \rfloor = 2$, y $\lfloor -2.1 \rfloor = -3$. |
| **growth factor** the multiple by which a quantity increases over time | U2-154 U3-222 | **factor de crecimiento** múltiplo por el que una cantidad aumenta con el tiempo |
| **growth rate** the rate of increase in size per unit of time; $r$ in the exponential growth model $f(t) = a(1 + r)^t$ | U2-154 U3-222 | **tasa de crecimiento** tasa de aumento de tamaño por unidad de tiempo; $r$ en el modelo de crecimiento exponencial $f(t) = a(1 + r)^t$ |
| | **H** | |
| **half-closed interval** an interval that includes one endpoint but not the other; also called a half-open interval | U3-145 | **intervalo medio cerrado** intervalo que incluye un punto final pero no el otro; también denominado intervalo medio abierto |
| **half-open interval** an interval that includes one endpoint but not the other; also called a half-closed interval | U3-145 | **intervalo medio abierto** intervalo que incluye un punto final pero no el otro; también denominado intervalo medio cerrado |

| English | | Español |
|---|---|---|
| **horizontal asymptote** a line defined as follows: The line $y = b$ is a horizontal asymptote of the graph of a function $f$ if $f(x)$ gets closer to $b$ as $x$ either increases or decreases without bound. | U3-145 | **asíntota horizontal** línea recta que se define de la siguiente manera: La línea $y = b$ es una asíntota horizontal del gráfico de una función $f$ si $f(x)$ se acerca a $b$ a medida que $x$ aumenta o disminuye sin límites. |
| **horizontal compression** squeezing of the parabola toward the $y$-axis | U2-175 | **compresión horizontal** contracción de la parábola hacia el eje $y$ |
| **horizontal stretch** pulling of the parabola and stretching it away from the $y$-axis | U2-175 | **estiramiento horizontal** jalar de la parábola y estirarla lejos del eje $y$ |
| **hypotenuse** the side opposite the vertex of the 90° angle in a right triangle | U5-309 | **hipotenusa** lado opuesto al vértice del ángulo de 90° en un triángulo rectángulo |

## I

| English | | Español |
|---|---|---|
| **identity** an equation that is true regardless of what values are chosen for the variables | U3-109 U5-309 U5-341 | **identidad** ecuación verdadera independientemente de los valores elegidos para las variables |
| **imaginary number** any number of the form $bi$, where $b$ is a real number, $i = \sqrt{-1}$, and $b \neq 0$ | U1-34 U3-109 | **número imaginario** cualquier número de la forma $bi$, en el que $b$ es un número real, $i = \sqrt{-1}$, y $b \neq 0$ |
| **imaginary unit, $i$** the letter $i$, used to represent the non-real value, $i = \sqrt{-1}$ | U1-34 U3-109 | **unidad imaginaria, $i$** la letra $i$, utilizada para representar el valor no real $i = \sqrt{-1}$ |
| **incenter** the intersection of the angle bisectors of a triangle | U5-171 U6-43 | **incentro** intersección de las bisectrices del ángulo de un triángulo |
| **increasing** the interval of a function for which the output values are becoming larger as the input values are becoming larger | U2-36 | **creciente** intervalo de una función para el que los valores de salida se hacen más grandes a medida que los valores de entrada también se vuelven más grandes |

| English | | Español |
|---|---|---|
| **increasing function** a function such that as the independent values increase, the dependent values also increase | U2-92 | **función creciente** función en la que a medida que aumentan los valores independientes, también aumentan los valores dependientes |
| **independent events** events such that the outcome of one event does not affect the probability of the outcome of another event | U4-2 U4-48 | **eventos independientes** eventos en los que el resultado de un evento no afecta la probabilidad del resultado de otro evento |
| **independent variable** labeled on the *x*-axis; the quantity that changes based on values chosen; the input variable of a function | U3-145 | **variable independiente** designada en el eje *x*; cantidad que cambia según los valores seleccionados; variable de entrada de una función |
| **infinity** going on without bound; represented by the symbol $\infty$ | U3-145 | **infinito** continuación sin límites; se representa con el símbolo $\infty$ |
| **inflection point** a point on a curve at which the sign of the curvature (i.e., the concavity) changes | U2-36 | **punto de inflexión** punto en una curva en el que cambia el signo de la curvatura (es decir, la concavidad) |
| **inscribed angle** an angle formed by two chords whose vertex is on the circle | U6-2 | **ángulo inscrito** ángulo formado por dos cuerdas cuyo vértice está en el círculo |
| **inscribed circle** a circle whose tangents form a triangle | U5-171 U6-43 | **círculo inscrito** círculo cuyos tangentes forman un triángulo |
| **inscribed quadrilateral** a quadrilateral whose vertices are on a circle | U6-43 | **cuadrilátero inscrito** cuadrilátero cuyos vértices están en un círculo |
| **inscribed triangle** a triangle whose vertices are on a circle | U6-43 | **triángulo inscrito** triangulo cuyos vértices están en un círculo |
| **integer** a number that is not a fraction or a decimal | U1-2 | **entero** un número que no es una fracción ni un decimal |
| **intercept** the point at which a line intercepts the *x*- or *y*-axis | U2-1 | **intercepto** punto en el que una línea intercepta el eje *x* o *y* |

| English | | Español |
|---|---|---|
| **intercept form of a quadratic function** the factored form of a quadratic equation, written as $f(x) = a(x - p)(x - q)$, where $p$ and $q$ are the x-intercepts of the function; also known as the *factored form of a quadratic function* | U2-2<br>U3-58 | **forma de intercepto de una función cuadrática** forma factorizada de una ecuación cuadrática, expresada como $f(x) = a(x - p)(x - q)$, donde $p$ y $q$ son los interceptos de $x$ de la función; también se conoce como la *forma factorizada de una ecuación cuadrática* |
| **intercepted arc** an arc whose endpoints intersect the sides of an inscribed angle and whose other points are in the interior of the angle | U6-2 | **arco interceptado** arco cuyos extremos intersecan los lados de un ángulo inscrito y cuyos otros puntos se sitúan en el interior del ángulo |
| **interior angle of a polygon** an angle formed by two sides of a polygon | U5-171 | **ángulo interior de un polígono** ángulo formado por dos lados de un polígono |
| **interior angles** angles that lie between a pair of parallel lines | U5-126 | **ángulos interiores** ángulos ubicados entre un par de líneas paralelas |
| **intersection** a set whose elements are each in both of two other sets. The intersection of sets $A$ and $B$, denoted by $A \cap B$, is the set of elements that are in both $A$ and $B$. | U4-2 | **intersección** conjunto cuyos elementos están todos en otros dos conjuntos. La intersección de los conjuntos $A$ y $B$, indicada por $A \cap B$, es el conjunto de elementos que se encuentran tanto en $A$ como en $B$. |
| **interval** the set of all real numbers between two given numbers. The two numbers on the ends are the endpoints. The endpoints might or might not be included in the interval depending on whether the interval is open, closed, or half-open/half-closed. | U2-154<br>U3-19<br>U3-145 | **intervalo** conjunto de todos los números reales entre dos números dados. Los dos números en los finales son los extremos. Los extremos podrían o no estar incluidos en el intervalo, según si el intervalo está abierto, cerrado, o medio abierto o medio cerrado. |

| English | | Español |
|---|---|---|
| **interval notation** a way of representing an interval using a pair of parentheses, a pair of brackets, or a parenthesis and a bracket | U3-145 | **notación de intervalos** modo de representar un intervalo con un par de paréntesis, un par de corchetes, o un paréntesis y un corchete |
| **inverse function** the function that results from switching the $x$- and $y$-variables in a given function; the inverse of $f(x)$ is written as $f^{-1}(x)$ | U2-204 | **función inversa** función que se produce como resultado de cambiar las variables $x$ y $y$ en una función determinada; la inversa de $f(x)$ se expresa como $f^{-1}(x)$ |
| **inverse operation** the operation that reverses the effect of another operation | U2-204 | **operación inversa** operación que revierte el efecto de otra |
| **irrational number** a number that cannot be written as $\dfrac{m}{n}$, where $m$ and $n$ are integers and $n \neq 0$; any number that cannot be written as a decimal that ends or repeats | U1-2 U3-19 U6-122 | **números irracionales** un número que no pueden expresarse como $\dfrac{m}{n}$, en los que $m$ y $n$ son enteros y $n \neq 0$; cualquier número que no puede expresarse como decimal finito o periódico |
| **isosceles trapezoid** a trapezoid with one pair of opposite parallel lines and congruent legs | U5-262 | **trapezoide isósceles** trapezoide con un par de líneas paralelas opuestas y catetos congruentes |
| **isosceles triangle** a triangle with at least two congruent sides | U5-171 | **triángulo isósceles** triángulo con al menos dos lados congruentes |

## K

| English | | Español |
|---|---|---|
| **key features of a quadratic** the $x$-intercepts, $y$-intercept, where the function is increasing and decreasing, where the function is positive and negative, relative minimums and maximums, symmetries, and end behavior of the function used to describe, draw, and compare quadratic functions | U2-36 U3-58 | **características clave de una función cuadrática** interceptos de $x$, intercepto de $y$, donde la función aumenta y disminuye, donde la función es positiva y negativa, máximos y mínimos relativos, simetrías y comportamiento final de la función utilizado para describir, dibujar y comparar las funciones cuadráticas |

| English | | Español |
|---|---|---|
| **kite** a quadrilateral with two distinct pairs of congruent sides that are adjacent | U5-262 | **cometa** cuadrilátero con dos pares distintos de lados congruentes que son adyacentes |

## L

| English | | Español |
|---|---|---|
| **leading coefficient** the coefficient of the term with the highest power. For a quadratic equation in standard form ($y = ax^2 + bx + c$), the leading coefficient is $a$. | U2-69<br>U3-19 | **coeficiente líder** coeficiente del término con la mayor potencia. En una ecuación cuadrática en forma estándar ($y = ax^2 + bx + c$), el coeficiente líder es $a$. |
| **least common denominator (LCD) of fractions** the least common multiple of the denominators of the fractions | U3-145 | **mínimo común denominador (LCD) de fracciones** múltiplo mínimo común de los denominadores de las fracciones |
| **least common multiple (LCM) of polynomials** with two or more polynomials, the common multiple of the polynomials that has the least degree and the least positive constant factor | U3-145 | **mínimo común múltiplo (LCM) de polinomios** con dos o más polinomios, el múltiplo común de los polinomios que tiene el menor grado y el menor factor constante positivo |
| **least integer function** also known as the ceiling function; a function represented as $y = \lceil x \rceil$. For any input $x$, the output is the smallest integer greater than or equal to $x$; for example, $\lceil -3 \rceil = -3$, $\lceil 2.1 \rceil = 3$, and $\lceil -2.1 \rceil = -2$. | U2-92 | **función de mínimo entero** también conocida como función techo; función representada como $y = \lceil x \rceil$. Para cualquier entrada $x$, la salida es el entero más pequeño mayor que o igual a $x$; por ejemplo, $\lceil -3 \rceil = -3$, $\lceil 2.1 \rceil = 3$, y $\lceil -2.1 \rceil = -2$. |
| **legs** congruent sides of an isosceles triangle | U5-171 | **catetos** lados congruentes de un triángulo isósceles |
| **like terms** terms that contain the same variables raised to the same power | U1-18<br>U3-1 | **términos semejantes** términos que contienen las mismas variables elevadas a la misma potencia |
| **limit** the value that a sequence approaches as a calculation becomes more and more accurate | U6-122 | **límite** valor al que se aproxima una secuencia cuando un cálculo se vuelve cada vez más exacto |

| English | | Español |
|---|---|---|
| **line segment** a part of a line that is noted by two endpoints, $(x_1, y_1)$ and $(x_2, y_2)$ | U5-1 | **segmento de recta** parte de una línea comprendida entre dos extremos, $(x_1, y_1)$ y $(x_2, y_2)$ |
| **linear function** a function that can be written in the form $f(x) = mx + b$, in which $m$ is the slope, $b$ is the $y$-intercept, and the graph is a straight line | U2-154 U2-204 | **función lineal** función que puede expresarse en la forma $f(x) = mx + b$, en la que $m$ es la pendiente, $b$ es el intercepto de $y$, y la gráfica es una línea recta |
| **linear pair** a pair of adjacent angles whose non-shared sides form a straight angle | U5-126 | **par lineal** par de ángulos adyacentes cuyos lados no compartidos forman un ángulo recto |
| **literal equation** an equation that involves two or more variables | U3-58 | **ecuación literal** ecuación que incluye dos o más variables |

## M

| English | | Español |
|---|---|---|
| **major arc** part of a circle's circumference that is larger than its semicircle | U6-2 | **arco mayor** parte de la circunferencia de un círculo que es mayor que su semicírculo |
| **maximum** the largest $y$-value of a quadratic equation | U2-2 U3-58 | **máximo** el mayor valor de $y$ de una ecuación cuadrática |
| **median of a triangle** the segment joining the vertex to the midpoint of the opposite side | U5-171 | **mediana de un triángulo** segmento que une el vértice con el punto medio del lado opuesto |
| **member** an item in a set; also called an element | U4-2 | **miembro** ítem en un conjunto; también se denomina elemento |
| **midpoint** a point on a line segment that divides the segment into two equal parts | U5-1 U5-171 | **punto medio** punto en un segmento de recta que lo divide en dos partes iguales |
| **midpoint formula** formula that states the midpoint of a segment created by connecting $(x_1, y_1)$ and $(x_2, y_2)$ is given by the formula $\left( \dfrac{x_1 + x_2}{2}, \dfrac{y_1 + y_2}{2} \right)$ | U5-1 U5-171 U6-197 | **fórmula de punto medio** fórmula que establece el punto medio de un segmento creado al conectar $(x_1, y_1)$ con $(x_2, y_2)$ está dado por la fórmula $\left( \dfrac{x_1 + x_2}{2}, \dfrac{y_1 + y_2}{2} \right)$ |

| English | | Español |
|---|---|---|
| **midsegment** a line segment joining the midpoints of two sides of a figure | U5-171 | **segmento medio** segmento de recta que une los puntos medios de dos lados de una figura |
| **midsegment triangle** the triangle formed when all three of the midsegments of a triangle are connected | U5-171 | **segmento medio de un triángulo** triángulo que se forma cuando los tres segmentos medios de un triángulo están conectados |
| **minimum** the smallest $y$-value of a quadratic equation | U2-2 U3-58 | **mínimo** el menor valor de $y$ en una ecuación cuadrática |
| **minor arc** part of a circle's circumference that is smaller than its semicircle | U6-2 | **arco menor** parte de la circunferencia de un círculo que es menor que su semicírculo |
| **monomial** an expression with one term, consisting of a number, a variable, or the product of a number and variable(s) | U1-18 U3-1 | **monomio** expresión con un solo término, que consiste en un número, una variable, o el producto de un número y una o más variables |
| **Multiplication Rule** the probability of two events, $A$ and $B$, is $P(A \text{ and } B) = P(A) \bullet P(B|A) = P(B) \bullet P(A|B)$; for independent events $A$ and $B$, the rule is $P(A \text{ and } B) = P(A) \bullet P(B)$. | U4-48 | **Regla de multiplicación** probabilidad de que dos eventos, $A$ y $B$, sea $P(A \text{ y } B) = P(A) \bullet P(B|A) = P(B) \bullet P(A|B)$; para eventos independientes $A$ y $B$, la regla es $P(A \text{ y } B) = P(A) \bullet P(B)$. |
| **mutually exclusive events** events that have no outcomes in common. If $A$ and $B$ are mutually exclusive events, then they cannot both occur. Mutually exclusive events are also called disjoint events. | U4-2 | **eventos mutuamente excluyentes** eventos que no tienen resultados en común. Si $A$ y $B$ son eventos mutuamente excluyentes, entonces no pueden producirse ambos. También se denominan eventos disjuntos. |

### N

| English | | Español |
|---|---|---|
| **neither** describes a function that, when evaluated for $-x$, does not result in the opposite of the original function (odd) or the original function (even) | U2-36 | **ni** describe una función que, cuando se evalúa para $-x$, no tiene como resultado lo opuesto de la función original (impar) ni la función original (par) |

| English | | Español |
|---|---|---|
| **non-rigid motion** a transformation done to a figure that changes the figure's shape and/or size | U5-18 | **movimiento no rígido** transformación hecha a una figura que cambia su forma o tamaño |
| **nonadjacent angles** angles that have no common vertex or common side, or have shared interior points | U5-126 | **ángulos no adyacentes** ángulos que no tienen vértices ni lados comunes, o que tienen puntos interiores compartidos |
| **null set** a set that has no elements, denoted by $\varnothing$. The null set is also called the empty set. | U4-2 | **conjunto nulo** conjunto que no tiene elementos, indicado con $\varnothing$. También se denomina conjunto vacío. |

## O

| English | | Español |
|---|---|---|
| **obtuse triangle** a triangle with one angle that is obtuse (greater than 90°) | U5-171 | **triángulo obtuso** triángulo con un ángulo que es obtuso (de más de 90°) |
| **odd function** a function that, when evaluated for $-x$, results in a function that is the opposite of the original function; $f(-x) = -f(x)$ | U2-36 | **función impar** función que, cuando se evalúa para $-x$, tiene como resultado una función que es lo opuesto a la función original; $f(-x) = -f(x)$ |
| **one-to-one** a relationship wherein each point in a set of points is mapped to exactly one other point | U2-204 | **unívoca** relación en la que cada punto de un conjunto de puntos se corresponde con otro con exactitud |
| **open interval** an interval that does not include its endpoints | U3-145 | **intervalo abierto** intervalo que no incluye sus extremos |
| **opposite side** the side across from an angle | U5-309 | **lado opuesto** lado al otro lado de un ángulo |
| **orthocenter** the intersection of the altitudes of a triangle | U5-171 | **ortocentro** intersección de las alturas de un triángulo |
| **outcome** a result of an experiment | U4-2 | **resultado** consecuencia de un experimento |

| English | | Español |
|---|---|---|

**P**

**parabola** the U-shaped graph of a quadratic equation; the set of all points that are equidistant from a fixed line, called the directrix, and a fixed point not on that line, called the focus. The parabola, directrix, and focus are all in the same plane. The vertex of the parabola is the point on the parabola that is closest to the directrix.

U2-2
U3-58
U6-155
U6-197

**parábola** gráfico de una ecuación cuadrática en forma de U; conjunto de todos los puntos equidistantes de una línea fija denominada directriz y un punto fijo que no está en esa línea, llamado foco. La parábola, la directriz y el foco están todos en el mismo plano. El vértice de la parábola es el punto más cercano a la directriz.

**paragraph proof** statements written out in complete sentences in a logical order to show an argument

U5-69

**prueba de párrafo** declaraciones redactadas en oraciones completas en orden lógico para demostrar un argumento

**parallel lines** lines in a plane that either do not share any points and never intersect, or share all points; written as $\overleftrightarrow{AB} \parallel \overleftrightarrow{PQ}$

U5-70

**líneas paralelas** líneas en un plano que no comparten ningún punto y nunca se cortan, o que comparten todos los puntos; se expresan como $\overleftrightarrow{AB} \parallel \overleftrightarrow{PQ}$

**parallelogram** a special type of quadrilateral with two pairs of opposite sides that are parallel; denoted by the symbol $\square$

U5-262

**paralelogramo** un tipo especial de cuadrilátero con dos pares de lados opuestos paralelos; se expresa con el símbolo $\square$

**parent function** a function with a simple algebraic rule that represents a family of functions. The graphs of the functions in the family have the same general shape as the parent function.

U3-145

**función principal** función con una regla algebraica simple que representa una familia de funciones. Los gráficos de las funciones en la familia tienen la misma forma general que la función principal.

**percent of change** $\dfrac{\text{amount of change}}{\text{original amount}}$, written as a percent

U3-222

**porcentaje de cambio** se expresa como porcentaje $\dfrac{\text{porcentaje de cambio}}{\text{cantidad original}}$

| English | | Español |
|---|---|---|
| **perfect square trinomial** a trinomial of the form $x^2 + bx + \left(\dfrac{b}{2}\right)^2$ that can be written as the square of a binomial | U3-19 U6-155 U6-197 | **trinomio cuadrado perfecto** trinomio de la forma $x^2 + bx + \left(\dfrac{b}{2}\right)^2$ que puede expresarse como el cuadrado de un binomio |
| **permutation** a selection of objects where the order matters and is found either using $n^r$, if repetitions are allowed, or by using $_nP_r = \dfrac{n!}{(n-r)!}$, where $n$ is the number of objects to select from and $r$ is the number of objects being selected and ordered. | U4-99 | **permutación** selección de objetos en la que el orden importa y se encuentra con el uso de $n^r$, si se permiten las repeticiones, o con $_nP_r = \dfrac{n!}{(n-r)!}$, donde $n$ es la cantidad de objetos de donde seleccionar y $r$ es la cantidad de objetos seleccionados y ordenados. |
| **perpendicular bisector** a line that intersects a segment at its midpoint at a right angle | U5-126 U6-43 | **bisectriz perpendicular** línea que corta un segmento en su punto medio en ángulo recto |
| **perpendicular lines** two lines that intersect at a right angle (90°). The lines form four adjacent and congruent right angles. | U5-126 | **líneas perpendiculares** dos líneas que se cortan en un ángulo recto (90°). Las líneas forman cuatro ángulos rectos adyacentes y congruentes. |
| **phi** (ϕ) a Greek letter sometimes used to refer to an unknown angle measure | U5-309 | **fi** (ϕ) letra del alfabeto griego que se utiliza a veces para referirse a la medida desconocida de un ángulo |
| **pi** (π) the ratio of circumference of a circle to the diameter; equal to approximately 3.14 | U6-2 | **pi** (π) proporción de la circunferencia de un círculo al diámetro; equivale aproximadamente a 3.14 |

| English | | Español |
|---|---|---|
| **piecewise function** a function that is defined by two or more expressions on separate portions of the domain | U2-92 | **función por partes** función definida por dos o más expresiones en porciones separadas del dominio |
| **plane** a flat, two-dimensional figure without depth that has at least three non-collinear points and extends infinitely in all directions | U5-126 | **plano** figura plana, bidimensional, sin profundidad, que tiene al menos tres puntos no colineales y se extiende infinitamente en todas direcciones |
| **point of concurrency** a single point of intersection of three or more lines | U5-171 U6-43 | **punto de concurrencia** punto único de intersección de tres o más líneas |
| **point of tangency** the only point at which a line and a circle intersect | U6-85 | **punto de tangencia** punto único de intersección entre una línea y un círculo |
| **point(s) of intersection** the ordered pair(s) where graphed functions intersect on a coordinate plane; these are also the solutions to systems of equations | U3-242 | **puntos de intersección** pares ordenados en los que se intersecan funciones representadas en gráficos en un plano de coordenadas; son también las soluciones a sistemas de ecuaciones |
| **polyhedron** a three-dimensional object that has faces made of polygons | U6-122 | **poliedro** objeto tridimensional que tiene caras compuestas por polígonos |
| **polynomial** a monomial or the sum of monomials | U1-18 U3-1 | **polinomio** monomio o suma de monomios |
| **polynomial function** a function whose rule is a one-variable polynomial; $P(x)$ is a polynomial function if $P(x) = a_n x^n + a_{n-1} x^{n-1} + \ldots + a_1 x + a_0$, where $n$ is a nonnegative integer and $a_n \neq 0$ | U3-109 | **función polinómica** función cuya regla es un polinomio de una variable; $P(x)$ es una función polinómica si $P(x) = a_n x^n + a_{n-1} x^{n-1} + \ldots + a_1 x + a_0$, donde $n$ es un entero no negativo y $a_n \neq 0$ |
| **postulate** a true statement that does not require a proof | U5-126 | **postulado** declaración verdadera que no requiere prueba |

| English | | Español |
|---|---|---|
| **power** the quantity that shows the number of times the base is being multiplied by itself in an exponential expression; also known as the exponent. In $a^x$, $x$ is the power/exponent. | U1-2 | **potencia** cantidad que muestra el número de veces que la base se multiplica por sí misma en una expresión exponencial; también se denomina exponente. En $a^x$, $x$ es la potencia o exponente. |
| **prime** an expression that cannot be factored | U3-19 | **número primo** expresión que no puede ser factorizada |
| **probability** a number from 0 to 1 inclusive or a percent from 0% to 100% inclusive that indicates how likely an event is to occur | U4-2 | **probabilidad** número de 0 a 1 inclusivo o porcentaje de 0% a 100% inclusivo que indica cuán probable es que se produzca un evento |
| **probability model** a mathematical model for observable facts or occurrences that are assumed to be random; a representation of a random phenomenon | U4-2 | **modelo de probabilidad** modelo matemático para hechos o sucesos observables que se presumen aleatorios; representación de un fenómeno aleatorio |
| **probability of an event** $E$ | U4-2 | **probabilidad de un evento** $E$ |
| denoted $P(E)$, and is given by $$P(E) = \frac{\text{number of outcomes in } E}{\text{number of outcomes in the sample space}}$$ in a uniform probability model | | se expresa como $P(E)$, y está dado por $$P(E) = \frac{\text{número de resultados en } E}{\text{número de resultados en el espacio de muestreo}}$$ en un modelo de probabilidad uniforme |
| **proof** a set of justified statements organized to form a convincing argument that a given statement is true | U5-70 U5-126 | **prueba** conjunto de declaraciones justificadas y organizadas para formar un argumento convincente de que determinada declaraciónes verdadera |
| **proportional** having a constant ratio to another quantity | U5-41 | **proporcional** que tiene una proporción constante con otra cantidad |

| English | | Español |
|---|---|---|
| **pyramid** a solid or hollow polyhedron object that has three or more triangular faces that converge at a single vertex at the top; the base may be any polygon | U6-122 | **pirámide** objeto poliedro sólido o hueco con tres o más caras triangulares que convergen en un único vértice en la parte superior; la base puede ser cualquier polígono |
| **Pythagorean identities** trigonometric identities that are derived from the Pythagorean Theorem: $\sin^2 \theta + \cos^2 \theta = 1$, $1 + \tan^2 \theta = \sec^2 \theta$, and $1 + \cot^2 \theta = \csc^2 \theta$ | U5-341 | **identidades Pitagóricas** identidades trigonométricas que se derivan de el teorema de Pitágoras: $\operatorname{sen}^2 \theta \cos^2 \theta = 1$, $1 + \tan^2 \theta = \sec^2 \theta$, y $1 + \cot^2 \theta = \csc^2 \theta$ |
| **Pythagorean Theorem** a theorem that relates the length of the hypotenuse of a right triangle ($c$) to the lengths of its legs ($a$ and $b$). The theorem states that $a^2 + b^2 = c^2$. | U5-341 U6-155 | **Teorema de Pitágoras** teorema que relaciona la longitud de la hipotenusa de un triángulo rectángulo ($c$) con las longitudes de sus catetos ($a$ y $b$). El teorema establece que $a^2 + b^2 = c^2$. |

## Q

| English | | Español |
|---|---|---|
| **quadratic equation** an equation that can be written in the form $ax^2 + bx + c = 0$, where $x$ is the variable, $a$, $b$, and $c$ are constants, and $a \neq 0$ | U3-2 U3-19 | **ecuación cuadrática** ecuación que se puede expresar en la forma $ax^2 + bx + c = 0$, donde $x$ es la variable, $a$, $b$, y $c$ son constantes, y $a \neq 0$ |
| **quadratic expression** an algebraic expression that can be written in the form $ax^2 + bx + c$, where $x$ is the variable, $a$, $b$, and $c$ are constants, and $a \neq 0$ | U3-2 | **expresión cuadrática** expresión algebraica que se puede expresar en la forma $ax^2 + bx + c$, donde $x$ es la variable, $a$, $b$, y $c$ son constantes, y $a \neq 0$ |

| English | | Español |
|---|---|---|
| **quadratic formula** a formula that states the solutions of a quadratic equation of the form $ax^2 + bx + c = 0$ are given by $x = \dfrac{-b \pm \sqrt{b^2 - 4ac}}{2a}$. A quadratic equation in this form can have no real solutions, one real solution, or two real solutions. | U3-19 U3-146 U3-242 | **fórmula cuadrática** fórmula que establece que las soluciones de una ecuación cuadrática de la forma $ax^2 + bx + c = 0$ están dadas por $x = \dfrac{-b \pm \sqrt{b^2 - 4ac}}{2a}$. Una ecuación cuadrática en esta forma tener ningún solución real, o tener una solución real, o dos soluciones reales. |
| **quadratic function** a function that can be written in the form $f(x) = ax^2 + bx + c$, where $a \neq 0$. The graph of any quadratic function is a parabola. | U2-2 U2-154 U2-204 U3-58 U6-155 U6-197 | **función cuadrática** función que puede expresarse en la forma $f(x) = ax^2 + bx + c$, donde $a \neq 0$. El gráfico de cualquier función cuadrática es una parábola. |
| **quadratic inequality** an inequality that can be written in the form $ax^2 + bx + c < 0$, $ax^2 + bx + c \leq 0$, $ax^2 + bx + c > 0$, or $ax^2 + bx + c \geq 0$ | U3-19 | **desigualdad cuadrática** desigualdad que puede expresarse en la forma $ax^2 + bx + c < 0$, $ax^2 + bx + c \leq 0$, $ax^2 + bx + c > 0$, o $ax^2 + bx + c \geq 0$ |
| **quadratic-linear system** a system of equations in which one equation is quadratic and one is linear | U3-242 | **sistema lineal cuadrático** sistema de ecuaciones en el que una ecuación es cuadrática y una es lineal |
| **quadratic polynomial in one variable** a one-variable polynomial of degree 2; it can be written in the form $ax^2 + bx + c$, where $a \neq 0$ | U3-109 | **polinomio cuadrático en una variable** polinomio de una variable de grado 2; se puede expresar en la forma $ax^2 + bx + c$, donde $a \neq 0$ |
| **quadrilateral** a polygon with four sides | U5-262 | **cuadrilátero** polígono con cuatro lados |

| English | | Español |
|---------|---|---------|
| | **R** | |
| **radian** the measure of the central angle that intercepts an arc equal in length to the radius of the circle; $\pi$ radians = 180° | U6-106 | **radián** medida del ángulo central que intercepta un arco de longitud igual al radio del círculo; $\pi$ radianes = 180° |
| **radian measure** the ratio of the arc intercepted by the central angle to the radius of the circle | U6-106 | **medida de radián** proporción del arco interceptado por el ángulo central al radio del círculo |
| **radical expression** an expression containing a root, such as $\sqrt[5]{9}$ | U1-2 | **expresión radical** expresión que contiene una raíz, tal como $\sqrt[5]{9}$ |
| **radical function** a function with the independent variable under a root. The general form is $y = a\sqrt[n]{(x-h)} + k$, where $n$ is a positive integer root and $a$, $h$, and $k$ are real numbers. | U2-92 | **función radical** función con la variable independiente bajo una raíz. La forma general es $y = a\sqrt[n]{(x-h)} + k$, donde $n$ es una raíz de entero positivo y $a$, $h$, y $k$ son números reales. |
| **radius** the distance from the center to a point on the circle; equal to one-half the diameter | U6-2 U6-155 | **radio** distancia desde el centro a un punto en el círculo; equivale a la mitad del diámetro |
| **random number generator** a tool to select a number without following a pattern, where the probability of any number in the set being generated is equal | U4-120 | **generador de números aleatorios** herramienta para seleccionar un número sin seguir un patrón, por lo que la probabilidad de generar cualquier número del conjunto es igual |
| **range** the set of all outputs of a function; the set of $y$-values that are valid for the function | U2-92 U3-146 | **rango** conjunto de todas las salidas de una función; conjunto de valores de $y$ que son válidos para la función |
| **rate** a ratio that compares measurements with different kinds of units | U3-146 | **tasa** proporción que compara medidas con distintos tipos de unidades |
| **ratio** the relation between two quantities; can be expressed in words, fractions, decimals, or as a percentage | U3-146 U5-309 | **proporción** relación entre dos cantidades; puede expresarse en palabras, fracciones, decimales o como porcentaje |

| English | | Español |
|---|---|---|
| **ratio identities** identities that define tangent and cotangent in terms of sine and cosine; the following two identities are ratio identities: $\tan\theta = \dfrac{\sin\theta}{\cos\theta}$ and $\cot\theta = \dfrac{\cos\theta}{\sin\theta}$ | U5-341 | **identidades de proporciones** identidades que definen tangente y cotangente en términos de seno y el coseno; las dos identidades siguientes son identidades de proporciones: $\tan\theta = \dfrac{\text{sen}\,\theta}{\cos\theta}$ y $\cot\theta = \dfrac{\cos\theta}{\text{sen}\,\theta}$ |
| **ratio of similitude** a ratio of corresponding sides; also known as the scale factor | U5-41 | **proporción de similitud** proporción de lados correspondientes; se conoce también como factor de escala |
| **rational equation** an equation that includes the ratio of two rational expressions, in which a variable appears in the denominator of at least one rational expression | U3-146 | **ecuación racional** ecuación que incluye la proporción de dos expresiones racionales, en la que aparece una variable en el denominador de al menos una expresión racional |
| **rational exponent** an exponent of the form $\dfrac{m}{n}$, where $m$ and $n$ are integers. If $m$ and $n$ are positive integers and $a$ is a real number, then $a^{\frac{m}{n}} = \left(\sqrt[n]{a}\right)^m = \sqrt[n]{a^m}$. | U3-222 | **exponente racional** exponente de la forma $\dfrac{m}{n}$, donde $m$ y $n$ son enteros. Si $m$ y $n$ son enteros positivos y $a$ es un número real, entonces $a^{\frac{m}{n}} = \left(\sqrt[n]{a}\right)^m = \sqrt[n]{a^m}$. |
| **rational expression** an expression made of the ratio of two polynomials, in which a variable appears in the denominator of a polynomial | U3-146 | **expresión racional** expresión formada por la proporción de dos polinomios, en la que aparece una variable en el denominador de un polinomio |
| **rational function** a function that can be written in the form $f(x) = \dfrac{p(x)}{q(x)}$, where $p(x)$ and $q(x)$ are polynomials and $q(x) \neq 0$ | U3-146 | **función racional** función que puede expresarse en la forma $f(x) = \dfrac{p(x)}{q(x)}$, donde $p(x)$ y $q(x)$ son polinomios y $q(x) \neq 0$ |

| English | | Español |
|---|---|---|
| **rational inequality** an inequality that includes the ratio of two rational expressions, in which a variable appears in the denominator of at least one rational expression | U3-146 | **desigualdad racional** desigualdad que incluye la proporción de dos expresiones racionales, en la que aparece una variable en el denominador de al menos una expresión racional |
| **rational number** any number that can be written as $\dfrac{m}{n}$, where both $m$ and $n$ are integers and $n \neq 0$; any number that can be written as a decimal that ends or repeats | U1-2 U3-20 | **números racionales** números que pueden expresarse como $\dfrac{m}{n}$, en los que $m$ y $n$ son enteros y $n \neq 0$; cualquier número que puede escribirse como decimal finito o periódico |
| **real numbers** the set of all rational and irrational numbers | U1-2 U1-34 U3-20 | **números reales** conjunto de todos los números racionales e irracionales |
| **reciprocal** a number that, when multiplied by the original number, has a product of 1 | U5-309 | **recíproco** número que multiplicado por el número original tiene producto 1 |
| **reciprocal identities** trigonometric identities that define cosecant, secant, and cotangent in terms of sine, cosine, and tangent: $\csc\theta = \dfrac{1}{\sin\theta}$, $\sec\theta = \dfrac{1}{\cos\theta}$, $\cot\theta = \dfrac{1}{\tan\theta}$, $\sin\theta = \dfrac{1}{\csc\theta}$, $\cos\theta = \dfrac{1}{\sec\theta}$, and $\tan\theta = \dfrac{1}{\cot\theta}$ | U5-341 | **identidades recíprocas** identidades trigonométricas que definen cosecante, secante y cotangente en términos de seno, coseno y tangente: $\csc\theta = \dfrac{1}{\text{sen}\theta}$, $\sec\theta = \dfrac{1}{\cos\theta}$, $\cot\theta = \dfrac{1}{\tan\theta}$, $\text{sen}\theta = \dfrac{1}{\csc\theta}$, $\cos\theta = \dfrac{1}{\sec\theta}$, y $\tan\theta = \dfrac{1}{\cot\theta}$ |
| **rectangle** a special parallelogram with four right angles | U5-263 | **rectángulo** paralelogramo especial con cuatro ángulos rectos |
| **reduction** a dilation where the scale factor is between 0 and 1 | U5-18 | **reducción** dilatación en la que el factor de escala está entre 0 y 1 |

| English | | Español |
|---|---|---|
| **Reflexive Property of Congruent Segments** a segment is congruent to itself; $\overline{AB} \cong \overline{AB}$ | U5-70 | **Propiedad reflexiva de congruencia de segmentos** un segmento es congruente con él mismo; $\overline{AB} \cong \overline{AB}$ |
| **relative frequency (of an event)** the number of times an event occurs divided by the number of times an experiment is performed | U4-2 | **frecuencia relativa (de un evento)** cantidad de veces que un evento se produce dividido por la cantidad de veces que se realiza el experimento |
| **remote interior angles** interior angles that are not adjacent to the exterior angle | U5-171 | **ángulos interiores remotos** ángulos interiores que no son adyacentes al ángulo exterior |
| **restricted domain** a subset of a function's defined domain | U2-92 | **dominio restringido** subconjunto del dominio definido de una función |
| **restricted range** a subset of a function's defined range | U2-92 | **rango restringido** subconjunto del rango definido de una función |
| **rhombus** a special parallelogram with all four sides congruent | U5-263 | **rombo** paralelogramo especial con sus cuatro lados congruentes |
| **right angle** an angle measuring 90° | U5-126 | **ángulo recto** ángulo que mide 90° |
| **right triangle** a triangle with one angle that measures 90° | U5-171 U5-309 | **triángulo rectángulo** triángulo con un ángulo que mide 90° |
| **rigid motion** a transformation done to a figure that maintains the figure's shape and size or its segment lengths and angle measures | U5-18 | **movimiento rígido** transformación que se realiza a una figura que mantiene su forma y tamaño o las longitudes de sus segmentos y las medidas de ángulos |
| **root** the inverse of a power/exponent; the root of a number $x$ is a number that, when multiplied by itself a given number of times, equals $x$ | U1-2 | **raíz** inversa de una potencia o exponente; la raíz de un número $x$ es un número que, multiplicado por sí mismo una cantidad determinada de veces, equivale a $x$ |
| **root(s)** solution(s) of a quadratic equation | U3-20 | **raíces** soluciones de una ecuación cuadrática |

| English | | Español |
|---|---|---|
| | **S** | |
| **same-side exterior angles** angles that lie on the same side of the transversal and are outside the lines that the transversal intersects; sometimes called consecutive exterior angles | U5-126 | **ángulos exteriores del mismo lado** ángulos que se ubican en el mismo lado de la transversal y están fuera de las líneas que corta la transversal; a veces se denominan ángulos exteriores consecutivos |
| **same-side interior angles** angles that lie on the same side of the transversal and are in between the lines that the transversal intersects; sometimes called consecutive interior angles | U5-126 | **ángulos interiores del mismo lado** ángulos que se ubican en el mismo lado de la transversal y están en medio de las líneas que corta la transversal; a veces se los denomina ángulos interiores consecutivos |
| **sample space** the set of all possible outcomes of an experiment | U4-2 | **espacio de muestreo** conjunto de todos los resultados posibles de un experimento |
| **scale factor** a multiple of the lengths of the sides from one figure to the transformed figure. If the scale factor is larger than 1, then the figure is enlarged. If the scale factor is between 0 and 1, then the figure is reduced. | U5-18 U5-309 | **factor de escala** múltiplo de las longitudes de los lados de una figura a la figura transformada. Si el factor de escala es mayor que 1, entonces la figura se agranda. Si el factor de escala se encuentra entre 0 y 1, entonces la figura se reduce. |
| **scalene triangle** a triangle with no congruent sides | U5-171 | **triángulo escaleno** triángulo sin lados congruentes |
| **secant** the reciprocal of cosine, $\sec\theta = \dfrac{1}{\cos\theta}$; the secant of $\theta =$ $\sec\theta = \dfrac{\text{length of hypotenuse}}{\text{length of adjacent side}}$ | U5-309 U5-341 | **secante** recíproco del coseno, $\sec\theta = \dfrac{1}{\cos\theta}$; secante de $\theta = \sec\theta$ $= \dfrac{\text{longitud de la hipotenusa}}{\text{longitud del lado adyacente}}$ |
| **secant line** a line that intersects a circle at two points | U6-2 | **línea secante** recta que corta un círculo en dos puntos |

| English | | Español |
|---|---|---|
| **second difference** in a set of data, the change in successive first differences | U2-154 | **segunda diferencia** en un conjunto de datos, el cambio en sucesivas primeras diferencias |
| **sector** a portion of a circle bounded by two radii and their intercepted arc | U6-106 | **sector** porción de un círculo limitado por dos radios y el arco que cortan |
| **Segment Addition Postulate** If $B$ is between $A$ and $C$, then $AB + BC = AC$. Conversely, if $AB + BC = AC$, then $B$ is between $A$ and $C$. | U5-70 | **Postulado de la suma de segmentos** Si $B$ está entre $A$ y $C$, entonces $AB + BC = AC$. A la inversa, si $AB + BC = AC$, entonces $B$ se encuentra entre $A$ y $C$. |
| **semicircle** an arc that is half of a circle | U6-2 | **semicírculo** arco que es la mitad de un círculo |
| **set** a collection or list of items | U4-3 | **conjunto** colección o lista de elementos |
| **Side-Angle-Side (SAS) Similarity Statement** If the measures of two sides of a triangle are proportional to the measures of two corresponding sides of another triangle and the included angles are congruent, then the triangles are similar. | U5-70 | **Criterio de semejanza lado-ángulo-lado (SAS)** Si las medidas de dos lados de un triángulo son proporcionales a las medidas de dos lados correspondientes de otro triángulo y los ángulos incluidos son congruentes, entonces los triángulos son similares. |
| **Side-Side-Side (SSS) Similarity Statement** If the measures of the corresponding sides of two triangles are proportional, then the triangles are similar. | U5-70 | **Criterio de semejanza lado-lado-lado (SSS)** Si las medidas de los lados correspondientes de dos triángulos son proporcionales, entonces los triángulos son similares. |
| **similar** two figures that are the same shape but not necessarily the same size; the symbol for representing similarity between figures is $\sim$ | U5-41 U5-309 | **similar** dos figuras que tienen la misma forma pero no necesariamente el mismo tamaño; el símbolo para representar similitud entre figuras es $\sim$ |

| English | | Español |
|---|---|---|
| **similarity transformation** a rigid motion followed by a dilation; a transformation that results in the position and size of a figure changing, but not the shape | U5-41 | **transformación de similitud** movimiento rígido seguido por una dilatación; transformación que tiene como resultado el cambio de posición y tamaño, pero no la forma, de una figura |
| **simple event** an event that has only one outcome; sometimes called a single event | U4-48 | **evento simple** evento que sólo tiene un resultado; a veces se denomina evento único |
| **sine** a trigonometric function of an acute angle in a right triangle that is the ratio of the length of the opposite side to the length of the hypotenuse; the sine of $\theta =$ $$\sin \theta = \frac{\text{length of opposite side}}{\text{length of hypotenuse}}$$ | U5-309 | **seno** función trigonométrica de un ángulo agudo en un triángulo rectángulo que es la proporción de la longitud del lado opuesto a la longitud de la hipotenusa; sen de $\theta =$ sen $\theta =$ $$\frac{\text{longitud del lado opuesto}}{\text{longitud de la hipotenusa}}$$ |
| **slope** the measure of the rate of change of one variable with respect to another variable; slope $$= \frac{y_2 - y_1}{x_2 - x_1} = \frac{\Delta y}{\Delta x} = \frac{\text{rise}}{\text{run}}; \text{ the slope}$$ in the equation $y = mx + b$ is $m$. | U2-37 | **pendiente** medida de la tasa de cambio de una variable con respecto a otra; pendiente $$= \frac{y_2 - y_1}{x_2 - x_1} = \frac{\Delta y}{\Delta x}; \text{ la pendiente en la}$$ ecuación $y = mx + b$ es $m$. |
| **slope formula** a formula that states the slope of the line through (or the line segment connecting) $A\,(x_1, y_1)$ and $B\,(x_2, y_2)$ is $\dfrac{y_2 - y_1}{x_2 - x_1}$ | U6-197 | **fórmula de pendiente** fórmula que determina la pendiente de la línea que atraviesa (o el segmento de recta que conecta) $A\,(x_1, y_1)$ y $B\,(x_2, y_2)$ es $\dfrac{y_2 - y_1}{x_2 - x_1}$ |
| **sphere** a three-dimensional surface that has all its points the same distance from its center | U6-122 | **esfera** superficie tridimensional que tiene todos sus puntos a la misma distancia de su centro |

| English | | Español |
|---|---|---|
| **square** a special parallelogram with four congruent sides and four right angles | U5-263 | **cuadrado** paralelogramo especial con cuatro lados congruentes y cuatro ángulos rectos |
| **square root** For any real numbers $a$ and $b$, if $a^2 = b$, then $a$ is a square root of $b$. The square root of $b$ is written using a radical: $\sqrt{b}$. | U2-92 | **raíz cuadrada** para cualquier número real $a$ y $b$, si $a^2 = b$, entonces $a$ es la raíz cuadrada de $b$. La raíz cuadrada de $b$ se expresa con un radical: $\sqrt{b}$. |
| **square root function** a function that contains a square root of a variable | U2-92 | **función raíz cuadrada** función que contiene una raíz cuadrada de una variable |
| **square root of a negative number** a number defined such that for any positive real number $a$, $\sqrt{-a} = i\sqrt{a}$. | U3-109 | **raíz cuadrada de un número negativo** número definido de forma tal que para cualquier número real positivo $a$, $\sqrt{-a} = i\sqrt{a}$. |
| **standard form of a quadratic function** a quadratic function written as $f(x) = ax^2 + bx + c$, where $a$ is the coefficient of the quadratic term, $b$ is the coefficient of the linear term, and $c$ is the constant term | U2-2 U3-58 | **forma estándar de función cuadrática** función cuadrática expresada como $f(x) = ax^2 + bx + c$, donde $a$ es el coeficiente del término cuadrático, $b$ es el coeficiente del término lineal, y $c$ es el término constante |
| **standard form of an equation of a circle** $(x - h)^2 + (y - k)^2 = r^2$, where $(h, k)$ is the center and $r$ is the radius | U3-242 U6-155 U6-197 | **forma estándar de ecuación de un círculo** $(x - h)^2 + (y - k)^2 = r^2$, donde $(h, k)$ es el centro y $r$ es el radio |
| **standard form of an equation of a parabola** $(x - h)^2 = 4p(y - k)$ for parabolas that open up or down; $(y - k)^2 = 4p(x - h)$ for parabolas that open right or left. For all parabolas, $p \neq 0$ and the vertex is $(h, k)$. | U6-155 U6-197 | **forma estándar de ecuación de una parábola** $(x - h)^2 = 4p(y - k)$ para parábolas que abren hacia arriba o hacia abajo; $(y - k)^2 = 4p(x - h)$ para parábolas que abren a la derecha o a la izquierda. Para todas las parábolas, $p \neq 0$ y el vértice es $(h, k)$. |

| English | | Español |
|---|---|---|
| **step function** a function that is a series of disconnected constant functions | U2-92 | **función escalonada** función que es una serie de funciones constantes desconectadas |
| **straight angle** an angle with rays in opposite directions; i.e., a straight line | U5-126 | **ángulo recto** ángulo con semirrectas en direcciones opuestas; es decir, línea recta |
| **stretch** a transformation in which a figure becomes larger; stretches may be horizontal (affecting only horizontal lengths), vertical (affecting only vertical lengths), or both | U5-18 | **ampliación** transformación en la que una figura se hace más grande; las ampliaciones pueden ser horizontales (cuando afectan sólo las longitudes horizontales), verticales (cuando afectan sólo las longitudes verticales), o en ambos sentidos |
| **subset** a set whose elements are in another set. Set $A$ is a subset of set $B$, denoted by $A \subset B$, if all the elements of $A$ are also in $B$. | U4-3 | **subconjunto** conjunto cuyos elementos están en otro conjunto. El conjunto $A$ es un subconjunto del conjunto $B$, indicado por $A \subset B$, si todos los elementos de $A$ se encuentran también en $B$. |
| **substitution** the replacement of a term of an equation by another term that is known to have the same value | U3-243 | **sustitución** reemplazo de un término de una ecuación por otro que se sabe que tiene el mismo valor |
| **supplementary angles** two angles whose sum is 180° | U5-126 U5-172 | **ángulos suplementarios** dos ángulos cuya suma es 180° |
| **Symmetric Property of Congruent Segments** If $\overline{AB} \cong \overline{CD}$, then $\overline{CD} \cong \overline{AB}$. | U5-70 | **Propiedad simétrica de congruencia de segmentos** Si $\overline{AB} \cong \overline{CD}$, entonces $\overline{CD} \cong \overline{AB}$. |
| **system of equations** a set of equations with the same unknowns | U3-243 | **sistema de ecuaciones** conjunto de ecuaciones con las mismas incógnitas |

| English | | Español |
|---|---|---|
| | **T** | |
| **tangent** a trigonometric function of an acute angle in a right triangle that is the ratio of the length of the opposite side to the length of the adjacent side; the tangent of $\theta$ = tan $\theta$ = $\dfrac{\text{length of opposite side}}{\text{length of adjacent side}}$ | U5-310 | **tangente** función trigonométrica de un ángulo agudo en un triángulo rectángulo que es la proporción de la longitud del lado opuesto a la longitud del lado adyacente; tangente de $\theta$ = tan $\theta$ = $\dfrac{\text{longitud del lado opuesto}}{\text{longitud del lado adyacente}}$ |
| **tangent line** a line that intersects a circle at exactly one point and is perpendicular to the radius of the circle | U6-2 U6-85 | **recta tangente** línea que corta un círculo en exactamente un punto y es perpendicular al radio del círculo |
| **term** a number, a variable, or the product of a number and variable(s) | U1-18 U3-2 U3-109 | **término** número, variable, o producto de un número y una o más variables |
| **test interval** for a polynomial or rational inequality in $x$, an interval on the $x$-axis formed by one or more critical numbers. The sign of the function on the test interval is the same as the sign of the function value at any $x$-value in the interval. | U3-146 | **intervalo de prueba** para una desigualdad polinómica o racional en $x$, intervalo en el eje $x$ formado por uno o más números críticos. El signo de la función del intervalo de prueba es el mismo que el del valor de la función en cualquier valor de $x$ en el intervalo. |
| **theorem** a statement that is shown to be true | U5-70 U6-197 | **teorema** declaración que se demuestra que es verdadera |
| **theta ($\theta$)** a Greek letter commonly used to refer to unknown angle measures | U5-310 | **teta ($\theta$)** letra griega que se utiliza por lo general para referirse a medidas de ángulos desconocidas |
| **transformation** adding or multiplying a constant to a function that changes the function's position and/or shape | U2-175 | **transformación** suma o multiplicación de una constante con una función que cambia la posición y/o forma de la función |

| English | | Español |
|---|---|---|
| **Transitive Property of Congruent Segments** If $\overline{AB} \cong \overline{CD}$, and $\overline{CD} \cong \overline{EF}$, then $\overline{AB} \cong \overline{EF}$. | U5-70 | **Propiedad transitiva de congruencia de segmentos** Si $\overline{AB} \cong \overline{CD}$, y $\overline{CD} \cong \overline{EF}$, entonces $\overline{AB} \cong \overline{EF}$. |
| **translation** transforming a function where the shape and size of the function remain the same but the function moves horizontally and/or vertically; adding a constant to the independent or dependent variable | U2-175 | **traslación** transformación de una función en la que la forma y el tamaño de la función permanecen iguales pero la función se traslada en sentido horizontal y/o vertical; suma de una constante a la variable independiente o dependiente |
| **transversal** a line that intersects a system of two or more lines | U5-126 | **transversal** línea que corta un sistema de dos o más líneas |
| **trapezoid** a quadrilateral with exactly one pair of opposite parallel lines | U5-263 | **trapezoide** cuadrilátero con exactamente un par de líneas paralelas opuestas |
| **trigonometry** the study of triangles and the relationships between their sides and the angles between these sides | U5-310 | **trigonometría** estudio de los triángulos y las relaciones entre sus lados y los ángulos entre ellos |
| **trinomial** a polynomial with three terms | U3-2 | **trinomio** polinomio con tres términos |
| **two-column proof** numbered statements and corresponding reasons that show the argument in a logical order | U5-70 | **prueba de dos columnas** declaraciones numeradas y las razones correspondientes que muestran el argumento en orden lógico |

| English | | Español |
|---|---|---|
| **two-way frequency table** a frequency table that shows two categories of characteristics, one in rows and the other in columns. Each cell value is a frequency that shows how many times two different characteristics appear together, or how often characteristics are associated with a person, object, or type of item that is being studied. | U4-48 | **tabla de frecuencia de dos vías** tabla de frecuencia que muestra dos categorías de características, una en filas y la otra en columnas. Cada valor de celda es una frecuencia que demuestra cuántas veces dos características diferentes aparecen juntas, o con qué frecuencia las características se asocian con una persona, objeto, o tipo de elemento que se está analizando. |

U

| English | | Español |
|---|---|---|
| **uniform probability model** a probability model in which all the outcomes of an experiment are assumed to be equally likely | U4-3 | **modelo de probabilidad uniforme** modelo de probabilidad en el que se presume que todos los resultados de un experimento son igualmente probables |
| **union** a set whose elements are in at least one of two other sets. The union of sets $A$ and $B$, denoted by $A \cup B$, is the set of elements that are in either $A$ or $B$ or both $A$ and $B$. | U4-3 | **unión** conjunto cuyos elementos están al menos en uno de otros dos conjuntos. La unión de los conjuntos $A$ y $B$, indicada por $A \cup B$, es el conjunto de elementos que están en $A$ o en $B$, o a la vez en $A$ y $B$. |
| **universal set** a set of all elements that are being considered in a particular situation. In a probability experiment, the universal set is the sample space. | U4-3 | **conjunto universal** conjunto de todos los elementos que se consideran en una situación particular. En un experimento de probabilidad, el conjunto universal es el espacio de muestreo. |

V

| English | | Español |
|---|---|---|
| **variable** a letter used to represent a value or unknown quantity that can change or vary | U3-2 | **variable** letra que se utiliza para representar un valor o cantidad desconocida que puede cambiar o variar |

| English | | Español |
|---|---|---|
| **Venn diagram** a diagram that shows how two or more sets in a universal set are related | U4-3 | **diagrama de Venn** diagrama que muestra cómo se relacionan dos o más conjuntos en un conjunto universal |
| **vertex angle** angle formed by the legs of an isosceles triangle | U5-172 | **ángulo vértice** ángulo formado por los catetos de un triángulo isósceles |
| **vertex form** a quadratic function written as $f(x) = a(x - h)^2 + k$, where the vertex of the parabola is the point $(h, k)$; the form of a quadratic equation where the vertex can be read directly from the equation | U2-2 <br> U3-58 | **fórmula de vértice** función cuadrática que se expresa como $f(x) = a(x - h)^2 + k$, donde el vértice de la parábola es el punto $(h, k)$; forma de una ecuación cuadrática en la que el vértice se puede leer directamente de la ecuación |
| **vertex of a parabola** the point on a parabola that is closest to the directrix and lies on the axis of symmetry; the point at which the curve changes direction; the maximum or minimum | U2-2 <br> U2-69 <br> U3-58 <br> U6-155 <br> U6-197 | **vértice de una parábola** punto en una parábola que está más cercano a la directriz y se ubica sobre el eje de simetría; punto en el que la curva cambia de dirección; el máximo o mínimo |
| **vertical angles** nonadjacent angles formed by two pairs of opposite rays | U5-126 | **ángulos verticales** ángulos no adyacentes formados por dos pares de semirrectas opuestas |
| **vertical asymptote** a line defined as follows: The line $x = a$ is a vertical asymptote of the graph of a function $f$ if $f(x)$ either increases or decreases without bound as $x$ gets closer to $a$. | U3-146 | **asíntota vertical** recta definida de la siguiente manera: La línea $x = a$ es una asíntota vertical del gráfico de una función $f$ si $f(x)$ aumenta o disminuye sin límites a medida que $x$ se acerca a $a$. |
| **vertical compression** squeezing of the parabola toward the $x$-axis | U2-175 | **compresión vertical** contracción de la parábola hacia el eje $x$ |
| **vertical stretch** pulling of the parabola and stretching it away from the $x$-axis | U2-175 | **estiramiento vertical** jalar y estirar la parábola lejos del eje $x$ |

| English | | Español |
|---|---|---|
| | **W** | |
| **wholly imaginary** a complex number that has a real part equal to 0; written in the form $a + bi$, where $a$ and $b$ are real numbers, $i$ is the imaginary unit, $a = 0$, and $b \neq 0$: $0 + bi$ | U1-35 | **totalmente imaginario** número complejo que tiene una parte real igual a 0; se expresa en la forma $a + bi$, donde $a$ y $b$ son números reales, $i$ es la unidad imaginaria, $a = 0$, y $b \neq 0$: $0 + bi$ |
| **wholly real** a complex number that has an imaginary part equal to 0; written in the form $a + bi$, where $a$ and $b$ are real numbers, $i$ is the imaginary unit, $b = 0$, and $a \neq 0$: $a + 0i$ | U1-35 | **totalmente real** número complejo que tiene una parte imaginaria igual a 0; se expresa en la forma $a + bi$, donde $a$ y $b$ son números reales, $i$ es la unidad imaginaria, $b = 0$, y $a \neq 0$: $a + 0i$ |
| | **X** | |
| **$x$-intercept** the point at which the graph crosses the $x$-axis; written as $(x, 0)$ | U2-2 U3-58 | **intercepto de $x$** punto en el que el gráfico cruza el eje $x$; se expresa como $(x, 0)$ |
| | **Y** | |
| **$y$-intercept** the point at which the graph crosses the $y$-axis; written as $(0, y)$ | U2-2 U3-58 | **intercepto de $y$** punto en el que el gráfico cruza el eje $y$; se expresa como $(0, y)$ |
| | **Z** | |
| **Zero Product Property** If the product of two factors is 0, then at least one of the factors is 0. | U3-20 | **Propiedad de producto cero** Si el producto de dos factores es 0, entonces al menos uno de los factores es 0. |
| **zeros** the $x$-values of a function for which the function value is 0 | U3-109 | **ceros** valores de $x$ de una función para la que el valor de la función es 0 |

# Formulas

# Formulas

## ALGEBRA

### Functions

| | |
|---|---|
| $f(x)$ | Function notation, "$f$ of $x$" |
| $f^{-1}(x)$ | Inverse function notation |
| $f(x) = mx + b$ | Linear function |
| $f(x) = b^x + k$ | Exponential function |
| $(f + g)(x) = f(x) + g(x)$ | Addition |
| $(f - g)(x) = f(x) - g(x)$ | Subtraction |
| $(f \bullet g)(x) = f(x) \bullet g(x)$ | Multiplication |
| $\left(\dfrac{f}{g}\right)(x) = \dfrac{f(x)}{g(x)}$ | Division |
| $\dfrac{f(b) - f(a)}{b - a}$ | Average rate of change |
| $f(-x) = -f(x)$ | Odd function |
| $f(-x) = f(x)$ | Even function |
| $f(x) = \lfloor x \rfloor$ | Floor/greatest integer function |
| $f(x) = \lceil x \rceil$ | Ceiling/least integer function |
| $f(x) = a\sqrt[3]{(x - h)} + k$ | Cube root function |
| $f(x) = \sqrt[n]{(x - h)} + k$ | Radical function |
| $f(x) = a\lvert x - h \rvert + k$ | Absolute value function |
| $f(x) = \dfrac{p(x)}{q(x)}; \quad q(x) \neq 0$ | Rational function |

### Symbols

| | |
|---|---|
| $\approx$ | Approximately equal to |
| $\neq$ | Is not equal to |
| $\lvert a \rvert$ | Absolute value of $a$ |
| $\sqrt{a}$ | Square root of $a$ |
| $\infty$ | Infinity |
| [ | Inclusive on the lower bound |
| ] | Inclusive on the upper bound |
| ( | Non-inclusive on the lower bound |
| ) | Non-inclusive on the upper bound |

### Linear Equations

| | |
|---|---|
| $m = \dfrac{y_2 - y_1}{x_2 - x_1}$ | Slope |
| $y = mx + b$ | Slope-intercept form |
| $ax + by = c$ | General form |
| $y - y_1 = m(x - x_1)$ | Point-slope form |

### Exponential Equations

| | |
|---|---|
| $A = P\left(1 + \dfrac{r}{n}\right)^{nt}$ | Compounded interest formula |
| Compounded... | $n$ (number of times per year) |
| Yearly/annually | 1 |
| Semi-annually | 2 |
| Quarterly | 4 |
| Monthly | 12 |
| Weekly | 52 |
| Daily | 365 |

# Formulas

## Quadratic Functions and Equations

| | |
|---|---|
| $x = \dfrac{-b}{2a}$ | Axis of symmetry |
| $x = \dfrac{p+q}{2}$ | Axis of symmetry using the midpoint of the $x$-intercepts |
| $\left( \dfrac{-b}{2a}, f\left( \dfrac{-b}{2a} \right) \right)$ | Vertex |
| $f(x) = ax^2 + bx + c$ | General form |
| $f(x) = a(x-h)^2 + k$ | Vertex form |
| $f(x) = a(x-p)(x-q)$ | Factored/intercept form |
| $b^2 - 4ac$ | Discriminant |
| $x^2 + bx + \left( \dfrac{b}{2} \right)^2$ | Perfect square trinomial |
| $x = \dfrac{-b \pm \sqrt{b^2 - 4ac}}{2a}$ | Quadratic formula |
| $(ax)^2 - b^2 = (ax+b)(ax-b)$ | Difference of squares |
| $(x-h)^2 = 4p(y-k)$ | Standard form for a parabola that opens up or down |
| $(y-k)^2 = 4p(x-h)$ | Standard form for a parabola that opens right or left |
| $F(h, k+p)$ | Focus for a parabola that opens up or down |
| $F(h+p, k)$ | Focus for a parabola that opens right or left |
| $y = k - p$ | Directrix for a parabola that opens up or down |
| $x = h - p$ | Directrix for a parabola that opens right or left |

# Formulas

## Exponential Functions

| | |
|---|---|
| $1 + r$ | Growth factor |
| $1 - r$ | Decay factor |
| $f(t) = a(1+r)^t$ | Exponential growth function |
| $f(t) = a(1-r)^t$ | Exponential decay function |
| $f(x) = ab^x$ | Exponential function in general form |

## General

| | |
|---|---|
| $(x, y)$ | Ordered pair |
| $(x, 0)$ | $x$-intercept |
| $(0, y)$ | $y$-intercept |

## Equations of Circles

| | |
|---|---|
| $(x - h)^2 + (y - k)^2 = r^2$ | Standard form |
| $x^2 + y^2 = r^2$ | Center at $(0, 0)$ |
| $Ax^2 + By^2 + Cx + Dy + E = 0$ | General form |

## Properties of Radicals

| |
|---|
| $\sqrt{ab} = \sqrt{a} \bullet \sqrt{b}$ |
| $\sqrt{\dfrac{a}{b}} = \dfrac{\sqrt{a}}{\sqrt{b}}$ |

## Imaginary Numbers

| |
|---|
| $i = \sqrt{-1}$ |
| $i^2 = -1$ |
| $i^3 = -i$ |
| $i^4 = 1$ |

## Radicals to Rational Exponents

| |
|---|
| $\sqrt[n]{a} = a^{\frac{1}{n}}$ |
| $\sqrt[n]{x^m} = x^{\frac{m}{n}}$ |

## Properties of Exponents

| Property | General rule |
|---|---|
| Zero Exponent | $a^0 = 1$ |
| Negative Exponent | $b^{-\frac{m}{n}} = \dfrac{1}{b^{\frac{m}{n}}}$ |
| Product of Powers | $a^m \bullet a^n = a^{m+n}$ |
| Quotient of Powers | $\dfrac{a^m}{a^n} = a^{m-n}$ |
| Power of a Power | $\left(b^m\right)^n = b^{mn}$ |
| Power of a Product | $\left(bc\right)^n = b^n c^n$ |
| Power of a Quotient | $\left(\dfrac{a}{b}\right)^m = \dfrac{a^m}{b^m}$ |

## Multiplication of Complex Conjugates

| |
|---|
| $(a + bi)(a - bi) = a^2 + b^2$ |

# Formulas

## DATA ANALYSIS

### Rules and Equations

| | |
|---|---|
| $P(E) = \dfrac{\#\text{ of outcomes in } E}{\#\text{ of outcomes in sample space}}$ | Probability of event $E$ |
| $P(A \cup B) = P(A) + P(B) - P(A \cap B)$ | Addition rule |
| $P(\overline{A}) = 1 - P(A)$ | Complement rule |
| $P(B\|A) = \dfrac{P(A \cap B)}{P(A)}$ | Conditional probability |
| $P(A \cap B) = P(A) \bullet P(B\|A)$ | Multiplication rule |
| $P(A \cap B) = P(A) \bullet P(B)$ | Multiplication rule if $A$ and $B$ are independent |
| ${}_nC_r = \dfrac{n!}{(n-r)!r!}$ | Combination |
| ${}_nP_r = \dfrac{n!}{(n-r)!}$ | Permutation |
| $n! = n \bullet (n-1) \bullet (n-2) \bullet \ldots \bullet 1$ | Factorial |

### Symbols

| | |
|---|---|
| $\varnothing$ | Empty/null set |
| $\cap$ | Intersection, "and" |
| $\cup$ | Union, "or" |
| $\subset$ | Subset |
| $\overline{A}$ | Complement of Set A |
| $!$ | Factorial |
| ${}_nC_r$ | Combination |
| ${}_nP_r$ | Permutation |

# Formulas

## GEOMETRY

### Symbols

| $\overset{\frown}{ABC}$ | Major arc length |
|---|---|
| $\overset{\frown}{AB}$ | Minor arc length |
| $\angle$ | Angle |
| $\odot$ | Circle |
| $\cong$ | Congruent |
| $\overleftrightarrow{PQ}$ | Line |
| $\overline{PQ}$ | Line segment |
| $\overrightarrow{PQ}$ | Ray |
| $\parallel$ | Parallel |
| $\perp$ | Perpendicular |
| $\bullet$ | Point |
| $\triangle$ | Triangle |
| $\square$ | Parallelogram |
| $A'$ | Prime |
| $\circ$ | Degrees |
| $\theta$ | Theta |
| $\phi$ | Phi |
| $\pi$ | Pi |

### Area

| $A = lw$ | Rectangle |
|---|---|
| $A = \dfrac{1}{2}bh$ | Triangle |
| $A = \pi r^2$ | Circle |
| $A = \dfrac{1}{2}(b_1 + b_2)h$ | Trapezoid |

### Trigonometric Ratios

| $\sin\theta = \dfrac{\text{opposite}}{\text{hypotenuse}}$ | $\cos\theta = \dfrac{\text{adjacent}}{\text{hypotenuse}}$ | $\tan\theta = \dfrac{\text{opposite}}{\text{adjacent}}$ |
|---|---|---|
| $\csc\theta = \dfrac{\text{hypotenuse}}{\text{opposite}}$ | $\sec\theta = \dfrac{\text{hypotenuse}}{\text{adjacent}}$ | $\cot\theta = \dfrac{\text{adjacent}}{\text{opposite}}$ |

### Trigonometric Identities

$\sin\theta = \cos(90°-\theta)$

$\cos\theta = \sin(90°-\theta)$

$\tan\theta = \dfrac{\sin\theta}{\cos\theta}$

$\csc\theta = \dfrac{1}{\sin\theta}$

$\sec\theta = \dfrac{1}{\cos\theta}$

$\cot\theta = \dfrac{1}{\tan\theta}$

$\cot\theta = \dfrac{\cos\theta}{\sin\theta}$

$\sin^2\theta + \cos^2\theta = 1$

### Pythagorean Theorem

$a^2 + b^2 = c^2$

### Volume

| $V = lwh$ | Rectangular prism |
|---|---|
| $V = Bh$ | Prism |
| $V = \dfrac{1}{3}\pi r^2 h$ | Cone |
| $V = \dfrac{1}{3}Bh$ | Pyramid |
| $V = \pi r^2 h$ | Cylinder |
| $V = \dfrac{4}{3}\pi r^3$ | Sphere |

### Distance Formula

$d = \sqrt{(x_2 - x_1)^2 + (y_2 - y_1)^2}$

### Dilation

$D_k(x,y) = (kx, ky)$

### Pi Defined

$\pi = \dfrac{\text{circumference}}{\text{diameter}} = \dfrac{\text{circumference}}{2\bullet\text{radius}}$

# Formulas

| Circumference of a Circle | |
|---|---|
| $C = 2\pi r$ | Circumference given the radius |
| $C = \pi d$ | Circumference given the diameter |

| Converting Between Degrees and Radians |
|---|
| $\dfrac{\text{radian measure}}{\pi} = \dfrac{\text{degree measure}}{180}$ |

| Midpoint Formula |
|---|
| $\left( \dfrac{x_1 + x_2}{2}, \dfrac{y_1 + y_2}{2} \right)$ |

| Inverse Trigonometric Functions |
|---|
| Arcsin $\theta = \sin^{-1}\theta$ |
| Arccos $\theta = \cos^{-1}\theta$ |
| Arctan $\theta = \tan^{-1}\theta$ |

| Arc Length | |
|---|---|
| $s = \theta r$ | Arc length ($\theta$ in radians) |

## MEASUREMENTS

| Length |
|---|
| Metric |
| 1 kilometer (km) = 1000 meters (m) |
| 1 meter (m) = 100 centimeters (cm) |
| 1 centimeter (cm) = 10 millimeters (mm) |
| Customary |
| 1 mile (mi) = 1760 yards (yd) |
| 1 mile (mi) = 5280 feet (ft) |
| 1 yard (yd) = 3 feet (ft) |
| 1 foot (ft) = 12 inches (in) |

| Volume and Capacity |
|---|
| Metric |
| 1 liter (L) = 1000 milliliters (mL) |
| Customary |
| 1 gallon (gal) = 4 quarts (qt) |
| 1 quart (qt) = 2 pints (pt) |
| 1 pint (pt) = 2 cups (c) |
| 1 cup (c) = 8 fluid ounces (fl oz) |

| Weight and Mass |
|---|
| Metric |
| 1 kilogram (kg) = 1000 grams (g) |
| 1 gram (g) = 1000 milligrams (mg) |
| 1 metric ton (MT) = 1000 kilograms |
| Customary |
| 1 ton (T) = 2000 pounds (lb) |
| 1 pound (lb) = 16 ounces (oz) |